Collier's *Junior* Classics

Series Editor
Margaret E. Martignoni

Series Titles	*Volume Editors*
A, B, C: GO!	**Rosemary E. Livsey**
ONCE UPON A TIME	**Elizabeth H. Gross**
MAGIC IN THE AIR	**Mary V. Gaver**
JUST AROUND THE CORNER	**Alice Brooks McGuire**
IN YOUR OWN BACKYARD	**Marian C. Young**
GIFTS FROM THE PAST	**Elenora Alexander**
LEGENDS OF LONG AGO	**Jane Darrah**
ROADS TO GREATNESS	**Louise Galloway**
CALL OF ADVENTURE	**Charlemae Rollins**
HARVEST OF HOLIDAYS	**Ruth Weeden Stewart**

harvest of
HOLIDAYS

A completely new selection of outstanding children's stories and poems compiled for enrichment reading by a distinguished editorial board of children's librarians.

Series Editor
MARGARET E. MARTIGNONI
Former Superintendent
Work with Children
Brooklyn Public Library

Editor-in-Chief
DR. LOUIS SHORES
Dean, Library School
Florida State University

Managing Editor
HARRY R. SNOWDEN, JR.

Volume Editor
RUTH WEEDEN STEWART
Former Coordinator
Work with Children
Brooklyn Public Library

Collier's *Junior* Classics Series

THE CROWELL-COLLIER PUBLISHING COMPANY • NEW YORK

Harvest of Holidays

Introduction

Collier's Junior Classics Series

We are children only once, and then only for a few brief years. But these are the most impressionable years of a lifetime. Never again will the world and everything in it be so eternally new, so filled with wonder. Never again will physical, mental, spiritual growth be so natural and unavoidable. During these years, habits become ingrained, tastes are developed, personality takes form. The child's whole being is geared toward learning. He instinctively reaches out for truth and, having no prejudices, seizes upon that which is good, just, beautiful. For these reasons, a child deserves what Walter de la Mare has called "only the rarest kind of best."

What do we mean by "best" in a book for children? Best books reflect universal truths with clarity and artistry. Such books reveal that man is essentially good and that life is infinitely worth living. They do not deny the existence of evil, but rather emphasize man's thrilling struggle against evil through faith, courage, and perseverance. They awaken the young reader's imagination, call forth his laughter as well as his tears, help him to understand and to love his fellow man. The reading of such books constitutes a rich heritage of experience which is every child's birthright.

The librarian-editors of *Collier's Junior Classics* have combed the best children's books of the past and present to assemble in a single series a sampling of the finest literature for boys and girls. High standards have been maintained for the art work also, which in most instances has been taken from the original book. No attempt has been made to cover all fields of knowledge or to include factual material for its own sake. The emphasis here is on good literature, chiefly fiction and biography, folk lore and legend, and some poetry. Special attention is given to the American scene and American democratic ideals, but many selections cover other cultures, geographical areas, and historical periods.

The purpose of *Collier's Junior Classics* is to introduce boys and girls to some of the best books ever written for children, to stimulate young readers to seek for themselves the books from which the selections have been drawn as well as other good books of similar appeal, and to encourage children to become discriminating, thoughtful, life-time readers. Author, title, and publisher are given at the foot of the page on which each selection opens. This enables readers to ask for the complete book at a library or bookstore. When necessary, brief introductions set the scene for the selection, while follow-up recommendations, complete with publishers' names, appear at the end of most stories.

v

Collier's Junior Classics is a series of ten individually indexed volumes. A, B, C: GO! has been lovingly compiled for the youngest, and consists of nursery rhymes, favorite folk tales, best-loved poems, and stories for reading aloud. Four volumes have been assembled for the intermediate group: ONCE UPON A TIME, a wonderous collection of fables, world folk tales, and modern fairy tales; MAGIC IN THE AIR, selections from great masterpieces of fantasy; JUST AROUND THE CORNER, excerpts from warm-hearted stories of other lands; and IN YOUR OWN BACKYARD, selections from stirring books about our own country. Four additional volumes cater to the interests of more mature boys and girls: GIFTS FROM THE PAST, memorable selections from world classics; LEGENDS OF LONG AGO, selections from great myths, epics, and American tall tales; ROADS TO GREATNESS, excerpts from biographies of some of the greatest men and women of the world; and CALL OF ADVENTURE, selections from action and suspense stories of today and yesterday. Finally, and most unusual of all, is the volume entitled HARVEST OF HOLIDAYS, a feast of stories, poems, documents, and factual material about twenty-two American national and religious holidays. Although perhaps of greatest interest to the intermediate group, HARVEST OF HOLIDAYS will intrigue and delight all ages.

The tables of contents for the ten volumes read like an all-time Who's Who of distinguished writers. A brief mention of only a few of these authors would include such names as Lewis Carroll, Kenneth Grahame, Charles Dickens, Mark Twain, Louisa May Alcott, Pearl Buck, Laura Ingalls Wilder, Eleanor Estes, Genevieve Foster, Robert Louis Stevenson, Robert McCloskey, Valenti Angelo, Carl Sandburg, A. A. Milne, Eleanor Farjeon, Elizabeth Enright, and Margaret Wise Brown. Among the illustrators, many of whom are also authors, are to be found the Petershams, the d'Aulaires, Wanda Gág, Louis Slobodkin, Helen Sewell, Lois Lenski, Roger Duvoisin, Maurice Sendak, Kurt Wiese, Marguerite de Angeli, Steele Savage, Howard Pyle, Lynd Ward, James Daugherty, Arthur Rackham, Fritz Kredel, and Gustave Dore.

Collier's Junior Classics is intended primarily for the home, although libraries will find the series valuable for browsing as well as for introducing children to many different books. Because each book is an individual volume, complete with its own index, it can be shelved where the librarian believes it will be most useful to the children.

No pains have been spared to make the individual volumes a series of stepping stones to all that is best in the magic world of children's books.

Margaret E. Martignoni
SERIES EDITOR

Contents

*Titles and authors of poems
and songs are set on one line.*

Harvest of Holidays

"January brings the snow,
Makes our feet and fingers glow"

. . . and it also begins the HARVEST OF HOLIDAYS, red-letter calendar days that bring color and excitement to every season. New Year's Day, Valentine's Day, Lincoln's and Washington's Birthdays—one on top of another—crowd the snowy season with fun and festivities.

As the crocuses peek through the newly-softened earth, Easter ushers in the spring with prayer and reverence, with bonnets and new suits. The green season overflows with occasions—Mother's Day, Father's Day, and Flag Day are only a few of the reasons for celebrating in the spring.

"Hot July brings cooling showers,
Apricots and gillyflowers"

. . . and firecrackers, flags, picnics, and parties that help us to herald the birthday of our country on the Fourth of July.

"Fresh October brings the pheasant,
Then to gather nuts is pleasant"

. . . nuts—to fill the trick or treat bags. Nuts—to decorate the Thanksgiving table.

December brings the year to a close with Hanukkah songs and Christmas carols, with eight-candled *menorahs* and sparkling Christmas trees. The year ends in gaily wrapped gifts surrounded by laughter and fun.

The year is many moods—some sad in memory of soldiers who have died, some happy in celebration of freedom and democracy. Others are thoughtful in hopes of lasting peace or thankful for the gifts which God has granted us. HARVEST OF HOLIDAYS tours a storied and poetic year, bursting with the richness of our literary heritage.

RUTH WEEDEN STEWART
Formerly Coordinator,
Work with Children,
Brooklyn Public Library

New Year's Day

JANUARY 1

"Bonne année!" they shout in Paris; "Feliz año nuevo!" in Spain. And beginning on December 31, streets and houses throughout the United States ring with the greeting, "Happy New Year!"

All people celebrate the New Year, but they do not all celebrate it on the same day or in the same way. The Chinese New Year, filled with festivity, falls on the first day of the Holiday Moon (usually in February). It is a birthday celebration for every Chinese, for whenever a Chinese child is born, he is considered one year old on New Year's day. The Jewish New Year is a solemn holiday of prayer which usually comes in September.

We owe our January first New Year to Julius Caesar, who changed the Roman New Year's day from March to January in honor of Janus, the god of beginning. Romans pictured Janus as a two-faced god: One face looked back at the old year, the other looked ahead to the new.

Now, on January 1, people all over the world think back about the year that has passed and ahead to the year to come. We bring in the New Year with bells ringing and noisemakers grinding, with dancing and laughter and song, and with a wish for health and happiness for ourselves and for the world.

Ringing in the New Year

BY CORNELIA MEIGS

Illustrations by Dawn Stoutsenberger

FRANKLIN Street was so empty that Julia Stone was singing to herself as she walked along through the snow. She did not sing very well, and so it was only when there was nobody near by to hear that she lifted up her voice and hummed a little song. Nobody else was moving down the street of the little New Hampshire village, where the thin veil of snow was falling everywhere. In every house, however, there was a glow of warm fires behind the windows and a bright holly wreath left over from Christmas hanging between the curtains. Above her, she could just barely see the tall spire of the church against the gray sky, with the cloud of falling snow wrapping it all around.

For Judy it was going to be a very special New Year indeed. Her mother had said that when she was eleven, she could sit up until midnight to see the old year out. Nancy Hyde, her best friend, had been told the same thing by her mother. And this year they were both eleven, although with Judy there was only one week to spare. She was going to sit up at Nancy's house and spend the night there. Yes, this was to be a new and exciting New Year's Eve.

The telephone rang just as she came into the house. Her mother and father had gone to see some friends in the next town ten miles away. Judy ran to answer and heard her mother's voice sounding faint and far away, for the telephone was not working very well.

"Judy, can you hear me? We'll have to spend the night with our friends. The road through Lyme Hollow will be drifted so deep we ought not to try it when it is getting dark. Anna will see that you have your supper and get safely over to Nancy's.

But I'm worried about one thing. You know your father and I always go on the last day of the year to see Mr. Townly and take him a load of firewood. Simon Hammonds was to bring it this afternoon. But the snow—"

The telephone sputtered and then gave no sound. The storm was interfering with it. Then suddenly it began to be clear again.

"Judy—Judy, are you still there? I'm afraid Simon can't get into town with his little truck. I know Mr. Townly will be out of wood because he expects ours. Ask Nancy's father if he won't send one of his trucks and see that Mr. Townly gets it somehow—"

Once more the telephone broke off. At last Central spoke. "I can't get the connection any more. The weight of the snow has brought down a wire or a pole somewhere."

Judy put down the receiver. Yes, of course, someone had to see that Mr. Townly got his wood. Mr. Townly was the pleasant old man who made the fires in the church and swept the Sunday-school rooms and always had such a kind word for every boy or girl in town. It was he who rang the bell in the tall spire of the church, rang it mornings and evenings, for Sunday services and for particular occasions. Mr. Townly was poor, and his little house at the end of the street could be very cold. Judy knew that on a winter night a low woodpile was a serious matter even in her own household.

In houses like Mr. Townly's there were no furnaces. In bitter weather someone often had to be up until morning to keep fires in stoves and fireplaces from going out. If you had nothing to burn, you could not just telephone a dealer down the street and have him bring a load of coal or wood. No, you had to send word to Mr. Hammonds, and he had to fetch it over three miles of bumpy road—if his truck would run. In this snow it probably would not.

Judy turned and ran out of the house. She was breathless when she got to Nancy's house, three blocks beyond the church. Nancy ran to take her wet coat, but Judy could not stop except to get her breath. She explained about Mr. Townly's wood, but Nancy's father had driven out to the power plant and her mother was out and would not be back until evening.

But Nancy's Cousin Martha Hand was sitting by the fire

knitting. She went to college and was here for the Christmas
vacation. Nancy's brother Tom had just come in and was still
in his big boots and heavy jacket. He had been shoveling snow
at the kitchen door.

Cousin Martha put down her knitting to listen, and Tom
stopped beating his snowy mittens against the fender. "That's
bad," Tom said. "Of course, Hammonds can't get in with the
wood. Poor old Mr. Townly!"

Everyone was fond of Mr. Townly. His father and his grandfather had rung the church bell before him. Every man, woman,
and child in the town got up by him, started to school by him,
went to church in the quiet of Sunday morning to his ringing.
He and those who had rung before him had never missed a
morning or a church service or a public festival. Everybody
knew that Mr. Townly had to be taken care of. And now all
the older people were out of reach and these younger ones must
do it. But how?

"There's the big truck out in the barn," Tom said. "Father
had it brought in last night from the plant. That could get out
to the Hammonds' place, but who's to drive it? I know how, but
I haven't got my license yet." Tom was fifteen, and the law
would not let him drive for another year. Cousin Martha jumped.

"I could drive it. I drove a truck when I was visiting on the
farm last summer. But how will we get the wood loaded if Mr.
Hammonds isn't there?"

"Oh, we can get plenty of people, like Jim Stevens and Polly
and the others. If there are enough of us we can get it on all
right. We'll pick them up as we go down the street."

They were off in no time at all. Martha, in her bright ski suit,
climbed to the high seat and shifted the big gears. The truck
groaned and creaked and began to creep backward out of the
shed. Martha backed it round neatly and came out onto the
road. The drifts were getting deeper, but the truck went plough-
ing steadily along. They stopped at one house after another
and explained the situation. Warmly clad boys and girls climbed
aboard at each stop.

Three miles is a long way in the snow, but they got to Mr.
Hammonds' house at last. He threw open the door when they
chugged into his yard and came running out. "There now, I'm

glad you came," he said. "I could never get into town myself with my small truck. I couldn't even get the wood loaded, for I'm trying to dig out a path to the stable and the sheep shed before the snow gets too much for me. The wood is piled back of the big barn. If each of you takes a stick at a time, you can get it loaded all right. It's lucky there are so many of you. But do you know how to take down a woodpile and load it in the truck? It has to be done right."

They all were sure that they could load the wood. Six of the boys and girls, Nancy and Judy among them, stood knee-deep in the snow and handed up the cut sticks, one at a time, to the other six in the truck. How they worked!

"We're all so plastered with snow, you'd think we had been

having a snowball fight," Martha said. "Climb on and hold tight. There will be plenty of bumps going home."

It was dark as they rumbled back to town, with the long fingers of the headlights feeling out the way ahead. The windows of all the houses were bright behind the holly wreaths as they rolled down Franklin Street. "Now run home to your suppers," Martha said, "and come back when we take the wood to Mr. Townly. It will have to be unloaded and piled up in his shed to do him any good."

It was quite late before they were all together again. People kept sending word. "Don't go without Jane, or Fred." "I have a package of cookies," or "Mr. Smith's overcoat that he isn't wearing." Anna and Martha were sewing up a flannel jacket for Mrs. Townly. It was really as late as everybody's bedtime when they were ready to start out again. But it was New Year's Eve tonight, and nobody's bedtime really mattered.

Judy thought she had never seen Mr. Townly's house look so small or so cold as it did that night. There must be only one light and one fire in it, and two people sitting close together, wondering how they could get through that bitter night.

What fun it was to shout, when the door opened, "Hello Mr. Townly, hello Mrs. Townly," to see their surprised faces, to put wood on the fireplace, to feed the cold stove in the kitchen until it roared. While some of the company stayed outside with Tom to pile the wood up in the shed, the others ran back and forth carrying in the boxes and bundles that had been sent. Martha had brought a can of milk and some packages in a basket, and she opened them in the kitchen. When all of them were gathered in the house at last, there was hot cocoa to hand around and there were plates piled up with cookies. They all sat down in front of the fire, most of them on the floor. Then Mr. Townly told them about when he was the age of Tom and went away to sea because the little New Hampshire town "seemed a sight too small for me."

He had had many adventures everywhere in the world. "But I came back in the end," he said. "When my father could not ring the church bell any more, I came back, first to help him, and then to keep on ringing it after he was gone. My son will do the same thing. He's out West now, driving cattle on

that big ranch in Montana that belongs to Tom's uncle. But
he'll come home, too. There are some jobs that are for the young
and some for those who are growing older. This is a good town
to come home to."

He looked at the big clock ticking on the wall. "Time's getting
on. I can't be late ringing the church bell to bring the New
Year in." He hurried into his worn old overcoat.

Tom had been out to look at the weather and came in stamping the snow off his boots. "The drifts are deep, Mr. Townly,"
he said. "We can't hope to drive the truck home tonight."

"Mr. Townly," asked Martha, "would it be so terrible if just
this one year the bell didn't ring for New Year's Eve?"

"Why, such a thing has never happened," he answered. "Do
you know that bell rang when the news came that the Declaration of Independence was signed in Philadelphia? It rang when
George Washington was made President, it rang when Abraham
Lincoln died, it rang for peace at the end of the last war. This
has been a hard year, and there's many who will listen for it.
If they don't hear it, they will think bad luck has come to the
town for certain. They'll begin the New Year with heavy hearts
and no courage. Oh, it has to ring!"

In spite of all they could say, he started out. Amongst them,
they managed to help him through the big drift at the gate, but
when they got out into the road the way was even harder. He
struggled on for a few yards, then stopped, and swayed. He
would have fallen if Tom had not caught him.

Somehow they got the old man back to his home and into
a big chair before the fire. Anxiously they clustered round, rubbing his hands, and helping Mrs. Townly to cover him with
warm blankets. No one noticed the time until Mr. Townly said,
feebly, "The bell! It must ring!"

The children looked at one another in dismay. It was a quarter
of twelve!

"We'll ring it for you," Julia said. "We'll ring it on time."

The children seconded her eagerly. In a moment, warmly
wrapped, they were out of the house and on their way. The
snow had stopped falling, but it lay so deep and smooth everywhere that it was hard to know places and corners and fence-
posts that marked the way. The clouds had broken and the

stars were out, very small and high in the cold air. Silently they pushed and fought their way through the deep snow, the older ones helping the little ones.

As they came nearer to the middle of the town, they found that some of the walks had been cleared and they could make more haste. Out of a few houses came the sound of voices, where there were parties going on. Then even these sounds ended, for it was nearly midnight and everyone was listening for the bell. The little town with its small, beautiful old houses, its broad street in the starlight, its yellow lights behind little windowpanes—we must not fail it, Judy thought. They could see the church spire, going up above them against the stars. Now they had reached it. They were on time.

Tom had Mr. Townly's lantern and watch and the big key. Inside, the church was very black and little warmer than was the clean, crisp air outdoors. The light of the lantern showed the narrow door and the steps going up, up into the dark. Tom went first, carrying the lantern. Martha came last with a tiny flashlight like a will-o'-the-wisp. They all climbed together, breathless from their struggle through the storm, their feet sounding hollow on the stairs. It was within one moment of twelve o'clock. At last they passed the little window that they had seen so often from far below. It was strange to look down on the sleeping roofs and the long snowy street beneath. Tom's voice sounded loud and echoing as he spoke from above.

"Here is the rope. Everybody take firm hold of the stair rail with one hand and a good grip on the rope with the other. When I say 'Three,' pull—pull together, one stroke for Liberty, one for Peace, one for George Washington, one for Abraham Lincoln, and all the rest for the New Year, one—two—three—"

The bell sounded terrifying, the first stroke was so loud in their ears. By the second they were a little more used to it. By the third they were pulling all together, evenly and smoothly. "Clang, clang, clang. Good luck, everybody. Be brave for the New Year, because it is going to be a good one. Good cheer, good courage, peace on earth, good will toward men."

Judy was singing it to herself, for no one could hear her in the great sound of the bell, ringing so splendidly overhead to bring in the New Year.

A Disastrous New Year's

BY RACHEL FIELD

Illustrations by Dorothy P. Lathrop

I might still be in the Van Rensselaer family and being exhibited to Isabella's grandchildren, if it had not been for the New Year's celebration. In those days, it was a far more important holiday than Christmas, and for weeks New York kitchens in that neighborhood had been active with preparations. Wonderful cakes were baked and iced, cookies and ginger nuts made, and mysterious bottles were brought up from the cellar to be ready for the hot toddies, eggnogs, and punches that would be served from New Year's Eve and on through the next day. Lily Van Rensselaer was pronounced of an age to receive callers with her mother and father in the drawing-room, but Harry and Isabella were still considered too young to take much part in New Year's doings. They made up for this the days before by stealing down into the kitchen and nearly driving the cook and maids distracted with their samplings of everything. But when the day itself arrived and they were banished to the nursery upstairs, they felt very rebellious and aggrieved.

From eleven o'clock on, there had been continuous rings at the front door bell and poundings at the knocker. The sound of voices and laughter and clinking china floated up to us. The streets were thronged with people going about to pay New Year's calls. It was for this reason Isabella had been charged not to poke her nose beyond the front door. It was not a day for little girls to be abroad, for a many of the gentlemen had been indulging in far too many toddies and eggnogs, and there were, besides, groups of rough men and ragamuffins from the poorer parts going about to get what they could from begging or taking. We could hear some of these gangs singing rowdy songs as they went by, some dressed in fantastic costumes they had collected from rag bags and ash barrels.

Isabella stood the nursery as long as she could. Harry was no help, being completely taken up with a new carpenter's chest that had been given him, and the maids all too busy to amuse her. The parlor was out of the question, since no amount of teasing had prevailed on her mother and father to let her in. She therefore hung over the banisters till she was dizzy with watching hats and canes being laid on hall furniture.

"I don't care if it is New Year's," I heard her say finally, "I'm going out myself. I guess I can make a call on Mr. Jenkins if I want to."

Mr. Jenkins was a friend of her father's, the same, in fact, to whom we had taken the sherry. He was a bachelor who lived in a big brownstone house and always made much of her. So presently Isabella had got herself into her outdoor things and with me in hand was slipping cautiously down the stairs. She waited behind the velvet portières of the drawing-room door, and when the hall was empty except for the tall silk hats and the canes, out she slipped. I knew it was very wrong of her, but I could not help a certain pleased excitement at the idea of being abroad by ourselves at such a time. Twilight was coming between the houses, but some faint sunset color still showed behind chimney pots and the trees of Washington Square. The sidewalks were thronged with hurrying people, and lights were beginning to stream out of windows on either side of the avenue. I think Isabella feared she might meet some friend of the family who would return her to the fold, so she decided to take a less familiar, roundabout way. Accordingly, we went west in the direction of Sixth Avenue.

Here all the shops were tightly shuttered, save for a chemist's or two, where great red or green jars threw out jets of colored light. Carriages and an occasional horse car rumbled by, but it was less crowded than on shopping days. Mr. Jenkins lived quite far uptown, in the "wilds of Twenty-third Street," Mr. Van Rensselaer used to say jokingly. Somehow, it seemed farther than usual that night, and I suspected that Isabella would not have minded turning back by the time we were nearing

Sixteenth Street. But once she had made her mind up, nothing could change it, not even her own feelings. So on we went. The wind blew a gale round all the corners and a few flakes of snow were beginning to fall. Suddenly, out of nowhere, or so it seemed, a crowd of urchins in blackened faces, cast-off hats, and an odd collection of old clothes bore down upon us. They must have been waiting in an alley for just such a chance to have sport with a well-dressed child out by herself. They were an odd-looking lot of boys of assorted sizes, with sticks and old umbrellas, which they waved with war whoops. They wanted pennies and I have no doubt if Isabella had had any to give them they would have let us pass peacefully.

But Isabella had no pennies, and seeing that no one was about to put a stop to their sport the boys set upon us fiercely.

"Tassels on her boots," screamed their leader, "get the tassels on her boots!"

What good they would be to those boys I could not make out, but go for them they did, though Isabella kicked out with all her might and used her fist. She had me in her other hand, which did not help matters.

"You'd better leave me alone," she cried, "or my father'll have you all put in jail."

"Ha, ha," mocked the leader, "my father'll have you put in the reservoir on Forty-second Street, and then you'll look a pretty sight. Oh, won't she, though, boys? Come on, let's take her there."

"Don't you dare to touch me," stormed Isabella, who was nearly in tears and at the same time stamping her foot with rage. "I can scratch and I can bite, too."

I could see from this that she had abandoned all hope of help from anyone but herself. Isabella was no coward. I hardly think many little girls would have stood up alone against that wild-looking troupe as she did. But of course she was no match for them, and in the end they had torn off her squirrel tippet and her ostrich feather, and one particularly unpleasant boy had snatched me rudely from her hand. The next thing I knew there was a whistle in the distance.

"Skip!" yelled the leader, and almost before the sound had died away the whole gang had scattered as by magic.

I had a glimpse of Isabella standing at the head of the alleyway, imperiously calling to a policeman and several passersby to come to her aid. Her hat with its red feather lay in at least six different bits, one sleeve was torn off at the shoulder, and the snow was falling on her disheveled hair and flushed face. I never saw anyone look quite so beautiful or so furious.

New Year's is anything but a name to give me pleasant associations. It would have brought tears to poor Miss Pinch's near-sighted eyes to see what those boys did to my fine outfit. They carried me away with Isabella's squirrel tippet for trophies. The tippet was taken by the leader, and since no one seemed particularly anxious for me, they decided I would make an excellent torch to set on fire.

Fortunately, they were then distracted by an invitation from some other boys to join a raid which was about to take place on a bakery shop. This turned into more of a fight than they had expected and presently there were more whistles and the word was passed round that the police had been sent for. Once more the gang scattered in different directions. One of the dirtiest boys stuffed me, headfirst, into his pocket with all my ruffles crushed and the lace of my underwear catching on buttons. Later, another boy thrust me roughly on the end of a stick and carried me like an effigy at the head of their procession. The point of the stick made a rent clear through to my chemise, and the snow, which was now falling steadily in big flakes, added to my bedraggled state. Up one street and down another they went—stealing ash cans and doorplates, throwing stones at unshuttered windows, raiding basement doors and unprotected passersby, and generally making a nuisance of themselves.

At last, the pangs of hunger sent them scattering to their various homes, if the crowded tenements and shanty cabins in vacant lots where they lived could be so called. I feared that I was going to be tossed into the gutter and trampled by the first horse's hoofs, when one of the gang asked if he might have me.

"For the kids at home," he volunteered, rather shamefacedly.

A hoot went up from the rest. But the boy who had been carrying me on the stick handed me over.

The next thing I knew I was the center of attention in a very different sort of room from the one I had left. An Irish cabdriver's family were eating their New Year supper in the kitchen of a tenement over a livery stable off Perry Street, and it was here that the boy, Tim Dooley, brought me. The table had no cloth, and the china was thick and cracked. It seemed to me that at least ten children of assorted sizes were gathered round it, all clamoring for the stew a big, red-faced woman was ladling from a kettle on the stove. As soon as the children caught sight of me, they turned their attention from the stew and all demanded me at once.

But Tim had plans of his own. A little cousin named Katie and her mother had come to spend New Year's with them and it was for her that he had saved me from the boys.

Dobry

BY MONICA SHANNON

Illustrations by Atanas Katchamakoff

BETWEEN Christmas and New Year, Grandfather was busy in a secret way, because Bulgarians give New Year presents instead of Christmas presents. Grandfather was busy especially, because in Bulgaria a peasant gives presents at New Year to those only who are younger than himself and naturally Grandfather's age made him the busiest and most secretive person in the whole village.

He looked over all his sashes, trying to make up his mind about which one Dobry would like best. At last he decided on a sash wider, longer even than the others and handwoven in green with a pattern of storks.

"It looks like April," Grandfather told himself.

He sorted out ancient Greek, Macedonian, and Turkish coins their family plow had turned up through the years and made two bracelets out of the coins, one for Roda and the other for Neda. Bracelets as strong as they were beautiful, the coins linked together by wrought iron links Pinu let him make in the blacksmith shop.

Remembering that Hristu had made him a pair of birthday shoes, Grandfather whittled a flute out of river linden and painted it with autumn colors for the shoemaker. And once started on flute making, he made up his mind to give Michael-acky, Semo, and Pinu each a new painted flute. But Grandfather could think of nothing for Asan, and he said to Roda:

"I can't think of a present for that narrow-faced, half-asleep boy. Nothing! If I could give him a flute now—but he already has the most wonderful flute anybody ever saw."

Roda relieved his mind and his curiosity, too, by showing

him a blouse she had woven for Asan and a golden-looking dress she had woven for Neda, because the two of them were without their mothers.

Dobry, too, was busy. He carved out a wooden lamb for Semo's baby, who was able to walk now. For Neda he made two fantastic slender animals out of the very hard wood of their mountain dran bush.

Dobry felt he had to make these animals out of dranwood, because the dran bush always begins its budding under snow in time for New Year's Eve, and a budding dran branch had come to mean New Year itself. First to leaf out under late snow and last to ripen its cranberry-like fruits, early snow often covered the dranka berries so that the dran bush was looked upon as the spirit of the year, alive to each season and friendly with snow.

On New Year's Eve everybody in the village carried dran branches, as a hint to winter that even the heartiest welcome may be worn out. These branches of sheathed buds were the image of spring. And eager for spring itself, the peasants now turned their backs on winter and were expecting spring to come faster than was possible in a high mountain village such as theirs.

Every peasant looked forward now to his bath as well as to spring's coming. The gypsies brought their massaging bear along in early spring, and if the bear would take his bath in the Yantra river then the villagers knew that the water was warm enough for themselves and they could wash and soak in the river without any fear of cramps.

Roda killed the oldest rooster in their courtyard for New Year's Eve. Only the oldest rooster was thought wise enough to predict the details of spring's arrival, and Roda had invited Semo, his peasant wife, and walking baby to a Weather-man Rooster supper.

And for the first time in his life, Dobry felt impatient of holiday ceremony, eager to be off to Neda with his fantastic animals and a story he had made up to go with them, a part of his New Year present to her.

But Na lay took possession of him when twilight took possession of the earth. Semo's walking baby came in at twilight, switched everybody with a dran branch, and said as best he could:

"Surva, Surva, survaknetca godina," or Happy New Year, a greeting all Bulgarians call out to each other. And a Bulgarian

is allowed to switch anybody older than himself when he
chants the New Year greeting.

Dobry no sooner thought of Na lay than he began to sing it
at the top of his lungs. Everybody sang the gypsy song with
him and when it was done Roda took up a dran branch, a
candle, and a little pot of incense. And Semo's baby, being the
youngest of them all, followed her on a small pilgrimage about
the house while Roda blessed each room in preparation for
the New Year.

The others were very quiet at table, waiting. Roda came back,
set the candle in the middle of the table, lifted the boy to his
stool, and for a moment everybody felt too excited to speak,
anticipating the pause and death of one year before another
year leaps to take its place.

Grandfather took up a dran branch, held it over the candle,
said, "Roda, this is your branch!" And Roda, anxiously watching, knew her luck by the number of leaf buds the flame popped
open. There were three buds on Roda's branch, two of them
popped, but if only one had opened, Roda would have expected little from this New Year. If no buds at all had opened,
Roda would have expected the year ahead to be a waste year.

Grandfather said, "Well, two is fairly good. If three leaf buds
had opened the year would have belonged to you, Roda. Now
you will have to belong a little to this New Year."

He told everybody's fortune by holding a dran branch over

the candle and then carved up the weather-wise rooster, saving out the wishbone for himself.

"I keep the weather man for myself," he said. "Why not? I see through him better than any of you do."

And his rooster meat eaten, Grandfather held its wishbone up to the candle flame, shut one eye, peered through the bone.

"Very clear. No snow. No clouds even," he declared. "Perfect! An early spring this year. The earliest spring I ever saw in a weather bone. All of the bone transparent. Perfect! Yes, the gypsy bear will be here before long and we'll take our baths! You'll see me rolling in the river like a buffalo. The water will be high this year, but I'll soak up a lot of river. And how we'll all feel after our baths! Perfect!" Grandfather made a big noise of snorting as if he already felt himself a water buffalo.

Dobry got up to go to Neda but Semo stopped him. "Wait a minute," Semo begged him. "I have to tell you about your New Year present. It's—well, your Nativity made me think of it, Dobry. I'm going to give you that little north room in the school and let you work there with your clay. An hour out of school time every day. Then——"

Roda interrupted the schoolmaster. "Wait, wait!" she cried to Dobry, gathered up the fortune-telling dran branches, putting them away carefully on a shelf under the jamal's hood to be the family's survaktcy for the coming year. The survaktcy is used when anybody hesitates about getting up at daybreak. An earlier riser beats a tattoo with a dran branch on the lazy one's bed, repeats, "Surva, surva, survaknetca godina!" until the laziest person in the world would rather get up than listen to the tiresome racket.

"Come here!" Roda called to Dobry and took out from her pocket a handful of gold coins. "The coins from my wedding dress," she told him. "I saved them for you, all of them. Coins from the head kerchief, coins from all around the hem of the skirt. They're for you—" Roda made her voice steadier. "They're for you so you can go to Sofia and grow to be an artist." Grandfather shook his head gravely. "You go in the spring, Dobry, after you've had your bath," he said. "I've saved all the money we got from the wood for your art education. That's a New Year present for you, too."

New Year's Day

By Rachel Field

Last night, while we were fast asleep,
   The old year went away.
It can't come back again because
   A new one's come to stay.

Welcome to the New Year

By Eleanor Farjeon

Hey, my lad, ho, my lad!
   Here's a New Broom.
Heaven's your housetop
   And Earth is your room.

Tuck up your shirtsleeves,
   There's plenty to do—
Look at the muddle
   That's waiting for you!

Dust in the corners
   And dirt on the floor,
Cobwebs still clinging
   To window and door.

Hey, my lad! ho, my lad!
   Nimble and keen—
Here's your New Broom, my lad!
   See you sweep clean.

Ring Out, Wild Bells

By Alfred, Lord Tennyson

Ring out, wild bells, to the wild sky,
  The flying cloud, the frosty light:
  The year is dying in the night;
Ring out, wild bells, and let him die.

Ring out the old, ring in the new,
  Ring, happy bells, across the snow:
  The year is going, let him go;
Ring out the false, ring in the true.

Ring out the grief that saps the mind,
  For those that here we see no more;
  Ring out the feud of rich and poor,
Ring in redress to all mankind.

Ring out false pride in place and blood,
  The civic slander and the spite;
  Ring in the love of truth and right,
Ring in the common love of good.

Ring out old shapes of foul disease;
  Ring out the narrowing lust of gold;
  Ring out the thousand wars of old,
Ring in the thousand years of peace.

Ring in the valiant man and free,
  The larger heart, the kindlier hand;
  Ring out the darkness of the land,
Ring in the Christ that is to be.

ILLUSTRATION BY ESTELLE HOLLINGWORTH

WITH MALICE TOWARD NONE

PRESENTED TO THE STATE OF ILLINOIS

Lincoln's Birthday

FEBRUARY 12

Abraham Lincoln "stood at the helm" during some of the stormiest years our nation has known. "If we do not make common cause," he said, "to save the good old ship of the Union in this voyage, nobody will have a chance to pilot her on another voyage." The Civil War proved there was a common cause, and Lincoln, the pilot, preserved the nation's unity.

Born on February 12, 1809, in a log cabin in the backwoods of Kentucky, Lincoln spent his early years in Kentucky, Indiana, and Illinois. As a youth he had perhaps a year of schooling in all. But the pioneer boy learned to read—and as he grew, books were his favorite companions.

In his young manhood, Lincoln studied law and set up law offices in Springfield, Illinois. He turned his hand to any task which would give him a living, but he was always reaching for more knowledge and education. Election to the state legislature opened the door to politics and pointed the way to his crowning achievement as sixteenth president of the United States.

Abraham Lincoln

BY INGRI AND EDGAR PARIN D'AULAIRE

Illustrations by the authors

HE wanted to read and to study, but school was far away, and he had to stay at home to help on the farm. The hard work made him big and husky, and he could outrun and outwrestle all the other boys of his age. Even quicker than his legs ran his wit, so he became leader of all the boys who lived around Little Pigeon Creek. Abe hadn't much time to play, but sometimes at night he and his friends stole out to a salt lick in the woods. There they hid behind trees and watched the shy deer licking the salty slabs. But Abe never went hunting as other boys and menfolk did. He loved the animals and wouldn't harm them.

For two happy years Abe and his family lived in the home in the woods near wolves and grumbling bears. But when he was nine a dangerous sickness came to the wilderness, and his mother took sick and died. Then the woods seemed gloomy and dark, and the days grew long for Sally and Abe.

A year or so later their father went off on a trip, and for many weeks Abe and Sally were left all alone. Then one day a big wagon, drawn by four horses, stopped in front of the cabin. Out of the wagon jumped their father and a kind, rosy-cheeked woman. She ran over to Abe and Sally and hugged them to her bosom. She had come to be their new mother.

The stepmother had brought her three children, and all her household goods. They unloaded a chest, a table, chairs, and feather beds, pots and knives and forks and spoons. So smooth and fine was the furniture that Abe could run his hands over it without getting splinters in his fingers. And the stepmother climbed up to the loft where Abe slept. She threw out the

leaves that had been his bedding, and gave him a soft feather
bed instead. Then she put the father to work to make a real
door, a window, and a wooden floor for the cabin. She washed
and scrubbed the cabin both high and low, and took charge
of the family right away.

"Let Abe have time to read," she said when she saw how eager
to learn he was. At night, after the others had gone to sleep,
she let him lie by the fireplace and study. In the flickering light
he practised writing and reading. He wrote with charcoal on

a wooden shovel, and read the Bible, stories about George Washington, "Pilgrim's Progress," and every other book he could get. Books were scarce in the wilderness, but Abe didn't mind walking twenty miles to borrow one.

When Abe grew too tired to read any more, he climbed up the pegs in the wall to his loft. Before going to sleep he hid the book he had been reading in a crack in the roof to keep it safe. But once a storm came up in the night, and when Abe woke up his book was soaking wet and spoiled. He had borrowed this book from a rich farmer, and for three long days Abe had to husk corn to pay for it. "No one can beat Abe Lincoln at farm work," said the neighbors. It was known for miles around how quick he was at splitting logs into fence rails. But when someone passed by, he would sit on the fence he had made and talk, asking questions to learn new things. Then the neighbors thought he was lazy. And when he walked between the handles of his plow reading a book, they thought he was queer.

Abe grew straight up into the air like a fir tree. Long and thin he was, with big hands and feet jutting out. His buckskin breeches were always too short and too tight, and made blue circles on his legs where they squeezed him.

"I can always wash your muddy footsteps from the floor," teased his stepmother, "but keep your head clean, Abe, so you won't be leaving tracks along my whitewashed ceiling." Abe grinned, scratched his head, and thought of a joke. When his stepmother went out for a while he took a little boy with muddy feet, lifted him up and walked him like a fly across the ceiling. "Abe, I should thrash you," said the stepmother when she came back. But she laughed at the joke instead. And with a pail of whitewash Abe made the ceiling white and clean again.

Often for days at a time Abe stayed alone in the woods chopping timber. It was so quiet in the forest, and he had plenty of time to think and dream. At mealtimes he shared his food with the squirrels, and in return they had to listen to the speeches he made up. The squirrels blinked their small brown eyes, and the trees seemed to sway and bow in agreement with what he said. He made a poem for his sister Sally, and when she married and left home, he read it at her wedding.

Abe also left home for a while to be a ferryman on the Ohio River. The great Ohio River flowed by some miles from Little Pigeon Creek, and it was there that he made his first dollar. Two elegant travelers gave him a shiny half dollar each for rowing them out to the steamboat that lay anchored in midstream. But as he stood there in his ferryboat, wondering that anyone could pay so much for so little work, one of the coins slipped out from between his fingers. Sadly Abe saw half of his new wealth vanish in the depths.

But Abe hadn't much time to grieve over his loss, too many things happened on the river. He looked wide-eyed at the boats, and listened to tales of the outside world. Then one day one of the neighboring farmers sent Abe himself out into the world. With a flatboat loaded with hogs and corn, the farmer's son and Abe set off to go all the way down to New Orleans to trade. They drifted with their boat down the Ohio and into the great Mississippi River. There Abe needed all his strength and quick thinking to steer clear of the many dangers. Paddle wheel steamers splashed up and down the river so hard that the water churned in a foam about them. Flatboats and keelboats and houseboats in strings drifted into their path. Dangers lurked behind every bend. Sandbars were washed up by the current and straggling trees, sticking up from the bottom, threatened to pin the boat up in the air like a beetle. Along the shores river pirates lay in hiding, waiting for nightfall to come.

One night, as Abe and his friend had made fast their boat at the bank, five vicious pirates came sneaking on board to rob them. But they hadn't counted on the strength of big Abe. He grabbed an oar, fought them all at once, and chased them far into the swamp. Abe could never forget this night, for the rest of his life he had a white scar over his eyebrow.

The further south they drifted the more Negro slaves they saw working in the cotton fields. And when, at last, they came to New Orleans, there were black slaves everywhere. Some were running about with loads on their heads, others were led in chains through the streets to be sold at slave markets. And Abe saw how Negroes were trotted up and down like horses to show that they were strong and healthy. The Negro mothers

were weeping, for they never knew if they would ever see their little black babies again when they were sold. Sometimes the one who bought the mother would refuse to take the children, and then they would be sold to someone else and the family would be broken up.

Abe Lincoln thought that was cruel. And when the cargo and the flatboat were sold, he was glad to go north again to his Indiana home where everyone was free.

There all the neighbors came to hear him tell of his adventures out in the big world. They never tired of hearing about the river pirates and slave markets. And they all grinned broadly when he told of the fortune teller who had said that he, Abraham Lincoln, would one day be President of the United States.

Abe's father was listening to stories about Illinois, the new prairie state, where folks said the grass grew greener than anywhere else.

"I reckon we'll be moving on," he said one day. So one early spring morning the Lincolns set off again, this time in a wagon so huge that a seven yoke ox team had to pull it. The wagon was crowded, for many relatives moved with them. They traveled on for two whole weeks through forests and swamps and rolling prairie. On long legs Abe walked in front to peddle pins and buttons, when once in awhile they passed a farm. When they came to the Sangamon River in Illinois they liked the land, and put up a cabin. Abe split mountains of rails for fences. One thousand rails he split for a neighbor to get himself a pair of jeans. That was much work for a pair of pants, but then his legs were long, too, so it took many yards of cloth to cover them. And when spring came he said goodbye to his father and his stepmother, put his belongings into a bundle, threw it over his shoulder, and set out into the world to try his luck. For now he had reached twenty-one years, and was free to do as he pleased.

A little further down the Sangamon River lay the village of New Salem. It had only a few dozen houses, but even Chicago did not have more at that time. There were several stores in New Salem, and a man named Offut was planning to open a new one. On one of his trips to the river Offut met tall Abe, and hired him as clerk in the store he was going to open.

But first he sent him down to New Orleans with goods to sell. Abe built a flatboat himself, and drifted down the Sangamon River. But off New Salem a miller had built a dam across the river, and on this milldam the flatboat stuck. All the people of the village stood on the bank and waited to see the flatboat sink. But Abe bored a hole in the boat and tipped it so the water could flow out, and slowly the flatboat slid over the dam. Then he put a wedge in the hole, and drifted on down the river. There was a mighty smart fellow, everyone said.

Offut went around bragging and betting that his huge new clerk was not only smart enough to outwit them all, but so strong that he could outrun, outjump, and outfight any man in the country. So when Abe came back to New Salem all the strong boys were strutting about like cocks, eager to measure their strength against his. And Abe had to make good Offut's words. He wrestled with the strongest and toughest of them all, and threw him to the ground. Then the beaten boy and all the people cheered and said Abe was the strongest man in the county. From that day they accepted him as one of them. They loved his funny ways and jokes. And they nicknamed him Honest Abe. Once he charged a woman six and a quarter cents too much, and he walked three miles to catch up with her and pay her back.

But Abe's honesty wasn't enough to keep Offut's store going. The debts grew bigger and bigger, and one morning Offut was gone. There stood Abe without a job. But just then the men of New Salem were called to war, for an Indian chief, Black Hawk, had come back to Illinois with his warriors. His tribe had sold the land to the "paleface," but Black Hawk said: "Man-ee-do, the great spirit, gave us the land, it couldn't be sold." "Sold is sold," said the people of Illinois, and went to war to chase the Indians out.

Abe Lincoln went to war as a captain. For the man from each village who had the longest row of men lined up behind him was elected captain. And twice as many men lined up behind Abe as behind his rival.

But his soldiers had never taken orders from any man before, and Captain Abe Lincoln struggled hard to make them obey him. That was all the fighting he had. For Black Hawk and his warriors fled before the soldiers. One day a peaceful old Indian came walking into camp. The soldiers were angry and wanted to kill him, but Abe said, "Anyone who touches him must fight me first." Because Abe was the strongest, they had to obey.

Soon after that Black Hawk was taken prisoner, and the Indian War was over.

Abe went back to New Salem, and he and another young man named Berry decided to open a store of their own. Both were poor, but Abe's word was good as gold, so they borrowed the money, bought the goods, and started to trade. Very soon Abe's friends were saying he was too clever to stand behind the counter all day long. He should go around making speeches so the people would elect him to go to the capital of Illinois.

Abe thought this a very good idea. So he began going

about making speeches and joking with the people. When he
had mounted a tree stump he started: "I am humble Abraham
Lincoln." And the people liked what he said and his funny
ways, and they elected him. Every spring he went to the capital. The rest of the year he took care of his store; but all
the time he wanted to study to become a lawyer. And it
happened that one day as he was standing in his store, a
covered wagon stopped at the door and a stranger came in

with a barrel of old stuff he wanted to sell. Abe had no need of the barrel, but he bought it for half a dollar to help the man. And when he opened the barrel he found at the bottom the book he needed to study law. From then on Abe lay most of the time on the counter and studied the book. And the schoolmaster helped him with grammar and English.

In the meantime Berry took care of the store. But instead of selling the goods, he ate and drank the whole day long, and at last he died. There was Abe with all the debts. It was more than a thousand dollars he owed. His store was taken away from him, and all that he owned was sold at an auction.

Abe's father had taught him: "If you make a bad bargain, hug it all the tighter." So instead of running away Abe stayed and toiled to pay back all the debts.

His friends believed in him, and most of all a girl, whose name was Ann Rutledge. She was sure he would become a great man some day, if he would just go on with his studies. And then they would be married, and be happy ever after.

But one day Ann Rutledge took sick and nothing could be done to save her life. From that day on it was as if there were two Abes. The one was gay and full of funny stories, the other was so sad and sorrowful that no one dared approach him. But he did his work and finished his studies, and one morning he took leave of his friends in New Salem. He borrowed a horse, and sad and penniless he rode off to Springfield, the capital of Illinois, to become a lawyer.

In Springfield he hitched up his horse on the main square and went into the store of Joshua Speed to ask the price of bedding. "I have no money, but if I succeed I'll pay you back," he said to Speed. But Speed felt sorry for sad-faced Abe and told him to take his things upstairs and share his own bed for nothing.

From that time on, Joshua Speed was Abe Lincoln's best friend. He took him to the homes of all his elegant friends. And Abe bought himself store clothes, put a stovepipe hat on his head, and by and by the country lad was changed into a well-known lawyer.

From the prairie all around people came to ask his advice, for they knew he would be fair and square. And the people in Springfield began to say that the two cleverest men in town were awkward Abraham Lincoln and stylish Judge Douglas. The one was fat and small, the other was lean and tall. And they both courted Mary Todd, a lady from Kentucky. She was dainty and witty, with a tongue so sharp that few people but Abe could tongue-tie her.

Little Miss Todd liked the tall Abe Lincoln, but she liked Judge Douglas too. He was elegant and important and Mary was as proud as she was witty. She had great plans for her future.

"The man I am going to marry will be President of the country," she said.

It took her a long while to make up her mind which one of her suitors to choose, for they were both very clever men. At last she chose Abe, and they were married. They did not have much to begin with, for Abe had debts which he had to pay back. But Mary saved and helped him. They paid off the debts, then they bought a house of their own. It was different from Abe's old home. It was painted white and had green shutters. There were many rooms with stylish furniture, lacy curtains, and plushy carpets.

In a few years they had three noisy little boys, who crawled all over long Abe when he lay reading on the soft carpet in the parlor.

His wife did not like him to lie on the floor, nor to open the door himself when the doorbell rang. Those were wilderness manners, she said. He should sit on a chair when he read and send the maid to the door. For now he was an important man; all over Illinois, people were talking about what a clever and honest man he was.

But it wasn't easy for anyone to change the ways of Abraham Lincoln. He milked his own cow, tended his horse, and was a friend of all the children in town. He was never too tired or busy to play and joke with them.

One evening some of his little friends tied a string across the street, so high up that everyone in town could pass under it but tall Abe Lincoln with his stove-pipe hat. Off flew the hat, and papers scattered in all directions. For instead of using a bag, Abe always stuffed his tall hat with bills and notes and important papers. While Abe stooped to gather them the boys ran out from their hiding places and threw themselves

upon him. Abe never lost his temper with them. He laughed at their pranks. He had been full of pranks himself when he was little.

Many months each year Abe spent driving from courthouse to courthouse out on the prairie. One evening, as he drove along a one-track prairie road, huddled up in his shawl, he met a husky fellow in a buggy. They both knew that the one who pulled aside risked getting stuck in the mud.

"Give way," cried Abe.

"Give way yourself," cried the other man.

Slowly Abe rose from his seat. "I'll tell you what I'll do if you don't give way," he shouted in a terrible voice.

And he rose higher and higher, till he looked like a giant against the setting sun.

"Don't grow any higher," pleaded the husky fellow, and drove right into the mud.

As Abe drove by, the man asked in a timid voice: "What is it you would have done?"

"I would have given way myself," chuckled Abe as he helped the man.

The stranger laughed—as the whole prairie laughed—even the judges had to laugh when Abe joked.

"Abe, you can even make a cat laugh," everyone said.

The years passed and people began to call him Old Abe. He still did not change. When the people of Illinois sent him to Congress, he walked up Capitol Hill in Washington with his pack of books in a red handkerchief slung over his shoulder. He was himself and did not care or even notice if people smiled. After his term in Congress was over he came home again to Springfield and hitched his horse to his buggy as before and rattled out over the prairie to faraway courthouses. There he sat with his feet on the table and seemed to be asleep. But when his turn came he stretched himself into shape, ruffled his hair and took off his coat and necktie. Then he began to speak, and everyone listened. There wasn't a man on the wide prairie who hadn't heard of Old Abe.

For fifteen years Abe Lincoln was too busy as a lawyer to have time for politics. It seemed as if Mary after all hadn't married a man who would be President. It was Judge Douglas who had become a great politician.

All this time there was a great quarrel between the States of the South and the States of the North.

"It is wrong to have slaves," said the Northerners; "let the black slaves go."

"Slaves they are and slaves they shall remain!" cried the Southerners, and they talked of leaving the United States and running their part of the country alone.

Judge Douglas traveled through Illinois making speeches. He said: "Let each state decide for itself whether it wants slavery or not." This aroused Abraham Lincoln. He stood up and said: "All men are created free and equal." There must be the same freedom in all of the United States, he felt, for "a house divided against itself cannot stand." And wherever Douglas made a speech, Lincoln made a speech against what he said.

From afar people came over dusty roads to hear the two best talkers of the state. Judge Douglas was elected senator from Illinois, but Old Abe's fame spread all over the United States.

Everywhere people began to wonder if Lincoln wasn't the man to keep the United States together. From the big towns in the East important men traveled to see him and asked if he would be willing to let the people vote for him as President. Abraham Lincoln thought it over for a long time. It was so friendly and peaceful on the prairie in Illinois.

But all over the North people cried: "We want Honest Old Abe." And at last he said yes.

Late one evening Lincoln got the message that he had been elected President of the United States. He went home to his wife, and said: "Mary, we are elected."

And Mary rejoiced. Her dream had come true.

Abe sold his horse and buggy and cow, and made ready to leave his home. And he grew a beard on his chin. He knew he wasn't handsome, and he thought a beard might make him look nicer.

On a drizzling morning he tied up his trunks. Then he went to the train at the station. He looked at the dear and homey faces of his prairie friends who had come to bid him good-bye. He was sad that he had to go, but the people of his country had called him.

"I bid you all an affectionate farewell," said Lincoln.

"Farewell, farewell," cried all his friends.

And with his wife and his boys Abraham Lincoln traveled to the White House in Washington.

Now Abraham Lincoln was master of the White House. But he was President of only part of the United States. For the Southern States had taken down the Star-Spangled Banner and raised the flag of the Confederacy in its stead. Sad and silent, Lincoln gazed through his spyglass at the Confederate flag that fluttered in the wind on the other side of the Potomac River in Virginia. He pondered how to get the Southern States back into the Union. He needed quiet to think what to do. But from morning till night the White House was crowded with people seeking his help. Lincoln wanted to listen to them all, but the days were too short. He grew haggard and care-worn, and scarcely had time to eat and to sleep. His servants at last put up a screen across the hall so Lincoln could pass unseen. But he was so tall that the top of his head showed above the screen when he tiptoed from room to room, and so gave him away to the visitors. Then he locked himself in his office with the men in the Cabinet, who were helping him with the government. No man ever loved peace more than Abraham Lincoln. But he firmly believed that his country could be great and strong only as long as all the states were united as one country. The Union must be saved.

With a heavy heart Lincoln called soldiers from the Northern States and sent them to war against the Southerners to force them back into the Union. The Civil War had begun.

At first his generals and the men in his Cabinet all thought they were much wiser than Abraham Lincoln who came from the wilderness. Lincoln just let them think so. He listened politely to their advices, but he did what he felt was best for the people. "Have you heard the story of the monkey who wanted a longer tail?" he said to his generals, when they asked for ever more honor and power.

"Once upon a time there was a tribe of monkeys that was going to war. The biggest and strongest of them was made their leader. But he didn't think his tail was grand and long enough. If he was to lead them to victory his tail must be longer, he said. And so the monkeys began to add to it with pieces of tail. But the longer they made it, the longer tail the monkey chief wanted. The tail became longer and longer—in scrolls and coils it lay all over the floor. At last it grew so long that it filled the room clear to the ceiling, and there sat the monkey leader, so entangled in tail that he couldn't move any more."

Thus everyone would fare, who wanted too much, meant President Lincoln.

The soldiers all loved their long, gangling President and his little son, Tad, who often rode at his side. For Mrs. Lincoln used to send Tad along with his father to make him take better care of himself.

Lincoln was father and friend to all the soldiers. They could go to him with their troubles, and he was never too busy to tell a story or laugh at a joke. One day when he was reviewing the troops, one of the generals gave him a wild horse to ride. But Abe Lincoln was an old ranger who knew how to keep in the saddle. He raced up and down the field, without even losing his hat. And the soldiers cheered till they were hoarse.

"We are coming, Father Abraham, four hundred thousand strong," they answered from all the Northern States, when Lincoln called for more soldiers.

And Lincoln helped them and grieved over those who fell on the battlefields as though they were his own sons. It was in memory of those men who had fallen at Gettysburg that he made his most famous speech, the Gettysburg Address.

He tried to make friends with the Southern States, and offered to buy the slaves' freedom, instead of using the money for war. But the South wouldn't listen to him. So on New Year's Day in 1863 Lincoln solemnly signed a paper that made the slaves free forever. It was called the Emancipation Proclamation.

The Southerners fought on, although they had less and less to eat, and had hardly any shoes to put on their feet. For several years Lincoln sought all over the North for a general who could end the war. At last he found General Grant. He was straightforward and brave, and did not waste his time just talking and writing.

"Can you make an end to the war?" asked Lincoln.

"If you give me soldiers enough I will," said Grant.

Once more Lincoln called for soldiers, and again men came from all over the North. And Grant did as he had promised. He forced the Southern soldiers out of Richmond, the capital of the Confederacy. Four years after the Civil War had begun the Star-Spangled Banner waved over Virginia again.

The next day President Lincoln walked into the town, holding little Tad by the hand. An old Negro recognized the long, thin man with the tall stove-pipe hat. "Here is our saviour," he cried, and threw himself at Lincoln's feet. And suddenly Lincoln was surrounded by Negroes, weeping and rejoicing as they cried: "Glory, glory hallelujah."

The Civil War had come to an end. The slaves were free, and the Union was saved. Most people in the Northern States wanted to make the Southerners pay for the four terrible years of war. But Lincoln said they should be received back into the Union "with malice toward none; with charity for all." He felt like the father of a great flock of children. Some had run away, but were now returning to their home.

He stood on a balcony of the White House, looking out over the cheering people who cried: "Speak, Father Abraham." Abraham Lincoln didn't answer with words. But he made the band play "Dixie," the favorite song of the Southerners, which had not been heard in Washington since the Civil War began. Then he sat down on his rocking chair to rest.

He had done what he should do. He had held together the great nation brought forth upon this continent by his forefathers.

Nancy Hanks

By Rosemary Benét

If Nancy Hanks
Came back as a ghost,
Seeking news
Of what she loved most,
She'd ask first
"Where's my son?
What's happened to Abe?
What's he done?

"Poor little Abe,
Left all alone
Except for Tom,
Who's a rolling stone;
He was only nine
The year I died.
I remember still
How hard he cried.

"Scraping along
In a little shack,
With hardly a shirt
To cover his back,
And a prairie wind
To blow him down,
Or pinching times
If he went to town.

"You wouldn't know
About my son?
Did he grow tall?
Did he have fun?
Did he learn to read?
Did he get to town?
Do you know his name?
Did he get on?"

A Reply to Nancy Hanks

By Julius Silberger

Yes, Nancy Hanks,
The news we will tell
Of your Abe
Whom you loved so well.
You asked first,
"Where's my son?"
He lives in the heart
Of everyone.

Lincoln's Gettysburg Address

November 19, 1863

Fourscore and seven years ago our fathers brought forth on this continent a new nation, conceived in liberty, and dedicated to the proposition that all men are created equal.

Now we are engaged in a great civil war, testing whether that nation, or any nation so conceived and so dedicated, can long endure. We are met on a great battlefield of that war. We have come to dedicate a portion of that field as a final resting-place for those who here gave their lives that that nation might live. It is altogether fitting and proper that we should do this.

But, in a larger sense, we cannot dedicate—we cannot consecrate—we cannot hallow—this ground. The brave men, living and dead, who struggled here have consecrated it, far above our poor power to add or detract. The world will little note, nor long remember, what we say here, but it can never forget what they did here. It is for us the living, rather, to be dedicated here to the unfinished work which they who fought here have thus far so nobly advanced. It is rather for us to be here dedicated to the great task remaining before us—that from these honored dead we take increased devotion to that cause for which they gave the last full measure of devotion—that we here highly resolve that these dead shall not have died in vain—that this nation, under God, shall have a new birth of freedom and that government of the people, by the people, for the people, shall not perish from the earth.

O Captain! My Captain!

By Walt Whitman

O Captain! my Captain! our fearful trip is done,
The ship has weather'd every rack, the prize we sought is won,
The port is near, the bells I hear, the people all exulting,
While follow eyes the steady keel, the vessel grim and daring;
  But O heart! heart! heart!
   O the bleeding drops of red,
    Where on the deck my Captain lies,
     Fallen cold and dead.

O Captain! my Captain! rise up and hear the bells:
Rise up—for you the flag is flung—for you the bugle trills,
For you bouquets and ribbon'd wreaths—for you the shores
 a-crowding,
For you they call, the swaying mass, their eager faces turning;
  Here, Captain! dear father!
   This arm beneath your head!
    It is some dream that on the deck
     You've fallen cold and dead.

My Captain does not answer, his lips are pale and still,
My father does not feel my arm, he has no pulse nor will,
The ship is anchor'd safe and sound, its voyage closed and done,
From fearful trip the victor ship comes in with object won;
  Exult O shores! and ring, O bells!
   But I with mournful tread,
    Walk the deck my Captain lies,
     Fallen cold and dead.

Valentine's Day

FEBRUARY 14

Valentine's Day is a whirl of hearts, candy, and good wishes in the form of red and white cards saying, "Be My Valentine."

The day derives from the old Roman feast of Lupercalia, the "lovers' festival," celebrated on February 15. However, in 496 Pope Gelasius changed the date to February 14, St. Valentine's day. The romance and fun of the Roman holiday have remained, tangled with many ancient customs and superstitions.

In England custom decrees that if a single girl walks around a certain church twelve times at midnight and says, "I sow hempseed, hempseed I sow, he that loves me best, come after me now," her true valentine will appear. In Sicily, it is said that if a young lady gets up at sunrise on Saint Valentine's day to peer through her window, the first single man to walk by, or someone like him, is the man she will marry.

The Valentine Box

BY MAUD HART LOVELACE

Illustrations by Charlotte Leveton

As Janice walked home to lunch on Valentine's Day, she did not feel happy. It was snowing hard, and once it occurred to her that perhaps her mother would not let her go back to school in the afternoon. Then Janice remembered that her mother would let her go if it were possible at all, because of the valentine box. And that's the very reason I don't want to go, because of the valentine box, Janice thought.

It was very mixed up. What made it harder was that she did not want her mother to know how queer she was feeling inside.

The box itself was beautiful. The fifth-grade children had made it, covering a pasteboard hatbox with red tissue paper, decorating it with white hearts, and cutting a slit in the top through which they would drop valentines this afternoon. The valentine box sat on the teacher's desk looking gay and important, and most of the children could hardly wait for the party. But Janice didn't have a single "party" feeling.

The trouble was that Janice was afraid she wouldn't get any valentines. She was new in the town of Oak Grove. She was going to a new school, and she didn't have any friends.

Back in Chickasaw City she had had plenty of friends, and one very special friend named Mary Lou. Janice and Mary Lou had always walked to school together, and after school they had gone skating, or had played games, or had cut out paper dolls, depending on the weather. Mary Lou was still her friend, of course, and they wrote letters to each other, but Janice needed a friend here in Oak Grove.

There was a girl in her grade she would like to have for a friend. Margaret was her name. Margaret was a large, rosy,

From *Jack and Jill*, October, 1946. Copyright 1945 by The Curtis Publishing Company and Maud Hart Lovelace.

smiling girl, with a mop of curly brown hair. She looked full of fun and she lived conveniently near to Janice, just in the next block. But Margaret had lived in Oak Grove all her life; she had plenty of friends, so she had hardly noticed Janice, who was small for her age, and dark, and quiet. Janice wasn't quiet after she got acquainted with people. She was as full of fun as anybody. But she didn't get acquainted easily.

I don't believe I'll have a single valentine in that box, she thought now, and hurried through the thickening snow.

In the doorway at home she took off her high boots and carried them into the house. A great gust of snow blew in with her.

"Mercy, what a day!" her mother said, brushing the wet flakes from Janice's snow suit. "If it wasn't Valentine's Day, I wouldn't let you go back this afternoon. And speaking of valentines, see what came in the morning mail!" She held up a big square envelope addressed to Janice.

"It's from Mary Lou!" cried Janice, and after examining the envelope from all sides, she carefully opened it. It was a beautiful valentine, trimmed with paper lace. Inside, Mary Lou had written, "You are my valentine." Janice liked the message even better than the paper lace. She read it over two or three times.

"It's very pretty," said Mother. "And you may get more in the valentine box at school." Then Mother grew serious. "I wouldn't expect many, though, if I were you, Janice. You must remember that you're new in this school."

"Of course," said Janice. "We're going to have refreshments at the party. That's the important thing."

But it wasn't really. The important thing was getting some valentines from friends who really liked you.

Janice ate her hot soup and sandwiches and an apple, and drank her cocoa. Then she climbed into the snow suit again.

"It's snowing so hard," her mother said, "that I'm going to lend you this old purse to carry your valentines in." She meant the valentines Janice was taking to school to put in the box for other children. Janice and her mother had made them together. They had had fun cutting and pasting and coloring, almost as much fun as Janice and Mary Lou had had making them in other years. Janice was giving one to her teacher and

one to Margaret, one to a boy named Bob who had loaned
her his eraser twice, and several others to children whom she
hardly knew.

"I think I'll take Mary Lou's valentine to school with me,"
she said suddenly.

"That's a good idea," answered her mother. "You can show
it to your teacher."

So Janice put the beautiful valentine into her purse. Then
she kissed her mother good-by, and started back to school
feeling happier. But the happy feeling did not last.

Across the street three other children were going to school
together. They were pushing one another into the drifts,
shouting, "Giving me a valentine?" "Like fun I am!"

That was the way she and Mary Lou used to joke on the
way to school on Valentine's Day.

Janice walked primly along on her side of the street with
her mother's purse under her arm.

The weather was even wilder than it had been before. The
wind was blowing the snow in dizzy circles, whipping the
shrubs to and fro, tossing the branches of trees. The snow
was beating into Janice's face, and once when she wiped it
away she wiped two big tears along with it.

But there wasn't really any chance to cry. She was too busy
keeping her feet on the ground and the purse tucked under
her arm. The wind was growing stronger all the time, and
as Janice reached the corner opposite the school, one terrific
gust almost sent her into a snowdrift.

"Oh! Oh!" she heard someone cry behind her.

Turning around, Janice saw Margaret with what seemed
at first to be a flock of birds swirling about her head. They
were envelopes which the wind had snatched from her hand.

"My valentines!" cried Margaret. "Oh, dear! I've lost them."

"I'll help you pick them up," Janice shouted.

"We can never find them," Margaret shouted back.

"Yes, we can," cried Janice. "Look, here's one, and here's
another!" And plowing into a drifted lawn, Janice rescued
two valentines, Margaret rescued a third, and Janice a fourth.
It was like a game, and they began to whoop with joy.

The wind entered into the fun. It blew one valentine into
a pine tree far over their heads.

"I'll get it," shrieked Janice. "I'm good at climbing trees."

"But pines scratch you."

"I'm Wonderwoman," Janice yelled, and dashed in among the needles, flashed up the tree and down.

Margaret chased another envelope down someone's cellar window.

"I'm Wonderwoman, too," she yelled.

They had a glorious time.

"There's one more," cried Margaret. The wind had veered suddenly, and this one was blowing in the opposite direction from the school. The envelope skipped over the drifts like a naughty child turning its back on the school. Margaret and Janice tumbled after the truant. The wind kept the envelope always ahead of them. Sometimes it would rest for a moment on a drift, but just as they caught up with it, the envelope would flutter away. Back at the school, a bell rang.

"Janice," cried Margaret. "Go back to school! You'll be late."

"No later than you'll be," Janice called. "I'm going to catch that valentine if it's the last thing I do."

The valentine blew on, getting farther and farther from school.

On the lawn before one of the houses some boys had made a snow man. He was a big, wonderful snow man, with a pipe stuck into his mouth. Now the wind blew the valentine envelope smack into the snow man. It stuck to his round head, like a jaunty cap. Janice and Margaret stopped to scream with laughter.

Then Margaret grabbed the envelope, took Janice's hand, and they raced for the school.

The hall was warm and unnaturally quiet. From the closed doors of the rooms on either side came a drone of voices. Margaret and Janice brushed the snow from each other, giggling.

"Your feet are sopping," Janice whispered. "How did you get so wet?"

"The snow went down inside my galoshes," whispered Margaret. "Do you think we're very late? Merrill will be furious."

"Ready to snap our heads off," Janice answered.

They both knew that Miss Merrill probably wouldn't be cross at all, but it was exciting to talk that way.

"Did I get all the valentines? Let's count them," Margaret said.

Taking off her wet mittens, she laid the damp envelopes in a row on the hall radiator. Together she and Janice counted them off: One for Miss Merrill, one for Bob, others for John, Susan, Peter, Tom.

There wasn't one for Janice. Janice and Margaret both noticed that at the same moment.

"It's too bad they're wet," Janice said hastily. "Mamma gave me a purse to carry mine — —" She broke off in a gasp. "Where is it?"

"What?"

"My purse. I must have dropped it while I was chasing the valentines."

They stared at each other in complete dismay.

"Don't you worry," Margaret said. "We'll go right back and find it."

"No," said Janice. "Anyway, not now. We'd better go and tell Miss Merrill first. We're late enough already."

They hurried off to the fifth-grade room, and Miss Merrill was very sympathetic after Margaret explained what had happened. "Did you have anything of value in the purse, Janice?" she asked.

"My valentines for the valentine box," said Janice. "And one other. It came from Mary Lou, my best friend back in Chickasaw City."

Miss Merrill looked thoughtful. She put her hands on the shoulders of Janice's snow suit, and looked down at the stout rubber boots. "You're perfectly snug," said Miss Merrill. "And there's time enough for you to run back and take a look."

"May I go along to help hunt?" Margaret asked. "It was on account of me that Janice lost the purse, you know."

Miss Merrill put her hands on Margaret's shoulders, and looked down at the galoshes which were oozing snow.

"No," she said. "Because you are wet. But Bob may go to help Janice if he wants to."

"Sure," said Bob.

Bob put on his boots and his warm jacket and cap, and he and Janice went out into the snow. At first Janice felt shy, but as they went up the street, she told him how she and Margaret had chased the valentines, and Bob laughed. They reached the snow man who had worn the valentine hat. And there, at the snow man's feet, Janice found her mother's purse. The snow had not yet covered the purse; it wasn't hurt at all; and the valentines inside were perfectly dry.

"This is the valentine from my friend Mary Lou in Chickasaw City," Janice said, showing it to Bob.

"Gee, that's neat!" Bob said. "Chickasaw City is a swell town, I'll bet. But you'll like Oak Grove, too, after you live here awhile."

Janice began to think that she would.

She was sure of it after they had gone back to the schoolroom and taken off their wraps and put her valentines into the box. For then Miss Merrill asked her to be postman. Janice went up to the front of the room and lifted the cover from the valentine box. Then she took out the envelopes, one by one, and called the names:

"Margaret. Joan. Bobby. Peter. Susan. Miss Merrill."

Three times there were valentines for Janice. She put them on her desk. And after the fun of being postman came the fun of opening them. One was a pink satin heart; it came from Miss Merrill. The second was a picture of a boy on a bike with his basket full of hearts. Janice thought that this valentine might be from Bob.

She hesitated a moment before opening the third one. It was big, and the envelope was made from drawing paper.

Janice opened it and then stared in surprise. The class, she realized, was looking at her. Especially Margaret was looking. In a moment Janice knew the reason why.

The valentine was the picture of a snow man, drawn with black crayon. He was smoking a pipe, and on his head he wore a square envelope cap. There were funny crayon pictures of two girls in snow suits, dancing wildly in the snow. And at the bottom of the page Janice found this message: "For my snowstorm valentine."

"It's from me," Margaret whispered. "I made it while you were out looking for the purse. Isn't it killing?"

"It's wonderful," Janice said.

Smiling, she folded it and placed it in her purse next to the valentine Mary Lou had sent her.

After the valentine box the fifth graders played games. And after the games they had refreshments. They had cookies and little candy hearts. Janice saved some to take home to her mother.

It was a lovely party, but not so nice as what came after. She and Margaret walked home together. It had stopped snowing, the wind had died down, and the afternoon sun sparkled on the drifts. "Can't you come over to my house," Margaret asked, "and play awhile? Maybe we could make a snow man like the one we saw today."

"I'll ask my mother," Janice said. "I think I can."

So they stopped in at Janice's house, and Janice said, "Mother, this is Margaret, my snowstorm valentine."

She and Margaret began to laugh, and Janice's mother laughed, too, as the girls told how they had chased valentines in the snow.

And after that, the two new friends went out to play together.

A Valentine

By Eugene Field

Go, Cupid, and my sweetheart tell
I love her well.
Yes, though she tramples on my heart
And rends that bleeding thing apart;

And though she rolls a scornful eye
On doting me when I go by;
And though she scouts at everything
As tribute unto her I bring—
Apple, banana, caramel—
Haste, Cupid, to my love and tell,
In spite of all, I love her well!

And further say I have a sled
Cushioned in blue and painted red!
The groceryman has promised I
Can "hitch" whenever he goes by—
Go, tell her that, and, furthermore,
Apprise my sweetheart that a score
Of other little girls implore
The boon of riding on that sled
Painted and hitched, as aforesaid;—
And tell her, Cupid, only she
Shall ride upon that sled with me!
Tell her this all, and further tell
    I love her well.

A Valentine

By Eleanor Hammond

Frost flowers on the window glass,
Hopping chickadees that pass,
Bare old elms that bend and sway,
Pussy willows, soft and gray,

Silver clouds across the sky,
Lacy snowflakes flitting by,
Icicles like fringe in line—
That is Outdoor's valentine!

A Valentine

By Laura E. Richards

O little loveliest lady mine,
What shall I send for your valentine?
Summer and flowers are far away;
Gloomy old Winter is king today;
Buds will not blow, and sun will not shine:
What shall I do for a valentine?

I've searched the gardens all through and through
For a bud to tell of my love so true;
But buds are asleep and blossoms are dead,
And the snow beats down on my poor little head:
So, little loveliest lady mine,
Here is my heart for your valentine!

Washington's Birthday

FEBRUARY 22

George Washington may never have chopped down the cherry tree that we've all heard about, and he may or may not have thrown a silver dollar across the Rappahannock River, but there is no doubt that he truly earned the title, "Father of His Country."

As a young statesman George Washington believed that every man had a right to liberty and property. When he felt that Great Britain was denying these rights, Washington joined the growing band of revolutionaries. When war broke, he served as Commander in Chief of the First American Army and helped win American independence. He advised his countrymen at the Constitutional Convention in 1787. Together they shaped the new government of the young nation.

As the first President of the United States, Washington upheld the spirit of freedom and fairness. He guided and watched his country grow, as a father guides and watches his son.

When the colonies belonged to England, they celebrated the birthday of British royalty. In 1782, the young nation honored its new leader, soon to be President of the United States, with the first official celebration of Washington's birthday.

Childhood on the Potomac

BY STERLING NORTH

Illustrations by Lee Ames

WHEN George Washington was born there were, of course, no automobiles, airplanes, locomotives or steamboats, nor was there electricity and modern plumbing. Men, animals, wind and falling water provided most of the harnessed energy. In that year young Louis XV was on the throne of France. George II was the King of England. The most widely known American was a 26-year-old Philadelphia printer named Benjamin Franklin. It would be two more years before Daniel Boone would be born—one of the few frontiersmen who would see more action in the wilderness than George Washington himself.

At the Pope's Creek plantation, George knew nothing of such matters. He ate, slept, played with his pets and watched long-legged colts frisking in the pastures. He was warned not to fall into the shallow waters of Pope's Creek. The fenced-in kitchen garden was a safe place for him to play. Here the mockingbirds sang by day and the whippoorwills called at night. Roses grew along the grassy walks between the well-kept beds of vegetables and flowers. The herb garden of sage, thyme, rosemary, pennyroyal and rue reminded him of the good odors of things cooking in the kitchen. George found ripe strawberries hiding under green leaves. All of his life he would enjoy gardens and orchards, planting and improving his fruit trees and his flowers.

When does memory begin? Perhaps George Washington's first clear recollections were of the bustle and confusion of moving from his birthplace to another great farm which Augustine owned farther up the Potomac at Little Hunting Creek. (This was a 2500-acre plantation that would later become famous as Mount Vernon.) What noise and excitement as the slaves and workmen prepared the furniture, farm tools and livestock for this big adventure!

It is probable that a small house already stood on the present site of the white-pillared mansion when the Washingtons moved

in 1735 to that imposing bluff above the "River of Swans" at the "Freshes" of the Potomac. The word "Freshes" refers to the fact that the water here is less salty than farther down the river, being constantly refreshed by the Great Falls of the Potomac some twenty-four miles upstream.

The members of the Washington family making this move were five in number: Augustine the father, Mary the mother, and their children George, Betty and Samuel, ages three, two and one. George's half-sister Jane had died within the year. His half-brothers, Lawrence and Austin, were still at school in England.

Three more children were to be born to Mary Ball Washington within the next few years: John Augustine, called "Jack," in 1736; Charles in 1738; and Mildred, in 1739—a child who did not survive infancy.

George, eldest and strongest of this tribe, quite probably led the others in their adventures. He would have been the first to learn the dangerous thrill of riding horseback on some small mount, with the wind in his ginger-colored hair and the ground speeding backward under flying hoofs.

Augustine would certainly have taken his children to see the mill he had built at Dogue Run for grinding flour and corn meal. One can imagine the row of youngsters standing entranced as they watched the clear water tumbling over the mossy water wheel. Inside the dusty mill, the rumble of the millstones and the groaning of the wooden cogwheels may have frightened the smaller children.

Equally exciting to the young Washingtons were the activities at the private wharf on the Potomac. Here, probably under some watchful adult eye, they could fish or lie in the sun idly viewing the barges being rowed by slaves across the water to the Maryland shore. Sails were often visible, tacking into the wind or skimming like floating leaves ahead of a stiff breeze. Wild ducks and geese wedged over, high above them.

On memorable occasions the children were chased off the wharf to watch from a safe distance the loading of huge hogsheads of leaf tobacco into a three-masted, ocean-going ship. This was the harvest of an entire season of planting being freighted off to some merchant in England. Here in its finished form was the crop they had watched all year, from the tiny green plants raised so carefully in covered beds, through the transplanting, cultivating, harvesting and stripping of the pungent leaves. What back-breaking labor had gone into the production of each of those great barrels of leaf tobacco upon which depended the entire success of the plantation!

Augustine and Mary made a long list of goods they wanted the ship's captain to bring back from England. They could grow most of their own food, but they needed from the mother country many things not made in Virginia. Fine cloth for suits and dresses, for example, was not to be had in the new land. Handkerchiefs, too, and bright ribbons, warm gloves and shoes of leather were obtainable only from abroad. Nor was that all. By British restriction, farming tools such as sickles, hoes, axes and saws could not be fashioned in the colonies, so these too must come from England. And, of course, green tea and Cheshire cheese; yes, even a few toys and sweets for the children if the tobacco fetched a good price that year. What a day it must have been when the ship returned loaded with at least some of these treasures (even if the shoes were not a perfect fit and a few of the items had been ruined by seawater)!

It was from this wharf that Augustine had sailed away on another worried business trip to England. He was to attend a conference concerning those troublesome iron mines and furnaces which were earning almost nothing for himself or for his English partners. Mary and her children must have watched the sails of that departing ship until they disappeared far down the Potomac on the way to the angry Atlantic Ocean. Months later the head of the family was safe at home again with news that Lawrence soon would be following. Already this big half-brother was something of a hero in the mind of six-year-old George.

But the happiness the Washingtons had known at Little Hunting Creek was suddenly threatened by the news that Augustine had again made the decision to move, this time to a little farm on the narrow Rappahannock. They would leave behind them the beautiful "River of Swans," the wide green meadows, the cool deep forests and the plantation house on the bluff—a place which from his childhood to the day of his death George Washington so greatly loved.

The new farm to which the Washingtons moved late in 1738 had an eight-room house situated pleasantly on high land overlooking the river. On the far shore lay the village of Fredericksburg. Some two miles up river, the Falls of the Rappahannock marked the head of navigation. Below the falls the water was deep enough for ocean-going vessels.

There were few waking moments in which a boy could have been unaware of this ribbon of water lying to the west of the house—a place to swim and fish, and a highway for the ships serving the tobacco port of Fredericksburg.

Tying the farm more closely to the river was the ferry which gave the name "Ferry Farm" to this new home of the Washingtons. The road to the ferry ran down a steep ravine so near the house that the shouting of the teamsters and the rumble of the heavy carts may have disturbed Mary. However, to George and the other children, the ferryboat plying back and forth across the river must have seemed continuously exciting.

Equally interesting was the little town of Fredericksburg

lying in neat squares on the far side of the Rappahannock. Here were tobacco warehouses; wharves; a stone quarry; and a scattering of houses. The town boasted a church, a prison, a tavern, and soon an apothecary shop where medicines were sold. Twice yearly to this village came the joyous and rowdy fairs.

Very little is known about Washington's early years. Several writers have invented unlikely stories. No one now believes that George cut down a cherry tree and then hurried to his father to confess, "I can't tell a lie, Pa; you know I can't tell a lie. I did cut it with my hatchet." This fable and many others were created from thin air by Parson M. L. Weems, a sentimental early biographer.

Equally doubtful are many of the stories about Washington's schooling. Was he instructed by a gravedigger named Hobby? There is no written evidence to prove it.

Possibly he went to a little school in Fredericksburg run by a Reverend James Marye. But if at this school he was a leader in the vigorous sports of the schoolyard, then Parson Weems must be in error when he pictures George as stopping every squabble between other boys, or rushing "instantly" to the school master to ". . . inform him of their barbarous intentions."

Somehow, between his seventh and eleventh years, he learned "reading, writing and ciphering" and a few words of Latin. He had at least one lesson in music. Obviously he mastered the art of copying his assignments in a clear, firm hand. Little more can be stated with assurance.

In view of the family tradition, it seems mysterious that George was not sent "back home" to England for a few years of study. Perhaps his father's financial troubles prevented it. Or possibly his mother wished to keep her eldest son beside her, fearing to let him cross the wind-swept North Atlantic. We *do* know that very soon she would be refusing to let him become a sailor.

The War for Independence

BY GENEVIEVE FOSTER

ON July 4, 1776, the United States was born. Exactly one year after Washington took command of the army, the colonies declared themselves free from England. Their Declaration of Independence had been written by Thomas Jefferson and signed.

George Washington did not sign it. On that day in July, when it was first read aloud to the members of Congress in Philadelphia, he was in New York City with his army. There, as soon as a copy came, he had it read aloud to the men. The soldiers, excited to hear that they were no longer subjects of George III, ran to the park, tore down his statue, knocked off his head and melted his lead horse into bullets.

George Washington did not approve of such disrespectful conduct, but he did approve of Independence. More than any one else, he was to make that Declaration, now only written on paper, become true. He believed that the colonies should be free and was willing to fight for their freedom.

And a long hard fight it was to be. Six years would pass from the time the first shots had been fired in Massachusetts until all firing ended at Yorktown, in Virginia; and two more years before the treaty was signed and the war was actually over.

Eight long discouraging years those would be for Washington. He had to carry on a war, when he had nothing to fight with—never enough soldiers—not enough guns and ammunition for those he did have—not enough clothes—not even enough food. And no pay for them, for Congress had no money.

Yet Congress would order him to do impossible things and blame him when he failed. Some of his officers were to lose faith in him, and form a plot to ruin him. One of those he most trusted was to turn traitor. Still he would keep steadily on through those eight years, doing the best he could with what he had and holding on—holding on.

Now the first year was over. The winter had been spent on the hills outside of Boston. In the Spring, the British had decided to leave the harbor. Through his spy glass, Washington had watched them as they boarded their ships and sailed away.

Following orders from Congress, Washington had then moved his patchwork army down to New York to try to keep that city from being captured next. But it proved impossible. For one thing, he had no warships to keep the British ships from entering the harbor. So General Howe sailed in. Having almost twice as many men, he defeated the Americans, drove them out of the city, chased them up the Hudson River, and across the river into New Jersey. That was enough for him. He went back to New York.

There he found Lord Cornwallis, who had just arrived from England, bringing Hessian soldiers, who had been hired to fight. So Howe sent them to carry on the chase. Week after week it went on. Month after month, down through New Jersey, Washington kept on retreating, with the enemy close upon his heels, like a pack of hounds chasing a fox.

Moving too fast to carry supplies, his cold, hungry troops began deserting. Some of his officers now turned against him. And when he had to cross the Delaware River into Pennsylvania, Congress was in a panic. Any day they expected to see Cornwallis and his soldiers come marching into Philadelphia.

But it was then December. The Delaware River was too difficult to cross, half frozen, full of floating ice cakes. So the soldiers, whom Cornwallis had sent on ahead of him, stopped short on the Jersey side in the town of Trenton. Christmas came. Feasting, drinking, singing songs of their homeland, the Hessians celebrated all day and far into the night.

During that night Washington re-crossed the Delaware. In the blinding snow and sleet, in small boats, he brought his men back across that half frozen river to the New Jersey side. At dawn, they rushed in upon the sleepy, groggy soldiers and captured them. Washington was still there, when Cornwallis arrived.

"I'll bag the old fox now," said Cornwallis, that night, planning to capture Washington in the morning. But next morning

he awoke to find that his "old fox" had been too sly for him. He had escaped!

While Cornwallis slept, Washington had slipped away in the dark. Leaving his campfires burning to fool the British sentinels into thinking he was still there, he had stolen silently around the enemy lines. By daylight, he and his soldiers were well away and on the road north again. A battle at Princeton, in which the British were defeated, ended the fighting for that winter. Cornwallis returned to New York. Washington went into winter camp in New Jersey. Martha came from Mount Vernon to be with him, and kept busy knitting stockings. She left in early summer when the fighting was expected to begin again.

Just where it would begin, or what city the British would try to capture next, Washington could only guess—until about the first of August.

Then his scouts brought word that General Howe had sailed

from New York harbor. Two weeks later, British ships were seen sailing into Chesapeake Bay. No doubt then. They were headed for Philadelphia!

Congress scurried away, and the "rebels" left in Philadelphia were terrified. Hoping to give them courage, Washington marched his soldiers through the streets and down past the Hall where the bold Declaration of Independence had so recently been signed. To the tune of "Yankee Doodle" on their fife and drums, the men and boys stepped along as briskly and bravely as they could, behind their devoted leader. Sprigs of green leaves were stuck in their ragged caps, to make them look a trifle less dilapidated.

Cheered by the rebels, the ragged troops were jeered and laughed at by the Tories. And there were many of them—many of those Americans who were still loyal to the King. They longed to hear and see the British entering their city. A battle or two, and they were there. Early in October, General Howe and his soldiers were marching into Philadelphia. The city was all theirs for a gay and comfortable winter.

Only twenty miles away, Washington and his soldiers suffered through the winter on the bleak, windswept hills at Valley Forge, half starved, half frozen. Many had no shoes, and their sore, cracked feet, wrapped in rags, left tracks of blood in the snow as they went about cutting down trees and building log huts to live in. Until the huts were finished, Washington stayed in a tent close to his men, and lived and ate as they did. Then he moved into a small stone house, down by the creek. Martha came, as usual, to spend the winter months. Bright days she trudged from hut to hut, with a basket on her arm, visiting soldiers who were ill. Every day but Sunday she was knitting socks and patching garments with wives of the other officers.

Washington lived through that winter with a heavy heart. He was distressed by the suffering of his soldiers. He was tormented by letters from Congress filled with blame and criticism, and offering no help. He discovered that a plot was being formed to ruin him and put another general in his place. Hurt by their lack of trust, Washington still kept up his courage, stood firm and held on. In time the cruel plot against him melted away and also that dreadful winter came to an end.

And it was Spring again—the Spring of 1778.

And with that Spring came news—GOOD news—GREAT news! WONDERFUL NEWS!

One day in May, the whole camp was given over to celebration and joy. So overjoyed was one young Major General, that he threw his arms around Washington and kissed him on both cheeks! This was the Marquis de La Fayette, a young French nobleman, just twenty years old. And the cause of his great joy?

France, his country—*France had now joined America in the war!* A treaty had just been signed by Louis XVI, the King of France, and Benjamin Franklin, who had gone there to ask France for help.

Only a year ago he, La Fayette, had left for America to help fight for Liberty. Then he had had to slip away to the seaport in disguise, with a black wig over his red hair, because the King had forbidden him to leave. Now the King had changed his mind. France was going to help America. French soldiers and French ships would soon be coming!

That news changed the plans of the British. General Howe had now returned to England, leaving another general in command. Hearing that a French fleet was sailing for New York, the British general felt he was needed there more than in Philadelphia. So he left, and, dragging after him a train of baggage wagons twelve miles long, returned to New York City. Washington followed, and went into camp not far off, where he could keep watch of the city and wait for the French fleet. As soon as the French ships came, Washington hoped, with their help, to recapture the city and drive the British from New York.

What a disappointment! The French ships got there in July, but their hulls were so deep that they dragged in the sand bar, got stuck and couldn't even enter the harbor. So the British stayed in New York and Washington and his troops stood guard nearby, to the end of the war.

And from then on to the end, most of the fighting was in the four southern states. It began in Georgia. By the Spring of 1780, the fifth year of the war, the British had marched up through Georgia, through South Carolina, and Lord Cornwallis, who was in command, had moved on into North Carolina, headed for Virginia. That was sad news for Washington, but there was also good news.

French soldiers had landed in America, and were in Newport, Rhode Island. Taking La Fayette with him, Washington went to confer with the friendly, old French general, whom his soldiers called "papa" Rochambeau. Again he was hoping to attack the British general in New York, but it seemed wiser not to try, until another French fleet reached America. Another was on its way. So there was nothing to do but wait, while that fifth year dragged slowly out. Early the next year, 1781, Washington heard from Thomas Jefferson, who was then governor of Virginia, that British troops were marching through Virginia, burning tobacco warehouses, and laying waste to the country. Washington sent La Fayette south at once, with all the soldiers he could possibly spare.

Soon he heard that Cornwallis was also in Virginia. He waited anxiously for La Fayette's letters.

At last, in early autumn, word came to hurry south as fast as possible.

The French fleet had arrived in Chesapeake Bay! The American generals had Cornwallis surrounded and he was bottled up in Yorktown.

Washington and Rochambeau started south at once. Soon the ragged American soldiers and the French troops, in their gorgeous uniforms, cheered by the people, were marching through Philadelphia, through Baltimore, and crossing the Potomac into Virginia. Late one night, the family at Mount Vernon were startled out of their sleep. There, to their surprise was Washington, himself! The next day, came "papa" Rochambeau. A fine feast was given them by the neighbors. And they were off again.

Jacky Custis went as an aide to Washington, saying what was to be a last goodbye to his three little girls and baby son. He would not return.

At Williamsburg, ten miles from Yorktown, Washington found La Fayette waiting, overjoyed to see his great and beloved general there at last.

On October 9, 1781, the siege of Yorktown began. Washington touched off the first cannon. For ten days the cannons boomed and clouds of smoke hung over the little town. Then the firing ceased.

Cornwallis surrendered.

At two o'clock in the afternoon, with the bright October sun shining on their scarlet coats, the British soldiers marched slowly out of Yorktown, while their band played a popular British tune, "The World Upside Down." They passed between rows of French and American soldiers drawn up in parallel lines. The troops stood in respectful silence, as Washington had told them to do, while the British soldiers laid down their arms.

The day after the surrender Cornwallis went to pay his respects to General Washington. And, shortly afterward, he was a guest at the dinner that Washington gave for the officers of the three armies.

Jacky Custis now lay desperately ill in Williamsburg. His wife and mother hurried from Mount Vernon. And just before he died, Washington promised to adopt his littlest girl, Nelly, who was two and a half, and his baby boy, named George Washington.

George Washington

BY MAUD AND MISKA PETERSHAM

Illustrations by the authors

WITH the booming of cannons and the ringing of bells, a great shout went up from a throng of people crowding the narrow street or clinging on nearby roof-tops. "LONG LIVE GEORGE WASHINGTON, PRESIDENT OF THE UNITED STATES."

This was in the year 1789. The crowds were gathered in front of Federal Hall in the City of New York. On the balcony of the Hall, above the cheering crowds, stood a tall, dignified

man. He was dressed in a dark brown suit with knee breeches and white stockings with silver buckled shoes. His white powdered hair was tied back in a small bag, the fashion of the times. His kindly face was serious as he bowed and acknowledged the cheers of the people.

George Washington had just taken the oath of office as the first President of the United States of America.

A new nation had been formed from the thirteen American colonies that had won their War of Independence. George Washington had been unanimously chosen to become the leader and the head of this new nation.

Wild uncultivated land and deep forest surrounded the farm where George Washington was born in Westmoreland county in Virginia. As a small boy he learned to ride and to hunt. He grew tall and straight as an arrow, but he cared little for books or study. His father died when he was eleven but under the firm guidance of his mother he learned to be independent and fearless.

At sixteen he was a competent surveyor, and he spent the next three years with his musket and his compass, mapping out a wild territory which crossed the Blue Ridge Mountains. He learned to take hardship and danger.

The royal governor of Virginia chose this young surveyor for a perilous mission far into the Ohio valley and sent him on a thousand mile journey through trackless forest.

Washington crossed steep mountains and icy, swollen rivers, and met with treacherous Indians, but he returned, with the mission accomplished.

George Washington became a colonel in the Virginia militia. He was over six feet tall, an excellent horseman and expert shot. As aide to the English General Braddock, he went to the frontier where Indians and the French were attacking American settlers. Washington knew the fashion of Indian warfare. Braddock insisted on arranging his troops in close formation. The bright red coats of the British soldiers made a sure target for the Indians in ambush. General Braddock was killed. Washington had bullet holes in his uniform and two horses shot from under him, but was uninjured. He saved from complete destruction the remnant of Braddock's army.

Washington's courage and judgment were known throughout the colonies. His leadership had begun.

The Colonists rebelled against the rule of England, and wanted the right to govern themselves.

Farmers became soldiers. They were ready to fight for their independence. They chose George Washington as their commander-in-chief.

Under an elm tree on the common in Cambridge, Massachusetts, General Washington drew his sword and took command of the Continental Army.

The calm, self-controlled general could be aroused to intense passion. He had determination, courage and faith. Through the long dark days of the American Revolution, he led his troops to final victory and the Colonies became a free and independent nation. Accepting no pay for his services, the commander-in-chief then bade farewell to his officers and men, and returned to the place he loved best—his plantation in Virginia.

Washington longed to live out his days at Mount Vernon as a planter, but the new nation needed its strongest, wisest men and again he was called back to public life. He presided over the Constitutional Convention in Philadelphia which drew up the new Constitution. And then after the Constitution was approved the people of the United States chose for their first President, the one man they all loved and trusted —George Washington. It was decided that in this new democratic country the President should not be addressed as "His Excellency" or "His Highness," but simply as "Mr. President."

Washington again proved himself a strong leader. He put the new rules of government to work and many problems facing the nation were solved. He served as President for two terms of four years each, but he refused a third term, and he retired to Mount Vernon.

As a man of twenty-one, George Washington had inherited from his half-brother the beautiful estate of Mount Vernon, overlooking the Potomac River. Here he had brought his wife Martha Custis and her two children. The estate was a little village in itself. There were fields and farms, a mill for grinding grain, a smoke house, a blacksmith shop and a small house for the spinning and weaving of cloth. There were slave cabins, and stables for the coach and saddle horses, and barns for a hundred cows. The stately home was always open to the many friends of George and Martha Washington.

Washington cared for all the details of the plantation. Each morning after his breakfast of corn bread, honey and tea, the master of the estate would ride about the farms, directing and planning. Under his careful supervision, the estate produced practically everything needed.

George Washington lived a little more than two years after he left the presidency. In his will he provided for the freeing of his many slaves. The first great president was beloved by the entire nation. He was the father of a country which was to become one of the strongest nations of the world.

Washington

By Nancy Byrd Turner

> He played by the river when he was young,
> He raced with rabbits along the hills,
> He fished for minnows, and climbed and swung,
> and hooted back at the whippoorwills.
> Strong and slender and tall he grew
> And then, one morning, the bugles blew.
>
> Over the hills the summons came,
> Over the river's shining rim.
> He said that the bugles called his name,
> He knew that his country needed him,
> And he answered, "Coming!" and marched away
> For many a night and many a day.
>
> Perhaps when the marches were hot and long
> He'd think of the river flowing by,
> Or, camping under the winter sky,
> Would hear the whippoorwill's far-off song.
> Boy or man, and in peace or strife,
> He loved America all his life!

George Washington

By Stephen Vincent Benét

Illustration by Estelle Hollingworth

Sing hey! for bold George Washington,
That jolly British tar,
King George's famous admiral
From Hull to Zanzibar!
No—wait a minute—something's wrong—
George *wished* to sail the foam.
But, when his mother thought, aghast,
Of Georgie shinning up a mast,
Her tears and protests flowed so fast
That George remained at home.

Sing ho! for grave George Washington,
The staid Virginia squire,
Who farms his fields and hunts his hounds
And aims at nothing higher!
Stop, stop, it's going wrong again!
George *liked* to live on farms,
But, when the Colonies agreed
They could and should and would be freed,
They called on George to do the deed
And George cried "Shoulder arms!"

Sing ha! for Emperor Washington,
That hero of renown,
Who freed his land from Britain's rule
To win a golden crown!
No, no, that's what George *might* have won
But didn't, for he said,
"There's not much point about a king,
They're pretty but they're apt to sting
And, as for crowns—the heavy thing
Would only hurt my head."

Sing ho! for our George Washington!
(At last I've got it straight.)
The first in war, the first in peace,
The goodly and the great.
But, when you think about him now,
From here to Valley Forge,
Remember this—he might have been
A highly different specimen,
And, where on earth would we be, then?
I'm glad that George was George.

Inscription at Mount Vernon

Anonymous

Illustration by Estelle Hollingworth

Washington, the brave, the wise, the good,
Supreme in war, in council, and in peace.
Valiant without ambition, discreet without fear, confident with-
out presumption.
In disaster calm; in success moderate; in all, himself.
The hero, the patriot, the Christian.
The father of nations, the friend of mankind,
Who, when he had won all, renounced all, and sought in the
bosom of his family and of nature, retirement, and in the hope
of religion, immortality.

Prayer for the Nation

By George Washington

Almighty God, we make our earnest prayer that Thou wilt
keep the United States in Thy holy protection; that Thou wilt
incline the hearts of the citizens to cultivate a spirit of subordi-
nation and obedience to government; to entertain a brotherly
affection and love for one another and for their fellow citizens
of the United States at large.

Saint Patrick's Day

MARCH 17

When he was a boy of sixteen, Patrick was taken from his home in Christian Britain by pirate raiders and sold as a slave in pagan Ireland. Patrick escaped and became a monk in France, but the six years he had spent in Ireland left him with a great desire to bring Christ to the people he had grown to love.

He returned to Ireland as a missionary, and for more than fifty years traveled the length and breadth of the rugged, beautiful island battling the Druid priests who held the land under a religion of fear and human sacrifice.

St. Patrick died in 461, after founding three hundred churches and Christianizing half of Ireland. He is the patron saint of the Irish, and on his feast day, all things Irish are honored.

Saint Patrick

BY ELEANOR FARJEON

Illustrations by Helen Sewell

MILCHO, a rich chief of Dalrhidia in County Antrim, stood bargaining on the shore with Nial Navigiallach, an Irish King who had come to that coast to trade. It was in the dawn of the Fifth Century, when the times were rough, and kings were pirates and raiders. The coasts of both Britain and Gaul had reason to fear the raids of Nial of the Nine Hostages. In his boats were many youths whom he had taken captive here and there, and one and another of these was hauled out by Nial's crew of Picts, for Milcho to consider. The rich man needed another slave, and he looked the boys over as a farmer does a horse or a cow in the market. He quarrelled with Nial about the price asked for each, and all the time he had his eye on a lad of sixteen, who sat in the boat with his hands tied together. Captive though he was, there was nothing cowed about him; he held his head up proudly, and Milcho thought he would make a likely slave. So presently, nodding carelessly towards the lad, he asked, "Are you selling that one?"

Nial said, "I might, if I got his price."

"What is he?" asked Milcho.

"One that we took in a raid off the Scottish coast."

"No, Nial," broke in one of his men, "it was in that raid off Wales—or would it be the one off Cumberland?"

"Neither," declared another, "we got that boy in Cornwall."

"You're wrong!" cried a third. "That's the one we took off a farm in Gaul."

While the Picts fell to quarrelling about where the boy came from, Milcho said to Nial, "It's all one. What do you want for him, anyhow?" And the chief and the king began their haggling all over again.

Nial had the boy fetched out of the boat, and said to Milcho, "There's a tall one for you!"

"I've seen taller," said Milcho.

"Mark the breadth of his shoulders," said Nial.

"I've known broader," said Milcho.

"Feel the muscles on him!" boasted Nial.

Milcho did so, and said, "I've felt tougher."

The king ran him up, and the chief ran him down, and so at last the bargain was concluded, and Milcho led the boy away to be his slave on the Mountain of Sleamish.

On the way the chief put questions to the boy, about whom the Picts had made so much argument. "Where did they take you?" he asked.

"From my father's farm at Enon," said the boy.

"Where might that be?"

"On the river's edge."

"What river, boy?"

"The river under Bonavem, where my father is a deacon of the church," said the boy proudly.

"Oho! Perhaps you hoped to be one too."

The boy knew himself to be a little careless of his religion; he answered, "My father hoped so."

"And hasn't your father a name of his own?" asked Milcho.

"His name is Calpurnius. My mother is called Conchessa. She is a Frank's daughter, but my father has the blood of patricians in him."

"And what may *your* name be, my young patrician?"

"Succath," said he.

"Well then, Succath, put away hopes of being a deacon like your da, it was off a farm, not off a church, they took you, and you shall keep my pigs, O well-born one!"

"First thrall to Picts, then thrall to pigs," observed Succath. "It's a queer thing life is surely." He stooped to pluck a tiny emerald leaf off the earth. "There's good things growing in this land however," thought he—"and evil ones too!" thought he again, as a viper hissed at him and darted away.

Thus Succath came to Dalrhidia on Mount Sleamish, and when Milcho's people asked, "Where was he born?" the chief replied, "Some say here and some say there," and the boy's birthplace remained for ever a matter of doubt.

Seven years Succath kept his master's pigs, and they were seven years of misery to the slave. But this they did for him, they led his mind, which was no man's slave, to God. His father's faith grew green in him, green as the three-leaved shamrock by the brown bog where the swine rooted. His labours began early in the dawn; but eager to serve God as well as his master, Succath rose still earlier than he need, and forestalled the daylight with his prayers.

Those seven years meant much to the boy's life. In them he came to speak the Irish tongue so well that you would take him for an Irishman itself, and he grew to know so much of the hearts of the folk that an Irish heart might have beat in his own breast. Moreover, Succath was no meek young man, but had a noble temper of his own, which made him still more like a hot-blooded son of Erin. At the end of the seven years, when he was three-and-twenty years old, he was more Irish than any other thing, and had a deep love for the island, the people, and the three-leaved shamrock which made the land so green. But some things in it he hated: such as the poison-snakes, whose venom was a danger to life, and the Druid priests, whose magic was a danger to the soul. And he hated his own slavery, which rendered him powerless to become, as was now his dearest wish, a priest of God, when he might fight against evils such as these. Meanwhile he did what he could with fasting and with prayers.

And then one night he heard a voice in his sleep: "Thou fastest well, and shalt soon return to thy country." And again the voice called: "Behold a ship is ready for thee."

When he awoke, Succath knew the time was come for him to go, and he rose and went under the cover of the night. The coast was many miles away, but he travelled safe till he reached it, and there, by God's power, was the ship. She was making ready to set sail for France.

Succath hastened his steps, and asked for passage in her.

"Can you pay?" said the Merchant Master of the ship.

"Yes, when we reach Bonavem," answered Succath.

But the Merchant stared at his mean garb, and roughly bade him be off. Not knowing what to do next he turned towards a little hovel on the shore, where he might hide himself; and as he went he began to say a prayer. It was not even ended, and he had not reached the hut before he heard a sailor shouting, "Turn back! He is asking for you!"—and when Succath came to the ship again, the Merchant simply said, "We will take you on trust." And so the ship set sail with Succath in her, and after three days was brought to beach in Brittany.

It was far from Succath's farmstead, a journey of at least a month, but the merchant-seamen decided to make it with their poor Christian passenger, who would recompense them at the end of it. They had with them their wares with which they hoped to trade in cities or at rich houses on the way. But they found none of these. It was at all times a hard, wild, stony country, and now it was desolate; for the savage Franks had lately ravaged it, taking the cattle and ruining the crops. After many rough and weary days they found themselves as cast away on land as ever at sea, and in a lonely forest, where they stayed exhausted, the Merchant thought they must all die of hunger. In his despair he turned to Succath and cried, "Christian! Is your God so powerful? Pray for us, lest we starve!"

"Have faith," said Succath, and fell on his knees and prayed. Soon there was a mighty stir in the forest, and a herd of wild pigs came trampling down the underbrush. With a shout the famished sailors sprang to their feet; and that night the forest was full of the smoke of wood-fires, and the smell of roast meat. The travellers stayed two days recovering their strength, and before they went from that place the Merchant came to Succath with wild honey in his hands. "See what I have found in a hollow tree," he said. "Take your share as an offering, Christian, and God be thanked."

So, after many years, when the young man came to his own door again, and the merchants took leave of him, he knew they carried with them something of his faith.

But Succath found he could not rest at home. The need to become a priest urged him elsewhere, for all the pleas of his friends and family; and chance or heaven led his feet south to Tours, whose bishop was the venerable Saint Martin. Martin was very old, Succath was young, but the younger and the elder met in their love of God. When Succath had spoken with the Saint in his green cabin on the banks of the Loire, where he

lived still like a hermit, Martin said: "If you wish to be my
disciple I will teach you all I can; and because you are of a
well-born Roman strain, you shall be called, not Succath, but
Patricius."

So Patricius, whom now we may at last call, in the Irish
manner, Patrick, realized his wish and became a monk, dwelling
in a sandstone cave by the river, as all Martin's disciples did.
From a monk he was to become a priest, from a priest a bishop.
While he was on the road, and still a young man, he had a
dream one night in which he saw written the words: "THE
VOICE OF THE IRISH." Then he heard sounds of voices crying from a thicket where people were lost in the dark: "We
entreat thee, O holy boy, come and walk again in our midst!"
And Patrick awoke, moved to the depths of his soul.

But the time was not ripe till he was a man in his prime,
when he heard that Pope Celestine thought of sending a mission to preach the Gospel in Ireland. Who was so fitted for that
mission as Patrick the bishop, who as Succath the slave had
learned to speak the tongue, and know the land, and love the
people? So once again a boat bore Patrick to the emerald isle,
even as one had borne him thirty years earlier; but this time
he went with unbound hands, that carried a bishop's crozier
into Ireland.

One April day the herdsmen of Lecale in County Down
looked over the sea and saw a boat coming, full of strange
men. Their coming meant one thing only to these simple fellows, and they took to their heels and ran to the great barn
where Dichu, their chieftain, was busy. "Master, make ready!"
they shouted, "for the marauders are upon us again!"

Dichu came out of his barn, and called to his servants to arm
and follow him; and he hastened down to the waterside, with
his shield on his arm and his spear in his hand. But when he saw
the boatful of men on the shore he was puzzled, for they were
unarmed, and their leader smiled peaceably upon him.

"Who are you, strangers?" asked Dichu.

The leader answered him in his own tongue. "My name is
Patrick, and once I was a slave in this land, yet in my soul I
was more free than you who live under the shadow of the

Druids. And now I am come to make you as free as I was."

"Step up to my house, Padruic, and tell me more," said Dichu. He signed to his followers to lower their spears, and brought Patrick and his monks into his hall, and made them welcome. When they had eaten, he bade the bishop speak, and Patrick stood up and said such things as had never before been said or heard in Erse. He had God's light in his heart, and God's gift on his tongue, and his eloquence was like fire that catches everywhere, and his reason like the tides that are according to heaven. Dichu had but to listen and believe, and he demanded instant baptism. But what then? There was no church handy, indeed, there was as yet none in all Ireland.

"Come into your own barn, Dichu," said the Saint, "and be baptized on your own threshing-floor."

And then and there divine worship was celebrated, among the tools and the grain, and Dichu and his servants were made Christians. Sabhall-Padruic, or Patrick's Barn, they called it ever after. Soon the whole place round about became known as Saul, out of the name of the barn, and it became Saint Patrick's favourite resting-place, after his long journeys here and there. Many journeys he made about the land, and now he was listened to, now driven away. Now he converted multitudes like the stones on the shore, now one or two only, like precious pebbles picked up in this place or that. It is no easy thing to change the faith of a people, or to lift from them a power that has lain on them for many hundred years. Fear of the Druids was the power over that land. Among those who would not listen was Milcho, in search of whom Patrick had gone on foot. His old master would not even see the Saint who once had kept his swine; and perhaps this time it was not fear of the Druids that was in it. But swiftly and slowly, and always steadily, Patrick's word was weakening the sway of the Irish magicians, and they themselves were growing aware of it.

Everywhere that men and women gathered in knots, miraculous tales were whispered from ear to ear.

"Have you heard? This Patrick has given back to blind Sheila the sight of her eyes!"

"Have you heard? When Sean was lying dead upon his bed, this Patrick came and raised him to life again!"

"Have you heard? He preached one cold morning on a moun-
taintop, and the limbs of his listeners froze, and they had neither
food nor fuel to warm them. This Patrick set them all to heap-
ing snowballs, and breathed upon the heap, and that white
heap of ice became a red-hot fire!"

"And have you heard how Lochu the Magus challenged him
to a trial of magic, and Lochu spread his hands and rose up in
the air halfway to the sky, but this Patrick only folded his and
said a prayer, and a white arm reached out of a cloud and flung
a snowball at Lochu, and he tumbled down head foremost at
Patrick's feet!"

"And this have you heard, how Patrick built a hut of green
wood and dry, and he challenged a Magus to sit in the green
half wearing a monk's robe, and in the dry half he sate the
Monk in the robe of the Magus, and then he set fire to the hut.
And it was the green wood that burned, and the Magus with
it, yet the holy habit was not even singed; and the dry timber
would not catch, and the Monk had not so much as a blister,
though the evil robe was shrivelled off him by the heat!"

"*Have you heard*" this and that wonder ran like wildfire from
place to place, and each new tale of Patrick spelled the Druids'
downfall. Till at last men were telling the tale of the great
encounter that finished them entirely.

The Saint had offered them his blessing, but they would have
none of it, and held by their magic obstinate as mules, though
Patrick told them, "Your magic is the curse of the country."

"Beware lest it be a curse on yourself," said they.

"On me, is it? Let *you* beware!" cried he. "If it comes to curs-
ing, there's none can do it better than a bishop when he's roused.
Yet I'd rather give you my blessing."

But when the Druids still sought to overthrow him with their
spells, even the holy Patrick knew they were past his prayers.
So he raised his hands over their fields, saying sternly: "I set my
curse on you!" The Druids' crops and pastures turned immediately into bogs, and they saw their chief means of living vanish
under their eyes.

"Will you let me bless you now?" asked Patrick.

"We can eat fish," they said. And they sat on the river-banks
with rod and line, and filled their creels, and went on playing
their tricks.

Then Patrick raised his hands over their rivers, crying again: "I set my curse on you!" The rivers ceased to have fish in them on the spot.

"Now shall I bless you?" asked Patrick.

"You shall not!" roared the Druids, and ran to their homes and put their kettles on. Heaven knows what dark spells they meant to brew over their fires, to destroy the holy terror they were no match for. But the Saint pursued them to their very hearths, and raising his hands over their kettles cried: "I set my curse on you!" And the kettles stopped boiling at once.

The Druids piled brushwood in armfuls on the red-hot peat, in vain. The wood flamed, the peat glowed, and the kettles stayed cold.

"Will you be blessed *now?*" said Patrick.

"We will not!" said they.

Then the Saint gave them up for a bad job. The land must be rid of its evils, and nothing was so evil in the land as they. He raised his hands for the fourth time, and pronounced his curse on their heads; and the earth opened under their feet and swallowed them up.

But the reptiles remained.

There never was a land so full of snakes. The reptiles he had hated in his slavery had multiplied out of all count, and now the tale went that this Patrick had sworn to rid Erin's soil of their poison, as he had rid her soul of the Druids' venom. A task indeed for any ordinary man! How would he set about it? *Have you heard?* He has made a vow: "I'll drum them out of the country!"

So he made himself a drum, and cut two stout sticks, and flourished them on his march across the land, drumming till his arms ached. Serpents, snakes, and scorpions fled before him! You never heard such drumming, or saw such flourishes! But his holy fervour nearly destroyed him entirely, for he struck the drum one such mighty blow that he knocked a hole through it. When next he struck, the virtue had gone out of the sound, and who knows what those millions of reptiles might not have done to him if an angel had not flown down out of heaven and patched up the hole? From that out, Patrick drummed more carefully, till the last little snake was driven into the sea; and then he blessed the land, so that they could never come back. Since then there has not been a snake or a Druid in Ireland.

It is one thing to destroy, it is another to build. If the land was cleared of the body of evil, superstition lingered on like its ghost. Patrick knew he had his chief work to do; he must teach the simple people of the country, and harder than that, the wise men of the cities.

Easter, the Christians' holy festival, was also a time of festival for the pagans, when they observed the Rites of Spring, and celebrated the sun's return to power. In the Temple of Temora on the Hill of Tara, King Leogaire and many princes and sages would assemble, and there would be gatherings on every height. Some days earlier all fires would be extinguished, as a symbol of the dark before the spring; and on a certain night the sacred fire in the Temple would be rekindled, a symbol that spring-fire had come back to the earth. Then the gatherings would flock to re-light their own fires from the sacred flame.

That Easter-Eve the twilight was thronged with watchers on the hills, waiting to see the tongue of fire on Tara, where the greatest crowd of all surrounded the King. The spring dusk showed no sign of light on earth, though heaven had begun to light her stars. The mystery and the revelation were near.

Suddenly there were murmurs of fear and dismay.

"Look yonder! yonder! there's a red spark shining."

"Where?"

"On the plains of Shane! There is fire on the earth, too soon!"

"Some one has broken our ritual!" cried the King.

"Sacrilege! sacrilege!" cried the angry crowd.

"O King!" said one of the wise men who was present, "this fire if it is not put out will vanquish ours."

The King leapt to horse, and galloped away towards Shane, followed by the sages with the peasants at their heels. Among them stumbled little Herc, a child. They reached the place where Patrick was with his monks, tending the fire which he had dared to light. Leogaire seated himself, and bade those with him do the same—"And let none rise," he commanded, "when the law-breaker stands before me."

Then Patrick was brought into Leogaire's presence. He looked so tall and noble in his bishop's robes that little Herc stood up and said, "A blessing on you!" That child became the Bishop of Shane one day. The Saint smiled on the child, but the King frowned on the Saint as he asked roughly why Patrick had broken the law of his gods.

"I have not broken the law of my God," said Patrick. "This fire is holy fire, the Pascal fire."

"We know not that fire," said the King, "and my sages say it is dangerous."

"Let me argue that with your sages," offered Patrick. "Let me come to Tara to-morrow in the morning, and tell you all the meaning of this fire." And so it was agreed.

On Easter Day Patrick went up to the Temple, and all were assembled to hear him dispute with the wise men. They questioned him on the doctrines of his faith, and Patrick silenced their questions with the eloquence of his answers. He had wanted nothing more than this chance to make Ireland hear the Doctrine of the Trinity. It would have been a hard thing for another to make plain to the clouded minds of the pagan princes and sages, but what did Patrick do? He stooped down and plucked a little emerald plant out of the ground, the three-leaved shamrock grown in their own soil, and he said:

"This plant, that you know as well as you know the thoughts in your head, see how its three joined leaves spring from a single stem. If this has never seemed strange to you, let me now tell you something just as natural." And keeping the three-leaved shamrock for a symbol, he spoke to them of the Triple Personality of God.

Many converts were made that Easter morning. Dubtach the Bard sprang up and cried, "From this day I vow my gift of song to your Christ!" And Conall, a brother of the King, was baptized. And although Leogaire himself was not, he was so far pleased that he gave Patrick leave to preach the Word of God wherever he would.

He preached it everywhere. In County Meath the chiefs gave him their sons to teach, and he left behind him a colony of Christians that flourished like the shamrock. In County Leitrim he destroyed the Crom-Cruach, the crooked monument where the Druids had sacrificed to the sun. In County Connaught he was found by the daughters of King Leogaire, chanting God's praise beside their father's fountain. Ethnea the Fair and Fethlima the Ruddy had come down to the fountain to bathe. Full of awe, they questioned the white-robed singer, and by sunrise had accepted all he told them, and were baptized in the water of the fountain. In Sligo and Roscommon he built churches; Lent he spent praying on Croagh Aigle in Mayo. In Firawley he baptized seven princes and twelve hundred peasants. In Wicklow Prince Deichin would have none of him, but the poor herd Killan slew his one cow to feed him. In Munster, where he baptized Aengus the Chief, he set by chance his crozier on Aengus's great toe. The toe was pierced, but Aengus thought, "This must just be a part of it," and never let a sound. He supposed the flowing of blood was to do with the rites, and Patrick did not know the thing he had done, till those standing round began to murmur: "Behold the Struth-fhuil, behold the Stream of Blood!" Struill they call the place to this very day.

More sad is the tale of the devout and simple Colmar, who during a great heat toiled in the harvest-field from morning to night. Such a thirst was on him that he could hardly endure it, yet because he had heard that Patrick had forbidden the drink before Vespers, he would not sip water. That was not the drink Patrick had in mind at all, but Colmar mistook his meaning, and laboured, ached, and thirsted all the day, and as the bell let fall cool drops of sound on the evening air, Colmar with a sigh lay down and died.

"There lies Colmar Stadhach, Colmar the Thirsty," said his fellows. And maybe after that St. Patrick made it plain that when he spoke of the drink he meant poteen. We may believe water his favourite drink, so many are the wells named after him; some say he drank poteen too, now and then, some even say he was the first one to distill it. What will they not say!

At the end of twenty years the Saint saw his work in Ireland nearly completed. For his See he chose a hill in County Armagh, a beautiful site. But when he asked the owner for it, this man, whose name was Daeri, answered, "No, I want the hill myself, you can have a bit in the valley." Patrick went meekly away. Then Daeri felt out with himself, and looked about for a present for the bishop. He found a huge cauldron, holding three firkins, and his churls carried it behind him to the place where Patrick was.

"There!" said Daeri. "This cauldron is for you anyhow."

"*Gratias agam!*" said the Saint, for sometimes he forgot and said thanks in Latin instead of in Erse.

Daeri scratched his head, and went home muttering, "Gratzacham! what's Gratzacham? Only a fool would say Gratzacham for a cauldron the like of that. Gratzacham indeed!" By the time he reached his door, he was so vexed that he shouted, "Churls! go fetch my cauldron back again!"

The churls went, and returned with the cauldron.

"What did he say?" asked Daeri.

"He said Gratzacham again."

"Gratzacham when I give! Gratzacham when I take!" Daeri burst out laughing. "If he's a fool, he's a good-natured one! For

that Gratzacham he shall have both the cauldron and the hill."
And he ran to Patrick himself to tell him so.

When Patrick went to view the site for his cathedral he found
a roe on the hill-top, suckling her fawn. The Saint carried the
fawn on his shoulders to a quiet spot, and the roe trotted beside
him; when they were happily together again, Patrick returned
to the hill, and marked the roe's warm bed as the place for his
altar. There, at the first synod held in Armagh, he celebrated
Mass.

And now, having done so much for his dear Ireland, he
turned his thoughts on Scotland over the water. His feet followed his thoughts, and that journey left the trail of his name
on Britain. There's Kilpatrick in Dumbartonshire, and Crag-
phadrig in Inverness. He had a church in Kirkpatrick, and
from Portpatrick he took boat for Westmoreland, where the
dale he preached in men called Patterdale; even as in Wales
they named where he walked Sarn-badrig, or Patrick's Cause-
way. The sea has swallowed up Sarn-badrig now, it is a shoal
in Carnarvon Bay that ships steer clear of. Patricks and Patters,
Badrigs and Phadrigs, he strewed his name over rocks and
churches, islands and valleys, causeways and cells, as a running stag scatters his scent. You could trace the Saint's journey
across Britain by the names he left behind him in three tongues.

But it was in Ireland, long time after, that he died, in Ireland
where he had baptized twelve thousand souls with his own
hand, and built as many churches as there are days in a year;
in Ireland, where he had served as a slave in his youth, as
a saint in his age, he closed his eyes at last when his work
was done. He was one hundred and twenty years old, they say.

"*Have you heard?* Our Bishop was taken ill in Sabhall-Padruic,
and thought it would be fitting to die in Armagh, so weak as
he was he set out. And on the way a blessed angel came down
out of heaven and turned him back to Saul, the place he
loved best."

It was on the Seventeenth day of March that Patrick died.
Since nobody quite knew when and where he was born, that
day became his feast, Ireland his country, and the three-leaved
emerald shamrock his own emblem, worn throughout Erin on
St. Patrick's Day.

April Fool's Day

APRIL 1

Almost all countries have a day very much like our April Fool's Day, when dignity is discarded and everyone plays practical jokes. Americans do their fooling on April 1 because the early Scotch, English, and French settlers brought the custom with them.

Also known as All Fools' Day, the occasion provides pranksters of every description an opportunity to play a wide variety of jokes upon their friends and neighbors.

RALPH A. TANKSLEY

Archie and the April Fools

BY B. J. CHUTE

Illustrations by Irving Leveton

Ted," said Jimmy Brewster, coming into the living room rather suddenly, "I hate to mention it, but there's a giraffe in the back yard."

His brother roused himself from the study of a photograph, gave Jimmy a puzzled look, then glanced at the calendar. A peaceful smile dawned upon his face. The calendar unquestionably proclaimed the fact that it was April first.

"Run away, my good man," said Ted. "I'm busy. You know, Jimmy, there's definitely a light leak in our camera. We've certainly got to get a new one, as soon as we have enough money."

"We're going to get a projector," Jimmy reminded him, "and, while I hate to mention it again, there *is* a giraffe in our back yard."

"I know, I know. And there's a baby hippopotamus in the kitchen sink, too, but don't bother me with that now. Just put April Fool's Day out of your mind." Ted sighed. "What kind of camera do you think we should get?"

"Projector," said Jimmy, gazing thoughtfully out the window. "I take it all back. There *isn't* a giraffe in the back yard."

Ted said, "That's better. You can't catch me on those old April Fool gags."

"He isn't in the back yard," said Jimmy, "because now he's in the side yard."

Ted fixed his brother with a glittering eye. "Now look here, you poor cluck, enough's enough. Once is funny, but—" he broke off, his gaze drawn to the window by Jimmy's intent stare, and made a noise like a drowning suction pump.

"You see?" said Jimmy reproachfully.

Ted saw. He rushed to the window and peered out wildly.

Jimmy nodded in sympathy. He knew how Ted felt. But there was no getting away from it—the large spotted object in the Brewster peony bed *was* a giraffe.

"I hope," said Jimmy, with dignity, "that this will be a lesson to you to trust me. I was deeply hurt—"

"Stop babbling," Ted requested, recovering slightly. "What are we going to do about this—this monster?"

Jimmy gazed out at the giraffe, which had left the peony bed and was munching a convenient tree, its head out of sight and its long thin neck looking like a large spotted serpent. "I read a book once," said Jimmy.

"This is no time to discuss your literary exploits," his brother told him fiercely. "Great howling buttercups! We've got to *do* something."

"This book," said Jimmy, undiscouraged, "said that giraffes can run faster than most horses."

"Yoicks! We've got to catch him. He probably belongs to the zoo."

"Maybe it would be better just to leave him alone," said Jimmy. "The book also said they kick with their hind legs, and, while naturally gentle, are capable of making a stout resistance."

Ted, who had been about to leave the house and organize a giraffe hunt, stopped in his tracks. "Stout resistance, huh? Perhaps we'd better call the zoo first."

"You watch the giraffe, and I'll call 'em." Jimmy grabbed for the phone book. "Circle 2-0123. Hurry, operator. . . . Hello, hello. Look, this is Jimmy Brewster, out on the Pine Road. We've got a giraffe here . . . A GIRAFFE. One of those things from Africa with long necks. . . . I want your what? Your accounting department? I do *not* want your accounting department. I want—" He broke off suddenly. "Look, what number is this? . . . Oh. Oh, I see. I'm sorry." He hung up, rather sadly. "That was the bank. They said I wanted their accounting department."

"Get going," Ted advised. "He's eating the lilac bush now."

"Circle 2-0123," Jimmy said again into the phone. "Ted, if you were a bank, would you refer a giraffe to your accounting department? . . . Hello. Is this the zoo? . . . Well, have you lost a giraffe? Yes. Yes? You have? . . . Well, it's here in our peony bed."

"Lilac," said Ted.

"Lilac bed," Jimmy corrected himself. "What do you want us to do?" There followed a brief, rather one-sided conversation, then Jimmy said, "Thank you. Yes, sure we will," and hung up.

"What'd they say?"

"It belongs to the zoo all right. They're sending men out with a truck, and we're to keep the giraffe here until they come." He paused. "Ted, there's a twenty-five dollar reward for the thing. He said we'd get it, if we caught the giraffe."

"Zowie!" Ted shouted. "We can get that camera."

"Projector," said Jimmy automatically.

"Camera," said Ted. "All we have to do—" He stopped short. "Faster than a horse, huh? Suppose it runs away when it sees us? Maybe it's scared of people."

"Frankly," said Jimmy, "that would make it unanimous. I'm scared of it."

Ted waved his hand airily. "Don't be difficult. Look, you go and get the encyclopedia and see what it says about giraffes, while I watch the beast out the window."

Jimmy dashed off and returned with the required volume. Ted, who had been watching the giraffe anxiously, said, "One of the advantages of living in the country is there's plenty of giraffe food around. He's eating the ivy now. Mother and Dad won't be pleased."

"Well, if they were home," said Jimmy reasonably, "they could tell Archie so."

"Archie?"

"That's his name. The zoo man told me." He began to read. "The giraffe or camelopard—good night, is that what he is? A camelopard!"

"Go *on*," said Ted.

Jimmy went on. "Native of Africa—occurs generally in herds of from five to forty. Whoops! Not here, I hope. Feeds on leaves and small branches of trees. Yes, we'd guessed that. Seven vertebrae in neck. Hey! That's all *I've* got. It hardly seems fair. Look at the length of his neck compared to mine."

"If you don't get a move on," Ted warned him dangerously, "there won't be any Archie here to have a neck."

Jimmy read on hastily. "No vocal chords—well, anyway he can't answer back then . . . Generally seeks safety in flight. That's not so good . . . Large, clear eyes. Nice for Archie, but no use to us. Ah, here we are!"

"About time," said Ted bitterly.

"What I said about their kicking with their hind legs," said Jimmy, "is true. But it seems they only kick lions."

"What do you mean, they only kick lions?"

"Well, the lion is their natural enemy, so, when attacked by a lion, they kick it—naturally."

"Very sensible point of view," Ted approved heartily. "Well, you and I aren't lions, therefore Archie won't kick us. Elementary, my dear Watson. Let's go."

Jimmy looked unhappy.

"Twenty-five dollars reward," Ted reminded him, "means we can get that camera."

"Projector," said Jimmy.

"Camera," said Ted. "Come on."

His brother came.

They let themselves cautiously out the back door and, by creeping, managed to get within ten feet of their giraffe before it noticed them. At that point, however, Jimmy fell over the garden hose and into an empty pail, and, the clatter being considerable, Archie withdrew his narrow head from the tree top.

"Shush," said Ted, fiercely.

Jimmy removed himself from the pail with as much dignity as possible. "I couldn't help it. Some silly idiot left that hose across the path."

"You did," said Ted. "Last night."

The giraffe was regarding them in a benign and lofty manner. "The man said to be awfully careful with him," Jimmy said. "He cost thirty-five hundred dollars."

"That thing?" Ted regarded Archie with profound respect. "Well, I'll be hornswoggled! What's he got that I haven't got?"

"More neck," said Jimmy, "and spots with white edgings."

Ted treated this remark with the contempt it deserved. "This is going to be quite simple," he announced suddenly, in a competent manner. "He's perfectly friendly." He stretched out one hand placatingly and began to advance, a step at a time. "Here, Archie, Archie. Nice Archie . . . Ooops!"

Archie gave him one look, shied violently, wheeled and departed around the corner of the house, his sloping body rolling in a ridiculous amble. "Now, look what you've done," said Jimmy. "There goes our projector."

"Camera," said Ted. "Come on. We've got to catch him."

They rushed in pursuit, and, rounding the house, stopped short. "There he is!" Jimmy panted, pointing. "He's stopped. Hey! Ought he to do that?" The giraffe had sighted a yellow crocus in the grass, and it had evidently roused in him a desire for dessert. Accordingly, he had spread his thin forelegs out at an impossible angle and was lowering his head earthwards, in a way that looked extremely perilous.

"He doesn't look safe to me," said Ted. "Besides, for all we know, crocuses aren't good for giraffes. Do they have crocuses in Africa?"

"I don't know," said Jimmy, "but I'll go and get the encyclopedia, while you figure out a way to—"

"Oh, no, you don't," Ted said firmly, grabbing his brother and hauling him back. "I've already figured out a way. How soon do they expect to get here from the zoo?"

"Dunno," Jimmy admitted regretfully. "It's quite a ways, and they may not find our place right off, although I gave 'em directions. Why?"

"If that giraffe leaves," said Ted, "our new camera leaves."

"Projector," said Jimmy.

Ted ignored him. "And the chances are that Archie isn't going to hang around just to oblige us. So *my* idea is to get him into our barn. It's got a good high roof, and—"

"May I ask just one simple little question?" said Jimmy. "*How* are you going to get him into the barn? You can't lead him, you know. He's all neck and legs—there's nothing to hang onto."

Ted said dramatically, "Look at his tail!" Jimmy looked. It was a goodish tail—not beautiful, perhaps, but certainly utilitarian—with a tuft on the end. It would be a most satisfactory tail to hang onto. "Well?" said Ted.

"I can think of two objections," Jimmy said. "One is, do you think you can pull a giraffe around backwards? Because, if so, I'm going to leave the whole thing to you, and you can have the projector all to yourself. I have my life to live."

"It's going to be a camera," Ted said firmly, "and we don't pull him, you goof. We urge him forward gently. The tail is just for emergencies, in case he starts to run."

"Oh," said Jimmy. "Well, the other objection is the location of his tail."

"It's in the usual place, I believe," Ted said stiffly.

"Well, naturally, but the usual place is so awfully near his heels." Jimmy looked mournful and quoted, "They kick with their hind legs and are capable of making a stout resistance."

"So what?" said Ted. "Archie won't attack anything but a lion. You read that yourself from the encyclopedia. We aren't lions, are we?"

There was a short pause. "I see what you mean," said Jimmy. "Are we men or are we lions?" There was another short pause. "Personally, I'm a mouse. You do it, Ted. You're more the executive type. I'll watch."

"You will not," Ted told him. "It's perfectly simple. I'll go in front and urge him on with some grass, and you go behind and hang onto his tail."

"Me?" Jimmy croaked. "Hang onto his tail?"

"Certainly. You just said I was the executive type, didn't you? Well, the executive type always leads. Come on, Jimmy." Ted gave him a shove from behind, and Jimmy staggered mournfully toward Archie's tail, stared at it for a moment, took a deep breath, and grabbed.

Things after that happened very quickly.

Archie's left hind leg kicked out at a fantastic angle and landed a powerful and accurate wallop. Jimmy described a parabola in the air, rolled over twice on the grass, got to his feet, and started running.

Ted joined him.

Archie galloped in enthusiastic pursuit.

His two would-be captors shot up into the branches of the nearest apple tree, and Archie came to a disappointed halt. Jimmy and Ted climbed upward as far as they could and came to rest near an abandoned bird's nest.

They looked at each other.

"Kicks only lions," said Jimmy bitterly. "The executive type—bah!"

"You read the book yourself," Ted accused and looked down thoughtfully at Archie's head, weaving around among the branches. The tree was not tall, and Archie was. After a moment, Ted broke off some juicy-looking leaves and handed them down to Archie, who accepted them courteously. Ted broke off some more.

Jimmy got the idea and began to help. "If we can only keep him here until the zoo men come—"

"I hope the tree lasts out," said Ted. "Sit down, Jimmy. You're rocking the boat."

"Thank you," said his brother with dignity. "I'm more comfortable standing up."

Ted said, "Oh," with polite sympathy, and Jimmy added, "In case you want to know, being kicked by an even-toed ungulate is the same as being kicked by anything else, only rougher."

"By a what?"

"An even-toed ungulate. That's what that thing down there is. And, personally, I wish he'd go off and ungulate somewhere else."

"Think of the camera," Ted urged.

"I am thinking," said Jimmy, "of the projector." He added broodingly, "So he wouldn't kick me, huh? He wouldn't kick me because I didn't have a mane. Phooey." He then said, "Whoops!" and nearly fell out of the tree.

A large, purposeful-looking truck had just turned into the driveway. "The zoo men!" Ted shouted. "The marines have landed. Jimmy, we're saved." He hesitated, and added, "I wish we weren't up here, though. It doesn't look so good. They might almost think Archie caught *us*."

"If they give that giraffe the reward," said Jimmy, "I shall blow a fuse."

"Hey!" said a voice. A stout man in blue overalls was peering up at them, one arm wound affectionately around Archie's neck. "What you doing up there?"

Jimmy said, "We've caught the giraffe for you," and there was a hearty burst of laughter in response.

"Look who's caught who, will you?" said the stout man. "A nice, tame, little fellow like Archie, too!"

"Tame!" said Ted under his breath, and then addressed the stout man quite coolly. "We couldn't find much for him to eat, and we thought feeding him was the best way to keep him here." He paused impressively. "We're up in this tree—where we can get more leaves."

The stout man was silenced in his turn, and Jimmy and Ted descended with admirable dignity. "Well," the man admitted finally, "that was pretty smart. Yessir, that was real bright. We're much obliged. I'll see you get that reward all right."

Indoors, Jimmy glared at the encyclopedia. "Only lions," he muttered.

"We can get our camera," Ted offered consolingly.

"PROJECTOR!" Jimmy howled.

"M'mmmm," said Ted, "I'll tell you what. We'll compromise. Next time we'll buy a projector. This time we'll buy a camera. Now run along and get some cookies, there's a pal. All that brain work has made me hungry."

Jimmy gazed upon his brother in mingled awe and fury, said "Compromise!" in a strangled voice, then departed suddenly. He came back, a moment later, both hands full of cookies and a strange glitter in his eyes.

"Ted," he said, "I hate to mention it. But there's a rhinocerous in the back yard."

Ted let out a wild scream and dashed into the kitchen. A moment later, Jimmy heard the back door slam. A gentle smile dawned on his face.

"Ah, well," he murmured, "we can't all be the executive type."

He looked affectionately at the calendar, which still proclaimed unmistakably that it was April Fool's Day, smiled again, and began to eat his cookies. He felt much better.

All Fools' Day

Anonymous

The First of April, some do say
Is set apart for All Fools' Day;
But why the people call it so
Nor I, nor they themselves, do know.
But on this day are people sent
On purpose for pure merriment.

April Pranks

By Ilo Orleans

A poodle ate
A doughnut,
And turned into a wheel.

A zebra said:
"Good morning!"
To a pretty diving seal.

A monkey found
Two drum-sticks,
And drummed upon the moon.

A cat sat down
To a banquet
With a fork and knife and spoon.

A bull bowed on
A fiddle,
On top of a hemlock tree.

Grandpa drank
A poem;
And he wrote a cup of tea.

A goat, a pig,
A rooster—
Went marching off to school.

I am a queen
On a golden throne!
What fun! It's APRIL FOOL!

ILLUSTRATION BY IRVING LEVETON

April Fool

By Elizabeth Coatsworth

"I saw an elephant walking down the road.
He had a book and was going to school.
He carried a satchel to hold his lunch—
APRIL FOOL!

"I saw your grandmother and your aunt
Fishing for suckers in the mill-stream pool.
They'd caught a dozen and maybe more—
APRIL FOOL!

"Mercy! whoever has mended your skirt?
The needle's still there and the thread and the spool.
Didn't you feel them there at the hem?
APRIL FOOL!"

UNITED PRESS INTERNATIONAL

Easter

Easter and spring arrive together, the first cele-brating the Resurrection of Christ and the beginning of His new life, and the second breathing new life into the world of nature. The word Easter comes from the festival of Eostre, Teutonic goddess of Spring. Easter falls on the first Sunday after the full moon following the spring equinox.

On Easter Sunday Christians attend church serv-ices and recall the Bible story that tells how Jesus disappeared from His tomb on the third day after His crucifixion. An angel appeared to His followers and announced, "He is risen."

Many secular symbols have come to be associated with Easter: lilies, bonnets, furry chicks. But the most popular symbol of all is the Easter bunny who is said to hide gaily decorated eggs in houses and yards. The bunny and the eggs are such old customs that no one knows how or when they were started. But we do know that both the eggs and rabbits have come to be symbols of birth and new life.

Nino's Easter

BY VALENTI ANGELO

Illustrations by the author

THERE was much excitement at Casa Checchi as Easter Sunday drew near. The courtyard was swept clean and the house scrubbed from ceiling to floor. Everything had to be in perfect order for the many guests who were expected. They would eat at a long table in the courtyard. In preparation for the occasion, the oven had been kept hot for several days.

Allinda had made huge piles of small cakes sprinkled with red, yellow, and pale blue sugar crystals; also there was panettone, a large cake filled with pine nuts, raisins, and chopped angelica. For the children she had baked little soldiers and roosters of cake dough glazed with a mixture of beaten eggs and sugar. Raisins were used for the buttons and eyes. They came from the oven slick and shining. Long lines of chocolate cookies lay on the table. Some were shaped like stars; others like half-moons and crescents; and still others took the form of balls. Next to the cookies lay the huge round sweet bread generously sprinkled through with aniseed and looking like a giant doughnut. Last of all, Allinda made the sweet green squash tarts sprinkled with cinnamon and sugar. These were immense and looked like cart wheels before they were cut into small pieces.

Nino seldom left his mother's side these days.

"Oh, let me braid the fancy loaves!" he would beg, or: "May I beat the eggs?" or: "I want to sprinkle the colored sugar, Mother. You know how I like doing that."

Allinda worked tirelessly, calling on her son from time to time. "Nino, bring me the big wooden spoon. Nino, wash this bowl," and more often: "Nino, get out from under my feet!"

Nino knew what fun Easter could be, with all the guests and the big table set out in the open air of the courtyard.

"Easter doesn't last long enough. It's like Christmas—it comes and goes too quickly," he said to himself.

At last Easter Sunday came, and Nino, looking out of his open window, saw a cloudless sky deep emerald in color. The song of the birds sounded sweeter than usual, and, in the distance, he could hear the voices of peasants singing in the clear morning air. He jumped from his bed and dressed quickly in the clean clothes his mother had laid out for him. Today would be too full to waste any part of it. While he was washing, he could hear Grandfather and one of the neighbors in the courtyard. They were busy setting up the long table which soon would groan with the weight of the holiday meal.

The morning sun climbed higher into the sky while Nino and Grandfather walked to church to attend Easter mass. As they walked along, Nino heard the bells ringing. Allinda, who had gone to the early mass, stayed at home to get ready for the guests, who would appear directly after the second mass was over.

Nino and Grandfather entered the church. They touched their fingers to the holy water at the font and made the sign of the cross. The mass had just started and the organ was playing in deep melodious tones. Today the altar decorations were even finer than usual. There were more lighted candles and many more flowers. There were more altar boys today, too, and the choir sounded louder than it did on other days.

"I would like to be an altar boy," Nino whispered to his grandfather, kneeling beside him on the small bench.

"Perhaps some day you may be," replied the old man quietly.

There was more kneeling than on other days, thought Nino, as he shifted his weight from one knee to the other. Glancing about, he noticed that some people knelt on only one knee. He tried this position too, but found it made little difference. His knees ached just the same.

"Be still, Nino," cautioned Grandfather.

The priest had just finished drinking from the sacred chalice and setting it down covered it with a spotless white napkin. He chanted the service in low sonorous tones. Two small altar boys held up the train of his sumptuous robe, which was covered with gold embroidery. It had a blue cross on the front and one on the back. Nino craned his neck to see him better. A boy kept changing the huge missal, a large book, from one side of the altar to the other. Another rang a little bell between the chants. The priest turned, bowed, and turned again with his back to the congregation. He bowed again. The smallest of all the altar boys ran back and forth with two small bottles of water and wine. He poured a little of each into the large silver and gold chalice that the priest held firmly in both hands. The priest blessed the congrega-tion, blessed himself, and then with both hands lifted the large chalice to his mouth and drained it to the last drop. The organ played a triumphant strain, and the voices of the choir rang out, almost drowning the priest's words.

Nino held a silver coin tight in one hand. When the collection box, which was fastened on a long handle, came round to him, he put his coin in it, noticing at the same time that the box was almost full. He was glad when the kneeling was over, and he sat back in the seat and thought of God and Easter.

Easter mass was over. The peasants, all dressed in their best clothes, streamed out into the sunshine which flooded the square facing the church. They stood around, greeting and saluting one another. Color filled the square. The blue, red, yellow, and green dresses of the village women mixed with the sober gray and black of the men. The rich colors blended harmoniously with the somber gray walls of the church.

The priest, who had changed from his altar robes to a long black cassock with a row of buttons running all the way down the front, walked through the crowd and chatted with the village folks. Nino watched him talking with Signor Patri, the fat and jovial Mayor of the village. The priest was bare-headed; he fingered a long string of beads that hung almost to the ground and wore a silver cross that glittered in the morning sun.

"Good morning, Father Bellarosa," said Nino as the priest turned from Signor Patri and walked towards the little group made up of Signor Ditto, the Signora, Julio, Jacobo the artist, the butcher, the cobbler, and Nino's best friend the pastry-cook. These and many more had been asked to come up to Casa Checchi for the feast.

"How are you, Nino?" said the priest. "How are you this fine Easter Day?" And he patted Nino's curly head.

"Oh, I'm so excited!" said Nino. "I'm so glad that you are coming to dinner today. I want to show you the rooster you gave me. It's still as good as new."

"All right, Nino. I'll be there. I would not miss your mother's cooking for anything, especially her baking," he said to Nino, as he walked over to talk with another group of villagers.

Nino was very fond of kind Father Bellarosa. He seldom scolded him at catechism and, besides, hadn't he given him the best toy he had?

Pigeons flew in and out of the belfry. Nino watched them circle the campanile and disappear in the rafters of the tower. Nino had been up in the tower once. He remembered how dizzy it made him feel when he looked down. He wondered if the pigeons didn't sometimes feel dizzy, too. Nino didn't like the way they stood around on the peaks of the roof and the eaves. Just then a pigeon alighted safely on the cross on top of the tower, and Nino knew why God had made wings.

Julio came up to where Nino stood, still looking upwards.

"What are you looking at?" asked Julio. "Haven't you ever seen the campanile before?"

"Yes, I have," said Nino. "I was just noticing how well the pigeons take care of themselves. See that one perched up on the cross?" he said pointing. "He's not at all frightened."

"They have wings, haven't they? I don't see why you worry about such things," said Julio, shrugging his shoulders.

A shy girl about Nino's age stood beside Julio. She was dressed in red, and a white embroidered apron fitted tightly high above her waist.

"Nino, this is my cousin, Gloria. She came all the way from Florence to spend a month with us," said Julio. "Won't we have fun now!" he said, jumping up and down like a marionette.

"I like the apron you're wearing, Gloria," said Nino. "Did your mother make it?"

"No, Nino," said Gloria in a shy voice. "It was bought for me in Florence."

Nino knew that Florence was a large city. He hoped that some day his mother would take him there. He had heard of all the fine things one could see in that "City of the Arts," which was what Grandfather often called Florence.

"Grandfather," said Nino, "may I go to Julio's house with him? He wants to stop for his new mandolin."

"Wait," said Signor Ditto. "There's something I want too."

"All right, Nino. Don't be long, though. Your mother is probably waiting for us all to come now," said the old man.

The four hurried off to the Dittos'. Julio found his mandolin, and his father went into the cellar and came out with an armful of bottles.

"*Viva il vino!* Hurray for wine!" he shouted, the bottles clinking against one another.

The four were panting with haste when they entered the courtyard. The long table stood under the wide grape arbor, covered with a coarse linen tablecloth which Nino's mother had woven on her loom.

There was already a large gathering of villagers in the courtyard. They talked and gesticulated, moving their arms, shrugging their shoulders, and occasionally glancing in the direction of the oven and the table. Allinda was bringing out huge bowls of thick soup and Signora Ditto followed with platters of bread cut in thick slices.

Julio went around poking his nose into this and that while Nino and Gloria walked over to the oven. The door was shut.

"Can't guess what's in there," Nino said to Gloria.

"Let's peek," she said.

Nino, with a finger to his mouth, said: "Sh!"

He opened the door of the oven just a little and they both peeked in.

"Um, um, that smells good!" said Gloria.

Nino's mother arrived just in time to give Nino a gentle box on the ear.

"Poky nose," she said.

"Mother, this is Gloria. She is Julio's cousin from Florence."

Allinda made a bow to the little girl and said: "We are happy to have you with us."

"I wonder why the pastrycook is so late," said Nino. "And the cobbler, he is late too," he added.

Julio said: "I'm hungry."

"Oh, they'll be here any minute," said Allinda as she walked toward the priest, who was shaking hands with the fat Signora Ditto for the second time that day.

"I didn't see you at mass today," said the good priest, pointing an accusing finger at Allinda. "Too busy with all this?" he said, waving a hand about the courtyard.

"No, Father," said Allinda. "I was at the early mass."

The old priest gave Allinda a gentle pat on the cheek and said: "My eyes are getting bad. I'm getting old, I guess."

Finally both the pastrycook and the cobbler arrived and everyone sat down to eat. Grandfather sat at one end of the huge table and the priest at the other. The jovial Mayor was placed in the middle with his dark-eyed wife by his side. Corrina and Pietro, their children, sat one on each side of them. Signor and Signora Ditto were across the table from the Mayor. Julio sat between Gloria and Nino, next to Grandfather. Friends of Grandfather and Allinda filled the rest of the table.

Father Bellarosa stood up. The kind priest raised one hand heavenward and while those seated about the long table bowed their heads he said: "O Lord in heaven, bless this food, and give strength to those who partake of it. Amen." Little shafts of sunlight streamed through the leaves from the arbor above.

Immediately after the priest had finished saying grace, Julio announced in a loud voice: "The soup smells good!"

Gloria giggled, and Nino said: "Hush!"

The priest sat down, smiling, and helped himself to the soup. The two huge bowls were soon emptied.

Signor Ditto said: "Don't put all the grated cheese in your soup, Julio."

Julio handed the cheese to Gloria, who in turn handed it to Nino.

"I like my soup plain," she said.

"A little cheese makes the soup taste better," Nino replied.

Grandfather rose and, holding his glass, said: "*Salute!* A happy Easter to all, and *salute* to Signor Ditto," he added, "who brought us this good old vintage."

Everyone except the children drank the wine.

Nino said to Gloria: "When I grow up, I'll drink wine too."

Julio told Gloria that he knew what wine tasted like.

Ravioli were served next. The little shells of dough filled with minced vegetables and chicken meat, and covered with brown mushroom sauce, were heaped high on huge terracotta platters.

"Oh!" said Julio. "That smells even better than the soup!"

Grandfather gave Julio a good plateful of ravioli, which disappeared fast. Everyone ate and enjoyed each other's company. The food was good, and all the guests praised Allinda's cooking.

Julio said: "Mother, why don't you make ravioli like these?"

Signora Ditto blushed a deep red and Signor Ditto looked daggers at his son.

The rack of lamb came out of the oven steaming hot and roasted to a juicy brown. Allinda cut the rack into chops. Heaps of fried squash, fried quail, and chicken followed.

"Isn't it a grand meal!" said Nino to Gloria, as he picked out a nice fat drum stick and put it on Gloria's plate.

Gloria smiled and said: "Thank you, Nino. I like the drum stick best of all the chicken."

Nino was pleased.

"Pass me a gizzard," Julio said to Nino, and Nino looked

about the platter for a gizzard, found one, stuck it with his fork, and put it on Julio's plate. "Don't you like gizzards?" Julio asked Gloria. "It's the chicken's stomach, you know. My mother found a penny in one once. The chicken had swallowed it."

In spite of his many threats, Grandfather after all had not had the heart to sacrifice his pet rooster for the Easter feast. The bird, with his flock of hens beside him, strutted about the courtyard now, occasionally sidling near the table to pick up a stray fallen crumb. Once in a while he crowed triumphantly, as though he had known all along that Grandfather would never put him in the oven, and the old man, picking on a chicken wing, thought how good it was to hear his voice still.

Caesar prowled round impatiently. He had to wait until the table was cleared before he would get his share.

The bones were removed from the plates before each person, and a big bowl of curly lettuce with chopped onions and garlic was passed around. Each guest stirred the oil and red vinegar at the bottom of the bowl before helping himself. But the children had eaten so much already that they shook their heads at the salad.

Julio leaned toward Gloria and said: "Now comes the part I like best!"

The table was covered with cakes and tarts and sliced panettone. The men dipped the slices in wine and ate them that way. The children fell upon the roosters and soldiers first, then went after the smaller cookies.

Julio, saying: "I begin to feel not so good," took a large piece of the squash tart.

Signora Ditto said: "Julio, you'll be sick. Don't make such a glutton of yourself."

Julio replied: "Oh, Ma!" his mouth so full it was all but running over.

Gloria, too, thought that Julio was overeating.

"Don't you think so?" she asked Nino.

"I don't know," said Nino. "Julio can eat an awful lot without feeling it. I remember the time when we ate green grapes together. I was sick, but he didn't even get a tummy ache."

Black coffee came next, along with cheese, nuts, and candy which the pastrycook had brought from his shop. The food was beginning to tell on some of the guests. They stretched their legs, belched politely, and loosened their sashes. The meal had lasted two hours. The children were the first to leave the table. Their elders still lingered over their coffee cups. The bottle of cognac went up and down the table. Almost everyone took a little in the black coffee.

Signor Ditto drank a toast to the house of Checchi, and Nino felt very proud indeed.

The afternoon sun hung bright over Casa Checchi and the shadow cast by the house crept slowly over the courtyard towards the arbor.

Easter Hymn

By Charles Wesley

Christ the Lord is risen today,
Sons of men and angels say:
Raise your joys and triumphs high,
Sing, ye heavens, and earth reply.

Love's redeeming work is done,
Fought the fight, the battle won:
Lo! our Sun's eclipse is o'er;
Lo! He sets in blood no more.

Vain the stone, the watch, the seal;
Christ hath burst the gates of Hell!
Death in vain forbids His rise;
Christ hath opened Paradise!

Lives again our glorious King:
Where, O Death, is now thy sting?
Once He died, our souls to save:
Where thy victory, O grave?

The Country Bunny and the Little Gold Shoes

BY Du BOSE HEYWARD

Illustrations by Marjorie Flack

WE hear of *the* Easter Bunny who comes each Easter Day before sunrise to bring eggs for boys and girls, so we think there is only one. But this is not so. There are really *five* Easter Bunnies, and they must be the five kindest, and swiftest, and wisest bunnies in the whole wide world, because between sunset on Easter Eve and dawn on Easter Morning they do more work than most rabbits do in a whole year.

When one of the Easter Bunnies grows old and can no longer run fast, the old, wise, and kind Grandfather Bunny who lives at the Palace of Easter Eggs calls the bunnies together from the whole world to select the very best one to take the place.

Often a mother bunny says to her child, "Now if you learn to be wise, and kind, and swift, some day you may grow up to be one of the Easter Bunnies." And all of the babies try their very best, so that they can grow up and go to work for the Grandfather Bunny at the Palace of Easter Eggs.

One day a little country girl bunny with a brown skin and a little cotton-ball of a tail said, "Some day I shall grow up to be an Easter Bunny:—you wait and see!"

Then all of the big white bunnies who lived in fine houses, and the Jack Rabbits with long legs who can run so fast, laughed at the little Cottontail and told her to go back to the country and eat a carrot. But she said, "Wait and see!"

The little girl Cottontail grew up to be a young lady Cottontail. And by and by she had a husband and then one day, much to her surprise there were twenty-one Cottontail babies to take care of.

Then the big white rabbits and the Jacks with long legs laughed and laughed, and they said, "What did we tell you! Only a country rabbit would go and have all those babies. Now take care of them and leave Easter eggs to great big men bunnies like us." And they went away liking themselves very much.

Cottontail stopped thinking about hopping over the world with lovely eggs for little boys and girls, and she took care of her babies.

And one day, when her children stopped being babies and were little girl and boy bunnies, she called them to her and said, "Now we are going to have some fun."

Then to two of them she gave little brooms and showed them how to sweep out the cottage, and two she taught how to make beds.

Two more went with her to the kitchen, and in no time at all had found out how to cook a good dinner. And with these went the two little dish-washers, and they made the glasses shine like crystal.

Two had little washtubs full of soapsuds, and they washed all the linen.

Two did the sewing and mending.

Two who had sweet voices were taught to sing and two more to dance and these amused all the others while they worked so that they were gay and happy.

Two others were soon digging in the garden.

To two she gave paints and crayons, so they could make pretty pictures for the walls.

And when Mother Cottontail had given out all of the tasks, she looked around, and there was only one little boy bunny left, and he was sad and lonely. Then Mother Cottontail said to him, "You are the most polite of all my children so I shall make you keeper of my chair. And whenever I come to dinner you shall seat me politely at table."

Then one day when the little rabbits were half grown up, she heard a great talk among the woods rabbits, and when she asked what it was about, they said, "Haven't you heard? One of the five Easter Bunnies has grown too slow, and we are all going to the Palace of Easter Eggs to see Old Grandfather pick out a new one to take his place."

So she called her little Cottontails and they all set off to the Palace to see the fun. But their mother was sad because she thought that now she was nothing but an old mother bunny, and could only look on, and that a big handsome white rabbit or long-legged Jack would be chosen.

When they came to the Palace of Easter Eggs there were bunnies everywhere on the great lawn, and the ones that hoped to be the Easter Bunny stood together, and all the others looked at them and clapped their paws. Then the big front door opened and the old, wise, and kind Grandfather came hopping slowly out. And he told the biggest and those with the longest legs to show what they could do. They jumped and ran and showed him their pretty white fur, and they were all very fast and very clever.

But still he did not pick one. And he said to them, "You are pretty and you are fast, but you have not shown me that you are either kind or wise."

Then his kind old eyes looked everywhere and at last they

rested on Little Cottontail Mother where she stood with her children around her. And he called her to come right up to the Palace steps. So she took her twenty-one children and went up and stood before him.

And when he spoke, his voice was so kind that she was not frightened at all. And he said, "What a large family you have, my dear. I suppose they take all of your time."

But she said, "When they were babies, that was so, but now they are so well trained that they do most of the work for me."

"Ah," he said, smiling, "you must be very *wise* to train so many children so well. But tell me, do they always look so happy, and do they always hold their ears up so prettily?"

"Indeed they do," she answered. "We never have a tear or

a cross word in our little country cottage. And if I do say it myself, they do carry their ears better than most bunnies."

"Then," he said, patting the nearest bunny on the head, "you must be very *kind* indeed to have such a happy home. It is too bad that you have had no time to run and grow swift, as I might then have made you my fifth Easter Bunny."

At that Mother Cottontail started to laugh, then she whispered to the little bunnies, and every rabbit on the lawn looked to see what would happen and the old Grandfather leaned forward to watch. Suddenly all of her twenty-one children raced away.

And Cottontail dashed after them, and in no time at all she had them all back again in front of the Palace.

Then the old, kind, wise Grandfather Bunny said, "I see that you are *swift* also. It is too bad that you cannot go to carry my eggs, because you will have to stay at home to take care of your children."

Mother Cottontail nodded her head to the little ones and they all formed a line and bowed low to the Grandfather. Then she stepped in front of them, and she said, "They will take better care of the house than I."

Then she called them up two by two, and as she put her hands on the heads of each pair she said, "These are my sweepers. They keep the cottage as clean as your hand. These make the beds without a wrinkle. These cook my dinner. These wash the dishes. These tend the garden. These wash and dry all the clothes. These do the mending. These sing, and these dance to keep us merry while we work. These are learning to paint pretty pictures for our walls. And this littlest one of all always pulls out my chair for me when I sit to table. So you see I can leave them to take care of the house until I come home."

Then the old, kind, wise Grandfather said, "You have proved yourself to be not only *wise*, and *kind*, and *swift*, but also very clever. Come to the Palace tomorrow afternoon, for that is Easter Eve, and you shall be my fifth Easter Bunny."

The next evening Cottontail knocked on the big front door and was admitted to the Palace. There she stood in her funny

country clothes but none of the other four Easter Bunnies laughed, for they were wise and kind and knew better.

They showed her all over the Palace, from room to room all piled high with eggs of gold and silver, and eggs that glittered like snow, chocolate eggs, marshmallow eggs, eggs for rich children and eggs for poor children, for children who were sick and children who were well all over the world.

Then, as soon as it was dark enough for the children to be asleep all over the world, the old, wise, kind Grandfather gave the word and the five bunnies set to work as fast as they could. First one, then another would take up a large egg or a pretty little basket and in a single hop would be out of the Palace and away out of sight. Then in a moment he would be back again, and before you could say Jack Robinson he would have whisked away again.

Slowly the night wore away, and the bunnies began to look tired as they kept returning for more and more eggs. And in the Palace the glittering piles grew smaller and smaller.

Poor little Cottontail was very tired, for this was the first time she had ever gone so far or so fast in her life, and she was beginning to hope that she could soon take the little basket that was set aside for her own children and go hopping home, when old, wise, kind Grandfather called her to him.

When she went close, she saw that he was holding in his hand the loveliest egg she had ever seen. It glittered like a diamond. "Peek through and see what you shall see," he said; so she peeked through the little hole in one end and she saw a beautiful scene with a sleigh, and a lake with people skating on the ice. And he said, "Because you have such a loving heart for children, I am going to give you the best but the hardest trip of all. Far off over two rivers and three mountains there is a great mountain peak. And in a little cottage on that peak is a little boy who has been ill for a whole year, and who has been so brave that never once has he cried or complained. The mountain is so high that there is ice on the top, and it will be hard to climb, but if you get there you will give more happiness than any other Easter Bunny."

Cottontail picked up the egg very gently and went hopping away on her journey.

She crossed the first river and then the second. She went

over the first mountain and then another mountain and yet
another until at last she reached the highest mountain of all.

She was very tired when at last she got to the bottom of
the great peak, and her heart failed her when she saw how high
it was, and how slippery with ice and snow on top. But, holding the egg very carefully, she started hopping up. At last she
reached the ice and snow and now she was almost to the top
and she could see the little cottage all covered with snow where
the little boy was sleeping. Then a terrible thing happened.

Her foot slipped and down she came—downward she flew
into snowdrifts. Then she left the ice and snow and rolling
and bouncing against the stones she felt the air getting warmer.

Down, down she went, and she crashed through a thicket
of budding laurel, rolled across a pasture, and finally struck
against the trunk of a great apple tree that was just getting
ready to bloom for Easter. And there she lay, with the egg still
safely clutched in her paw, but with a great pain in her leg.

She tried to rise again, because she saw a lovely pink light in the sky and she knew that in a few minutes more it would be day, and the little boy would be sad if she did not get his egg to him. But the pain was so bad she fell down. Then she felt something touch her shoulder, and she looked up, and there, right before her, way off there in that distant land, was old, wise, kind Grandfather Bunny.

And he smiled at her and he said, "You are not only *wise*, and *kind*, and *swift*, but you are also the *bravest* of all the bunnies. And I shall make you my very own Gold Shoe Easter Bunny." And he reached over and she saw for the first time that he was holding a tiny pair of gold shoes in his hand. And he bent down and put them on her feet. Suddenly all the pain left her leg, and she stood up and picked up the precious egg. Then, before she knew what was happening, she felt a sudden motion, and she found herself flying high in the air: over the pasture she flew, over the laurel, over the stones, until at last, when she landed, she looked back and she saw that one single jump had carried her halfway up the mountain. Then she jumped once again and there she was at the cottage door. Quickly she squeezed through the tiny crack that had been left open just in case the bunny did come all that way, and in the hand of the beautiful sleeping boy, she placed the egg.

Then, just as the Easter Morning sun rose over the edge of the world, she jumped quickly back to the Palace, where she found her little basket for her own little bunnies, and went hopping back home to give them a happy Easter.

Mother Cottontail found that the garden was tended.

And sure enough, just as she had said, everything was in order. The floors were swept and there were two lovely new pictures painted and hanging on the wall.

The dishes were washed and shone in the cupboard.

The clothes were washed and mended and nicely hung away. And her twenty-one children were all sound asleep in their little beds.

And the little house of Mother Cottontail can always be told now from the homes of all other bunnies. Because in a special place on the wall, on a very special hook, hangs a pair of very tiny little gold shoes.

Easter

By Elizabeth Coatsworth

On Easter morn,
On Easter morn,
The sun comes dancing up the sky.

His light leaps up;
It shakes and swings,
Bewildering the dazzled eye.

On Easter morn
All earth is glad;
The waves rejoice in the bright sea.

Be still and listen
To your heart,
And hear it beating merrily!

Easter Parade

By Marchette Chute

My button gloves are very white,
　My parasol is new,
My braids are braided nice and tight,
　And there are very few
Of all the people that I see
Who are as beautiful as me.

An Easter Carol

By Christina Rossetti

Spring bursts today,
    For Christ is risen and all the earth's at play.

    Flash forth, thou Sun,
The rain is over and gone, its work is done.
    Winter is past,
Sweet Spring is come at last, is come at last.
    Bud, Fig and Vine,
Bud, Olive, fat with fruit and oil and wine.
    Break forth this morn
In roses, thou but yesterday a Thorn.
    Uplift thy head,
O pure white Lily through the Winter dead.
    Beside your dams
Leap and rejoice, you merry-making Lambs.
    All Herds and Flocks
Rejoice, all Beasts of thickets and of rocks.
    Sing, Creatures, sing,
Angels and Men and Birds and everything.
    All notes of Doves
Fill all our world: this is the time of loves.

Pippa's Song

By Robert Browning

The year's at the spring
And day's at the morn;
Morning's at seven;
The hillside's dew-pearled;
The lark's on the wing;
The snail's on the thorn;
God's in his heaven—
All's right with the world!

Arbor Day

The state of Nebraska was once a tree-less land in the heart of what was called the "Great American Desert." Mr. and Mrs. J. Sterling Morton pioneered to Nebraska in 1850 and devoted their lives to filling the barren prairie with trees and urging others to do the same. On April 10, 1872, the state of Nebraska observed the first Arbor Day. One million trees were planted that year.

The ceremony of tree planting, now observed across the nation, is performed on various dates throughout the country, depending on the proper season for planting. Thus in the South, Arbor Day comes earlier in the season than in the North.

Although Arbor Day became a holiday in the late nineteenth century, the idea has always been a popular one. Many ancient cultures observed planting festivities. The Aztec Indians planted a tree when a baby was born, giving the tree and the baby the same name. Today, many nations around the world celebrate their own Arbor Day.

Mr. Plum and the Little Green Tree

BY HELEN EARLE GILBERT

Illustrations by Margaret Bradfield

THERE was once a little green tree which stood all alone in a little green square in a big noisy city. On two sides were busy streets with crowds of buses and cars and trucks and people going up and down, up and down, all day long.

But the little green tree turned its back on the rushing cars and trucks and the hurrying people and the stop lights and tall buildings. And it leaned instead toward the south, where the sun shone into a short quiet street in which old-fashioned brick houses leaned against one another.

Some of the houses had funny little shops in them, and one of these was occupied, upstairs and down, by an old man whose name was Mr. Plum.

Mr. Plum was a shoemaker. All day long he sat on a bench in his shop downstairs and put soles onto shoes, and patches onto shoes, and heels onto shoes, and straps and buttons and buckles and bows onto shoes and slippers and sandals. And every once in a while he would push his glasses up onto his forehead (so that he could see better) and look up from his work and gaze at the little green tree.

"How beautiful my little green tree is!" Mr. Plum would say to himself in a happy, pleased sort of way. "My-*tree*, my-*tree*, my-*tree*!" And with his hammer he would keep time: tap-*tap*, tap-*tap*, tap-*tap*!

Now Mr. Plum knew as well as anyone that city trees belong to everybody, not to any one person. But he liked to say, "My tree."

In the spring Mr. Plum watched the tight brown buds burst into blossom. In the summer he looked at the beautiful green leaves and felt cooler because of them. In the fall he listened to the rustle of the dry leaves. In the winter he saw the soft white snow sift down upon the bare branches.

Once, when the snow lay so heavily on the little tree that its branches bent almost to the ground, Mr. Plum went quietly over early in the morning and shook off the weight of snow.

And once, when it had not rained for weeks and the leaves of the little green tree had grown dusty and dry, Mr. Plum went quietly over late at night and poured a pail of water down among the thirsty roots.

One warm summer morning, as Mr. Plum sat tapping away, a City truck turned into the quiet street and parked almost in front of Mr. Plum's shop. Three men got out and went straight toward the little green square.

They stepped over the low iron fence, tramped down the grass with their big dirty shoes, and stood there, staring at the little green tree.

It made Mr. Plum very uneasy. He put down his work and pushed his glasses up (so that he could see better). He saw the men go back to the truck, and take out an ax, a crosscut saw, and a long strong rope.

Mr. Plum glared at the men. He was growing worried.

The three men crossed the street again, carrying the rope, the ax, and the saw. They walked around the little green tree and squinted at it from all sides.

Mr. Plum laid down the shoe he was fixing. He took his glasses off completely (which was what he did when things got really bad) and hurried out of his door and across the street.

"What are you going to do to my tree?" he demanded.

"Cut it down," one of the men said. And he threw the rope up over a branch—the one with the robin's nest in it.

"Cut it down!" repeated Mr. Plum. "Who said so?"

"The Mayor," the three men replied.

"Dear, dear!" cried Mr. Plum. He looked around in despair.

The clock on the tall building across the street said twenty minutes to eleven. Mr. Plum had an idea.

"Will you wait half an hour?" he asked. "I am going to see the Mayor." The men paid no attention.

"My home," went on Mr. Plum, "is up over my shop. Right over there. Where it says *Arthur Plum . . . Repairs the Finest Shoes*. You must be hot, working so hard. And tired. If you would like to go upstairs and sit down, I think you'll find a chocolate cake in the breadbox and some lemonade in the icebox."

The men began to think that Mr. Plum was rather nice. "Well, half an hour," they said.

Mr. Plum rushed across the street and upstairs. He put on his glasses and combed his hair. He got out his Sunday coat and his best hat. But he was in such a hurry that he forgot to take off his apron. It was a long shoemaker's apron with ever so many pockets in it for his tools—an awl to make holes with, nails of all sizes, needles and thread, shears—even a small hammer.

Mr. Plum hurried down again to the street. A white-and-yellow taxicab was speeding along, and Mr. Plum waved to it.

It stopped, and the driver opened the door. Mr. Plum stepped in just as if he rode in taxicabs every day of his life.

"The Mayor's office!" he shouted.

"You mean City Hall," said the driver.

"Very well," replied Mr. Plum.

Now that he was on the way, he began to feel a little scared. He had never seen a Mayor, except once in a parade.

He set his glasses straight, dusted the front of his coat, and tried to think what he would say to the Mayor. All at once the city seemed very big and his tree very small.

The taxi stopped. "City Hall!" called the driver and opened the door.

"Oh dear!" said Mr. Plum. But not out loud. He got out the money to pay the driver, and gave him five cents besides.

Then he went through the big door and followed some men into an elevator.

So many people crowded in that Mr. Plum was pushed to the back. He felt lost, and bumped, and he couldn't see.

"The Mayor's office!" he cried, very loudly.

Everyone in the elevator turned to look at him.

Mr. Plum took off his glasses and felt his tie. But the elevator boy spoke in a friendly way.

"That's on the top floor," he said.

A few at a time, the people got off. At the sixth floor only Mr. Plum and the boy were left.

"Going to see His Honor?" asked the boy with a sidewise look. He did not often see anyone in the elevator wearing a shoemaker's apron.

"Yes," said Mr. Plum, thinking of what he was going to say.

"Here you are!" the boy called, and swung back the door.

Mr. Plum got out and put on his glasses.

Right in front of him was a door with the word MAYOR printed on it in black letters. Mr. Plum swallowed, took off his glasses, and opened it.

There was no one in the room. Beyond a desk he saw another door. This one had MAYOR printed on it in gold. He walked over and turned the knob.

Inside he could see an enormous desk, and behind it a red, unhappy face. It was the Mayor.

Mr. Plum stepped in. "Good morning, your Honor," he said softly.

The Mayor glared.

"WHO ARE YOU?" he roared.

Mr. Plum jumped. If he had not thought of his little tree he would have turned and run. Instead, he stepped a little closer. Then he saw that one of the Mayor's feet was stretched out on a chair.

"Well?" snapped the Mayor.

"My name is Plum, Arthur Plum," Mr. Plum began. "I came about the tree in the little square—"

"Ouch!" yelled the Mayor. "My foot!" And he bent over the foot on the chair.

So did Mr. Plum.

"I think I know what's the matter with your foot," he said.

The Mayor stared.

Mr. Plum pushed up his glasses and looked again. "Your shoe's too tight," he said wisely.

"Is *that* all?" the Mayor cried.

Mr. Plum touched the shoe gently.

"I think so," he said, almost forgetting the little green tree.

He put his hat down on the Mayor's desk. "I think I could fix it, if you want me to."

"Right now?" the Mayor asked, starting to take off the shoe.

Mr. Plum nodded.

From one pocket of his long shoemaker's apron he drew out his sharp little shears. From another he pulled a neat little leather patch. And in two minutes Mr. Plum had clipped a hole in the side of the Mayor's shoe and was stitching the patch firmly in place. He snipped, he sewed, he hammered a little. In two more minutes it was done.

"Try it now," said Mr. Plum to the Mayor.

The Mayor put on the shoe and stood up. A smile began to curl around his face. He took a step or two c-a-r-e-f-u-l-l-y. Then he walked across the room, turned, and laughed out loud.

"It doesn't hurt AT ALL!" he cried. And he stamped his foot to prove it.

Mr. Plum beamed. He tucked his tools away in the pockets of his shoemaker's apron. "It's a good thing I forgot to take that off!" he thought.

Just then, outside, the big clock in the City Hall began to strike eleven.

Mr. Plum suddenly remembered his tree.

"Well," the Mayor was saying, "how did you happen to come up here anyway?"

Hurrying very much, Mr. Plum told him all about his little green tree and the men in the truck.

The Mayor walked around as he listened. He rocked up and down on the sore foot, but he could not make it hurt.

"So you don't want the little tree cut down, eh?"

The Mayor pulled the telephone across the desk toward him.

"What's your number?" he asked. And in one minute he was talking to one of the men at Mr. Plum's house.

"Hello," he said. "This is the Mayor. You are not to cut down that tree across from the shoemaker's shop. Go on up to the Park and find one. Thanks."

"I'm the one to say thanks," said Mr. Plum. He smiled and smiled. So did the Mayor.

"Perhaps we both are," the Mayor said.

The next afternoon, as Mr. Plum was tap-tapping away at

his work, another City truck drove up. Once again three men got out. But these men did not carry an ax, a saw, and a long strong rope. They carried a shovel, a crowbar, and two pails.

They dug up the hard dirt around the little green tree, so it could get more water when it rained. They piled rich earth over its roots and planted fresh green grass all around.

And the little tree grew greener and lovelier every day.

And every day (and sometimes oftener) Mr. Plum would push his glasses up over his forehead (so that he could see better) and look out at the little tree and smile.

"My-*tree*, my-*tree*, my-*tree*!" he would say, while his hammer went tap-*tap*, tap-*tap*, tap-*tap*, keeping time.

Why the Old Man Planted Trees

BY DAN MURDOCH

A NOBLEMAN was once riding along the road and saw a very old man digging in his garden. Beside the old man, on the ground, lay a sapling tree, ready to be planted. The nobleman stopped to watch, and after a few minutes called out to the old man, "What kind of tree are you planting there, my good man?"

The old man wiped his brow and picked up the sapling. "This is a fig tree, sir," he said.

"A fig tree?" cried the astonished nobleman. "Why, how old are you, may I ask?"

"I am ninety years old," said the other.

"What!" cried the nobleman. "You are ninety years old, and you plant a tree that will take years and years to give fruit?"

"Why not?" replied the old man.

The nobleman pointed to the tree. "Surely you don't expect to live long enough to get any benefit from the hard work you are doing with this sapling."

The old man leaned on his shovel and looked around his garden. Then he smiled and said, "Tell me, sir, did you eat figs when you were a boy?"

"Certainly." The nobleman sounded puzzled. "Why?"

The old man smiled again. "Then tell me this," he said, "who planted the trees from which those figs were picked?"

The nobleman hesitated. "Why—why, I don't know."

"You see, sir," the old man continued, "our forefathers planted trees for us to enjoy, and I am doing the same for those who come after me. How else can I repay my debt to those who lived before me?"

The nobleman was silent for a moment and then said, "You are very wise, old man, and I have been foolish."

"Thank you, sir," said the old man. "May I ask your name?"

"It doesn't matter," said the nobleman. "You are far more important than I am. Good-by."

The old man nodded his head in farewell and began to dig again, while the nobleman clucked to his horse and rode off, one arm raised in salute to the wise old man.

Trees

By Joyce Kilmer

Illustration by Dawn Stoutsenberger

I think that I shall never see
A poem lovely as a tree.

A tree whose hungry mouth is prest
Against the earth's sweet flowing breast;

A tree that looks at God all day
And lifts her leafy arms to pray;

A tree that may in summer wear
A nest of robins in her hair;

Upon whose bosom snow has lain;
Who intimately lives with rain.

Poems are made by fools like me,
But only God can make a tree.

Trees

By Harry Behn

Trees are the kindest things I know,
They do no harm, they simply grow

And spread a shade for sleepy cows,
And gather birds among their boughs.

They give us fruit in leaves above,
And wood to make our houses of,

And leaves to burn on Hallowe'en,
And in the Spring new buds of green.

They are the first when day's begun
To touch the beams of morning sun,

They are the last to hold the light
When evening changes into night,

And when a moon floats on the sky
They hum a drowsy lullaby

Of sleepy children long ago . . .
Trees are the kindest things I know.

Arbor Day

By Dorothy Brown Thompson

To plant a tree! How small the twig,
And I beside it—very big.

A few years pass; and now the tree
Looks down on very little me.

A few years more—it is so high
Its branches seem to touch the sky.

I did not know that it would be
So vast a thing to plant a tree!

Mother's Day

In 1907, Miss Anna Jarvis arranged for a church service to honor all mothers, to be held on the anniversary of her own mother's death. The idea caught on, first in Philadelphia, then in other cities. "Mother's Day" became so popular that on May 8, 1914, President Woodrow Wilson issued a proclamation making the second Sunday in May a day for "public expression of our love and reverence for the mothers of our country."

My Mother is the Most Beautiful Woman in the World

BY BECKY REYHER

Illustrations by Ruth Gannett

ONCE upon a time, long, long ago, when the harvest season had come again in the Ukraine, the villagers were all busy cutting and gathering the wheat. For this is the land from which most Russians get the flour for their bread.

Marfa and Ivan went to the field early each day, as did all their children. There they stayed until sundown. Varya was Marfa's and Ivan's youngest little girl, six years old. When everyone went to the fields in harvest time, Varya went, too. Her legs were so short she had to run and skip to keep up with her mother's and father's long steps.

"Varyachka, you are a little slow poke!" her father said to her. Then, laughing loudly, he swung her up on his shoulder where she had to hold tight to his neck, for his arms were full carrying the day's lunch and the long scythe to cut the wheat.

In the field, in the long even rows between the thick wheat, Varya knew just what she must do. First, she must stay at least twenty or thirty paces behind her father, who now took even greater and bigger steps, so that he might have plenty of room to swing wide the newly sharpened scythe.

"Stand back, Varyachka! Mind the scythe!" her father warned. Swish, swish, swish, went his even strokes, and down came the wheat, faster and faster, as he made his great strides.

Soon Marfa began to follow Ivan. She gathered the wheat in

sheaves or bunches just big enough to bind together with a
strand of braided wheat. Varya, eager to be useful, helped
gather the wheat, and held each bunch while her mother tied
it. When three sheaves were tied, they were stacked against
each other in a little pyramid.

"Careful, Varyachka!" her mother cautioned, wheat side up!

After a while, instead of long rows of wheat, there were long rows of sheaves, standing stiffly.

Sometimes Varya forgot to follow her mother. On very hot days she stopped to rest upon the warm ground, and let her tired, bare feet and toes tickle the dark, moist earth. A while later she ran and caught up with her mother, and then her mother hugged her to her and wiped her dripping face. Even though her mother's arms and bosom were hot and damp, they felt cool and restful to Varya.

Day after day, Ivan, Marfa, and Varya went to the field, until all the wheat was cut and stacked and none was left growing in the ground. Then a big wagon came and everyone pitched the wheat up to the driver who packed it in solidly, and carefully, and took it to the threshing barn.

When the harvest was over, Ivan, Marfa, Varya, and everyone in the village prepared for the feast day. And what a feast they had!

The Russian sun shines with a warm glow that makes Russia's wheat the most nourishing in the world, and her fruit and vegetables the most delicious that ever grew. The cherries are the reddest, largest and juiciest, the apples the firmest and crunchiest to the teeth, the cucumbers the most plentiful on the vine. As for the watermelons, only someone who has seen a Ukrainian watermelon really knows what watermelons should be.

The villagers worked tirelessly throughout the summer. Their muscles ached, but there was a song in their hearts, and there were merry chuckles on their lips. Hard work produced a rich harvest. There would be wheat for everybody. It was time, then, for a grand celebration.

When Varya was five years old, a year ago, she was allowed to share in the excitement of preparing the feast. That summer she helped her mother bake the little cakes of plaited flat dough, stuffed with meat or cabbage. *Piroghki,* they were called.

When all the cakes were rolled out, Varya's mother said: "And for you, Varyachka, a special one, a *piroghochok.*" That meant, in Russian, a darling little cake. It also meant that harvest day was a holiday, and that Varya's busy mother could take the time to bake a special cake for her.

Besides the *piroghki,* Varya and her mother brought *blini* to the feast. These are flat, rolled, browned, little pancakes,

filled almost to bursting, with jelly or cheese. They are eaten
smothered with thick cream, or plain, held between sticky
fingers.

Varya had taken her turn at rolling out the dough for the
piroghki, for the thinner the dough, the lighter the *piroghki.*
This was one of the housewifely lessons she had to master.

The feast always took place after church in the very heart
of the village. Varya came with her parents. Everybody was
there. The grandmothers whom Russians call Baboushka, and
who always wear a gay kerchief tied below their chin. The
mothers with babies in their arms. The strong, broad-shouldered
fathers. And the many children, all with roses in their cheeks.

Tolya, the village leader, played the accordion. The minute
his music started, everybody's feet began to keep time. The
boys whistled, and stamped their feet, and everybody clapped
their hands.

Tolya stood in the center, all eyes upon him. He danced a
jigging step or two, his fingers never leaving the accordion,
and shouted: "Too quiet, my friends. A little more nonsense.
A little more noise. A few more smiles. Sing! Sing! My friends,
this is a holiday! Come! Everyone on their feet! We must have
a dance!"

Men, women, and children joined in the singing, as Tolya swung his accordion into rollicking dance tunes.

The men wore polished knee high, heavy boots, but they danced as if their feet were bare. As the music grew faster and faster, their feet grew lighter and nimbler. It was as if they and their partners had wings that carried them swiftly by those who were watching. To Varya it seemed that the older girls' braids flew by like birds in the wind.

The girls wore lots of petticoats under a skirt so wide you could not tell where it began, or where it ended. Around their

necks were many strings of beads that shone as bright as a
Christmas tree, all tied with trailing strings of many colored
ribbons.

Some of the little girls were dressed almost as grandly. But
not Varya, nor most of them.

Varya kept asking her mother: "When am I going to have
a beautiful dance costume with lots of beads?"

And Varya's mother would say: "When you are a grown up
young lady, Varya."

Always it seemed to Varya she just could not wait until she
was grown up.

Varya was an impatient little girl. Her impatience was like
a teasing toothache. Today it was so great she felt choked, as
if she had swallowed a whole watermelon. For today was the
last day for gathering the wheat. By evening all the wheat
would be cut, stacked in pyramids, and waiting for the wagon
to take it to the threshing barn. Tomorrow another wonderful
feast day and celebration would come around again. Varya
could hardly wait for the feast day to begin.

Bright and early Marfa, Ivan, and Varya went to the wheat
field. "We must get to it," warned Ivan, "this is our last day
to get the wheat in!"

"It has been a good crop, Ivan, hasn't it?" asked Marfa.

"Indeed, yes!" Ivan answered heartily. "And it will mean a
good warm winter with plenty to eat. We have much to be
thankful for."

Marfa and Ivan worked quicker and harder than ever. They
did not seem to notice the hot sun. The wheat swished almost
savagely as it came rushing down.

But to Varya the day seemed the longest she had ever lived.
The sun seemed hotter than on any other day, and her feet
seemed almost too heavy to lift.

Varya peered into the next row of wheat which was not yet
cut. There it was cool and pleasant and the sun did not bear
down with its almost unbearable heat. Varya moved in just a
little further to surround herself with that blessed coolness.
"How lucky I am!" she thought, "to be able to hide away from
the hot sun. I will do this for just a few minutes. Surely Mamochka will not mind if I do not help her all the day."

Soon Varya grew sleepy, for in so cool a place, one could curl up and be very quiet and comfortable.

When Varya woke, she jumped to her feet and started to run toward her mother. But her mother was nowhere in sight.

Varya called, "Mama," "Mama," "Mamochka," but there was no answer.

Sometimes her mother got ahead of her and was so busy with her work she did not hear.

"Maybe if I run along the row, I will catch up with her," Varya thought.

She ran and ran, and soon she was out of breath, but nowhere could she see her mother.

"Maybe I have gone in the wrong direction," she said to herself. So she ran the other way. But here, too, there was no trace of her mother.

Varya was alone in the wheat fields, where she could see nothing but tall pyramids of wheat towering above her. When she called out, her voice brought no response, no help. Overhead the sun was not so bright as it had been. Varya knew that soon it would be night and that she must find her mother.

Varya cut through the last of the wheat that had not yet
been cut, breaking her own pathway, which bent and hurt
the wheat. She would not have done this, had she not been
frightened.

When it was almost dark, Varya stumbled into a clearing
where several men and women had paused to gossip after the
day's work. It took her only a second to see that these were
strangers, and that neither her mother nor father were among
them.

The little girl stared ahead of her, not knowing what to do.
One of the men spied her and said in a booming voice which
he thought was friendly, "Look what we have here!"

Everyone turned to Varya. She was sorry that with so many
strangers looking at her, she had her hair caught back in a tiny
braid with a bit of string, and that she was wearing only her
oldest, most faded dress. Surely, too, by now her face and
hands must be as streaked with dirt as were her legs and dress.
This made her burst into tears.

"Poor little thing," cried one of the women, putting her arms
around Varya, "she is lost!" But this sympathy, and the strange
voices made Varya want her mother all the more. She could not
help crying.

"We must know her name, and the name of her mother and
father. Then we can unite them," said the women.

"Little girl, little girl," they said, "what is your name? What
is your mother's and father's name?" But Varya was too unhappy to speak.

Finally because her longing for her mother was so great,
she sobbed out:

"My mother is the most beautiful woman in the world!"

All the men and women smiled. The tallest man, Kolya,
clapped his hands and laughingly said, *"Now* we have something to go on."

This was long, long ago, when there were no telephones and
no automobiles. If people wanted to see each other, or carry
a message, they went on their two feet.

From every direction, friendly, good-hearted boys ran to
village homes with orders to bring back the beautiful women.

"Bring Katya, Manya, Vyera, Nadya," the tall man, Kolya,
called to one boy.

"Ay, but don't forget the beauty, Lisa," he called to still another boy.

The women came running. These were orders from Kolya, the village leader. Also the mothers, who had left the fields early to get supper for their families, thought perhaps this was indeed their child who was lost.

As each beautiful woman came rushing up, blushing and proud that she had been so chosen, Kolya would say to her: "We have a little lost one here. Stand back, everyone, while the little one tells us if this is her mother!"

The mothers laughed and pushed, and called to Kolya: "You big tease! What about asking each mother if this is her child? We know our children!"

To Varya this was very serious, for she was lost and she was desperate without her mother. As she looked at each strange woman, Varya shook her head in disappointment and sobbed harder. Soon every known beauty from far and near, from distances much further than a child could have strayed, had come and gone. Not one of them was Varya's mother.

The villagers were really worried. They shook their heads. Kolya spoke for them. "One of us will have to take the little one home for the night. Tomorrow may bring fresh wisdom to guide us!"

Just then a breathless, excited woman came puffing up to the crowd. Her face was big and broad, and her body even larger. Her eyes were little pale slits on either side of a great lump of a nose. The mouth was almost toothless. Even as a young girl everyone had said, "A homely girl like Marfa is lucky to get a good husband like Ivan."

"Varyachka!" cried this woman.

"Mamochka!" cried the little girl, and they fell into each other's arms. The two of them beamed upon each other. Varya cuddled into that ample and familiar bosom. The smile Varya had longed for was once again shining upon her.

All of the villagers smiled thankfully when Varya looked up from her mother's shoulder and said with joy:

"This is my mother! I told you my mother is the most beautiful woman in the world!"

The group of friends and neighbors, too, beamed upon each other, as Kolya repeated the proverb so well known to them, a proverb which little Varya had just proved: *"We do not love people because they are beautiful, but they seem beautiful to us because we love them."*

Next day was the feast day. In the evening Varya sat cuddled in her mother's lap, and happily watched the dancing. As the music played, she brought her mother's head close to her own and whispered: "Mamochka, the dancers, they are so beautiful. I love to watch them."

Her mother patted Varya and whispered back: "This is the harvest feast day. Everyone is wearing their best clothes, and their best smile. Of course it is fun to watch them!"

Varya was so happy and felt so safe, she was able to speak of the dark, awful moments when she was lost.

"Mamochka," she said, haltingly, as if she could not find the right words, "some of the children have teased me. They laughed about my calling you the most beautiful woman in the world. They say the angels, the Czarina, the Princesses, the Queens, the rich, their own mothers, are the most beautiful. One of *them* is the most beautiful woman in the world.

"Mamochka," Varya went on, "I know that some of those women have more beads than you. Some have bigger and wider skirts. Maybe some of them can sing and dance better than you can. But, Mamochka, to me, you are the most beautiful woman in the world!"

Varya's mother, Marfa, kissed her, smiled happily and said: "Some people, Varyachka, see with their eyes alone. Others see with their hearts, too. I am grateful and lucky that you see with your heart, as well as with your eyes."

The Mother Sings

By Eleanor Farjeon

Rockaby, my baby,
Slumber if you can.
I wonder what you're going to be
When you're grown a man.

If you are a monarch
On a gold and silver throne,
With all the lands of East and West
For to call your own,
I know you'll be the greatest monarch
Ever was known.

If you are a poet
With the magic of the word,
A swan's quill to write with
And a voice like a bird,
I know you'll be the greatest poet
Ever was heard.

But whether you're a monarch
And make your bride a queen,
Or whether you're a poet
With men's hearts to glean,
I know you are the sweetest baby
Ever was seen.

Rockaby, my baby,
Slumber if you can,
I wonder what you're going to be
When you're grown a man.

Night and Morning

By Dorothy Aldis

Illustration by Dawn Stoutsenberger

The morning sits outside afraid
Until my mother draws the shade;

Then it bursts in like a ball,
Splashing sun all up the wall.

And the evening is not night
Until she's tucked me in just right
And kissed me and turned out the light.

Oh, if my mother went away
Who would start the night and day?

Memorial Day

MAY 30

A day that honors dead soldiers is always one of mixed emotions. We are proud of the glory they have won, proud of the job they have done to keep us free. And we are sad that good men had to suffer and die.

Memorial Day was called Decoration Day when, on May 30, 1868, General John A. Logan, Commander in Chief of the Grand Army of the Republic, issued the order that, ". . . every post of the G.A.R. should hold suitable exercises and decorate the graves of their dead comrades with flowers."

Memorial Day originally reminded us of those who died during the Civil War, a battle in which our countrymen fought each other, North against South, brother against brother, father against son. Those who died for the South and states' rights were just as sure they were right as those who died for the North and the Union.

Today, Memorial Day, celebrated on May 30 in most states, honors the dead of all our wars.

Light Bread and Apple Butter

BY HAROLD KEITH

Illustrations by Emil Weiss

SUMMER passed, and with the coming of autumn the Kansas troops at Rolla were issued warm woolen gloves and long blue overcoats. Jeff was satisfied with everything but the food. He would always be hungry, he reckoned. They never got enough to eat.

He was issued three days' rations during a march and could have eaten it all in one day. And now that cooler weather had arrived, his appetite had burst its fetters. He was hungrier than a woodpecker with a headache.

One Sunday afternoon in October, after inspection, he took Dixie for a walk down the leaf-strewn road to the clay pits, hoping to find some ripe persimmons. It was good to be out in the tingling air.

The north wind held just enough of a sting in it that his short coat felt comfortable. From somewhere back in the quiet timber he heard the splintering thud of an ax. His nose caught the sour, winy odor of a cider press. A sharp pleasure came over him. It was good to get away from the camp, where for three long hours the officers had kept him busy cleaning his quarters and scrubbing his buttons and buckles with a fresh corncob in advance of the brigade commander's weekly inspection visit.

The Missouri woods reminded him of his mother's brilliantly colored rag rug that lay on the split-log floor beside her bed, back in Linn County. The blackjack seedlings seemed aflame in the genial sunshine. The young hickories glowed in livid gold. The oaks couldn't seem to agree on an appropriate color; some wore a subdued foliage of yellow and pale green, others were gay in bronze and bright red. A cardinal flew leisurely

out of a tall, coppery sweet gum, and Jeff thought at first it was
a falling leaf. Dixie trotted along contentedly at his side.

Soon they came to a rude clearing and Jeff saw a small, un-
painted clapboard house with crude leather hinges on the door.
Behind the house were several apple trees, heavy with fruit.
A small patch of big orange pumpkins lay in a garden nearby.

The red apples looked so tempting that for a moment Jeff
hesitated. It would be easy to help himself. Curbing his fierce
appetite, he decided to ask first and, walking up a small pas-
sageway of pulverized white rock, knocked vigorously on the
thin-planked door.

A woman opened it, frowning suspiciously at his blue uniform. With a gnarled hand she raked the black hair out of her
eyes. Jeff snatched off his army cap.

"Mam," said Jeff, twisting the cap in his hands bashfully,
"I'm real hungry. Could I have some of those apples yonder?"
With his cap, he pointed at the fruit trees nearby. He saw a
small boy's white, scrubbed face peering curiously at him from
behind the woman's skirts.

"Begone with ye," the woman snapped, in a tired, strained

voice. "Iffen I feed one of ye, ye'd come back tomorrey, an' bring the whole army with you. We ain't got enough fer ourselves." She started to shut the door.

Jeff stepped back, disappointment in his face. "Mam," he said politely, "I wouldn't bring the army down on you. And I'll be glad to work for the apples. I was raised on a farm in Kansas. You got any man's work needs to be done around here? Anything you want lifted, any fence to fix?"

Now it was the woman's turn to look surprised. Hopefully Jeff watched her. When she glanced at his blue uniform she scowled. But when she looked into his boyish face, her hard features began to soften and her distrust to fade.

"I reckon it's all right," she whined, wearily. "Just help yo'sef to the apples. Ye don't need to work fer 'em. Most soldiers woulda jest taken 'em and not even bothered to knock."

Relief flooded Jeff, like a warm shaft of sunshine.

"Yes, mam," he said, "I come pretty near doing that myself, mam, I was so famished."

She seemed pleased with his honesty and opened the door wider. A small girl with curly yellow hair thrust her head bashfully around the jamb. When Jeff smiled at the children, the boy opened his mouth and smiled back and Jeff saw he had two upper front teeth missing.

"Ye don't look like a soldier nohow," the woman said. "Ye look more like a schoolboy. Ye orter be home with yer mother."

"Yes, mam," grinned Jeff.

That grin must have done something to her, because now she stepped back. "Why don't ye come in?" she invited. "Sit down. We ain't got much ourselves but mebbe we can do better fer ye than jest raw apples."

She indicated a kitchen table covered with oilcloth. "Sit thar." She went back into the shed room. Gratefully Jeff stepped inside and sat down.

"Do ye like light bread and apple butter?" she called from somewhere inside the house.

Jeff could feel his mouth puckering with hunger. "I sure do, mam. I'd like it even if it had bugs on it."

She came back carrying a stone jar of apple butter, part of a round loaf of fresh light bread and a tall blue-glass bottle of cold milk. "It ain't much. But it ain't got no bugs on it. Hep yersef."

"Yes, *mam*. Thank you, mam."

With a long, sharp, bone-handled knife, she planed off three slices of the bread. Jeff could smell the fragrant yeast. With an effort he restrained himself.

"Mam," he said, "may I give my dog some of this? I'll bet she's almost as hungry as me."

The woman said, "You jist go ahead, now, and eat yore vittles. I'll feed yore dog."

"Yes, mam," Jeff said. "Thank you, mam."

Overjoyed at his good fortune, he ate ravenously while the two children, fingers in mouth, stared shyly at him.

"My name's McComas," the woman said, returning and sitting at the other side of the table. "We're lucky to hev any food at all these days. One army or t'other's on us all the time."

"We get rations," Jeff explained between bites, "but they aren't much. Just a little bacon and corn meal and coffee."

"Ye talk different than us," the woman said. "Where'bouts was ye raised?"

"In Linn County, Kansas, mam, close to the Missouri border," Jeff said. "My mother was a schoolteacher back in Kentucky before she got married. She taught all of us our speech." He told them all about his home, his family, and the bushwhackers.

The woman's eyes grew hard at the mention of the bushwhackers. "There's bushwhackers in both no'th an' south," she said, smoothing her faded gray apron over her knee. "I got a sister livin' near Neosho, close to the Kansas border. They was raided twict by Montgomery's Jayhawkers from Kansas an' got cleaned out both times. Bushwhackers, no matter which side they's on, is the lowest critters on God's green earth."

"Yes, mam," agreed Jeff. With the back of his hand he wiped the bread crumbs off his mouth. Feeling full for the first time in weeks, he arose to go.

"Mam, are you sure you haven't got some chores or something I could help you with around here? I've a little time before I have to go back."

Appreciative, she showed him an ax and several long blackjack logs piled together in the yard. Taking off his coat, Jeff

picked up the ax and began to swing it in the crisp fall air. He
enjoyed the exercise. He hadn't used an ax since he had left
home. Soon he had cut enough wood to keep the fireplace going
several days. He carried part of it inside for her, stacking it
neatly on the hearth.

She thanked him, wiping her rough hands on her apron.
"Thet'll last us a week. My man's in the army. It's hard to
keep going without him."

"Mam," said Jeff, just before he left, "could I take a blouse-
ful of those apples back to my messmates in camp? I'd take the
ones on the ground. And I wouldn't tell them where I got them.
They're hungry, too."

She gave him an old tow sack. Jeff filled it with windfalls.

As he and Dixie walked away, he looked back and saw them
all three standing in the doorway watching him. He waved.
The boy and the girl waved back.

Barbara Frietchie

By John Greenleaf Whittier

Illustration by Irving Leveton

Up from the meadows rich with corn,
Clear in the cool September morn,

The clustered spires of Frederick stand
Green-walled by the hills of Maryland.

Round about them orchards sweep,
Apple and peach-tree fruited deep,

Fair as a garden of the Lord
To the eyes of the famished rebel horde,

On that pleasant morn of the early fall
When Lee marched over the mountain wall;

Over the mountains winding down,
Horse and foot, into Frederick town.

Forty flags with silver stars,
Forty flags with crimson bars,

Flapped in the morning wind: the sun
Of noon looked down, and saw not one.

Up rose old Barbara Frietchie then,
Bowed with her fourscore years and ten;

Bravest of all in Frederick town,
She took up the flag the men hauled down;

In her attic window the staff she set,
To show that one heart was loyal yet.

Up the street came the rebel tread,
Stonewall Jackson riding ahead.

Under his slouched hat left and right
He glanced; the old flag met his sight.

"Halt!"—the dust-brown ranks stood fast.
"Fire!"—out blazed the rifle blast.

It shivered the window, pane and sash;
It rent the banner with seam and gash.

Quick, as it fell, from the broken staff
Dame Barbara snatched the silken scarf.

She leaned far out on the window-sill,
And shook it forth with a royal will.

"Shoot, if you must, this old gray head,
But spare your country's flag," she said.

A shade of sadness, a blush of shame,
Over the face of the leader came;

The nobler nature within him stirred
To life at that woman's deed and word;

"Who touches a hair of yon gray head
Dies like a dog! March on!" he said.

All day long through Frederick street
Sounded the tread of marching feet:

All day long that free flag tost
Over the heads of the rebel host.

Ever its torn folds rose and fell
On the loyal winds that loved it well;

And through the hill-gaps sunset light
Shone over it with a warm good-night.

Barbara Frietchie's work is o'er,
And the Rebel rides on his raids no more.

Honor to her! and let a tear
Fall, for her sake, on Stonewall's bier.

Over Barbara Frietchie's grave,
Flag of Freedom and Union, wave!

Peace and order and beauty draw
Round thy symbol of light and law;

And ever the stars above look down
On thy stars below in Frederick town!

The Blue and the Gray

By Francis Miles Finch

By the flow of the inland river,
  Whence the fleets of iron have fled,
Where the blades of the grave-grass quiver,
  Asleep are the ranks of the dead:
    Under the sod and the dew,
      Waiting the judgment-day:
    Under the one, the Blue;
      Under the other, the Gray.

These in the robings of glory,
  Those in the gloom of defeat,
All with the battle-blood gory,
  In the dusk of eternity meet:
    Under the sod and the dew,
      Waiting the judgment-day:
    Under the laurel, the Blue;
      Under the willow, the Gray.

From the silence of sorrowful hours
  The desolate mourners go,
Lovingly laden with flowers
  Alike for the friend and the foe:
    Under the sod and the dew,
      Waiting the judgment-day:
    Under the roses, the Blue;
      Under the lilies, the Gray.

So with an equal splendour,
  The morning sun-rays fall,
With a touch impartially tender,
  On the blossoms blooming for all:
    Under the sod and the dew,
      Waiting the judgment-day:
    Broidered with gold, the Blue;
      Mellowed with gold, the Gray.

So, when the summer calleth,
  On forest and field of grain,
With an equal murmur falleth
  The cooling drip of the rain:
    Under the sod and the dew,
      Waiting the judgment-day:
    Wet with the rain, the Blue;
      Wet with the rain, the Gray.

Sadly, but not with upbraiding,
  The generous deed was done,
In the storm of the years that are fading
  No braver battle was won:
    Under the sod and the dew,
      Waiting the judgment-day:
    Under the blossoms, the Blue;
      Under the garlands, the Gray.

No more shall the war cry sever,
  Or the winding rivers be red;
They banish our anger for ever
  When they laurel the graves of our dead!
    Under the sod and the dew,
      Waiting the judgment-day:
    Love and tears for the Blue;
      Tears and love for the Gray.

Sheridan's Ride

By T. Buchanan Read

Illustration by William Colrus

Up from the South at break of day,
Bringing to Winchester fresh dismay,
The affrighted air with a shudder bore,
Like a herald in haste, to the chieftan's door,
The terrible grumble, and rumble, and roar,
Telling the battle was on once more—
  And Sheridan twenty miles away.

And wider still those billows of war
Thundered along the horizon's bar;
And louder yet into Winchester rolled
The roar of that red sea uncontrolled,
Making the blood of the listener cold,
As he thought of the stake in that fiery fray—
  And Sheridan twenty miles away.

But there is a road from Winchester town,
A good, broad highway leading down;
And there, through the flush of the morning light,
A steed as black as the steeds of night
Was seen to pass as with eagle flight;
As if he knew the terrible need,
He stretched away with his utmost speed;
Hills rose and fell; but his heart was gay,
  With Sheridan fifteen miles away.

Still spring from those swift hoofs, thundering South,
The dust, like smoke from the cannon's mouth,
Or the trail of a comet, sweeping faster and faster,
Foreboding to traitors the doom of disaster.
The heart of the steed and the heart of the master,
Were beating like prisoners assaulting their walls,
Impatient to be where the battlefield calls;
Every nerve of the charger was strained to full play,
  With Sheridan only ten miles away.

Under his spurning feet the road,
Like an arrowy Alpine river flowed,
And the landscape sped away behind
Like an ocean flying before the wind,
And the steed, like a bark fed with furnace fire,
Swept on, with his wild eye full of fire.
But lo! he is nearing his heart's desire:
He is snuffing the smoke of the roaring fray,
    With Sheridan only five miles away.

The first that the general saw were the groups
Of stragglers, and then the retreating troops.
What was done—what to do? A glance told him both.
Then, striking his spurs, with a terrible oath
He dashed down the line, 'mid a storm of huzzas,
And the wave of retreat checked its course there, because
The sight of the master compelled it to pause.
With foam and with dust the black charger was gray;
By the flash of his eye, and the red nostrils' play,
He seemed to the whole great army to say:
"I have brought you Sheridan all the way
    From Winchester town to save the day."

Hurrah! hurrah for Sheridan!
Hurrah! hurrah for horse and man!
And when their statues are placed on high,
Under the dome of the Union sky,
The American soldiers' Temple of Fame,
There, with the glorious general's name,
Be it said, in letters both bold and bright:
"Here is the steed that saved the day,
By carrying Sheridan into the fight,
    From Winchester, twenty miles away!"

The Sword of Robert Lee

By Abram J. Ryan

Forth from its scabbard, pure and bright
   Flashed the sword of Lee!
Far in the front of the deadly fight,
High o'er the brave in the cause of Right,
Its stainless sheen, like a beacon bright,
   Led us to Victory.

Out of its scabbard, where, full long,
   It slumbered peacefully,
Roused from its rest by the battle's song,
Shielding the feeble, smiting the strong,
Guarding the right, avenging the wrong,
   Gleamed the sword of Lee.

Forth from its scabbard, high in air
   Beneath Virginia's sky—
And they who saw it gleaming there,
And knew who bore it, knelt to swear
That where that sword led they would dare
   To follow—and to die.

Out of its scabbard! Never hand
   Waved sword from stain as free,
Nor purer sword led braver band,
Nor braver bled for a brighter land,
Nor brighter land had a cause so grand,
   Nor cause a chief like Lee!

Forth from its scabbard! How we prayed
   That sword might victor be;
And when our triumph was delayed,
And many a heart grew sore afraid,
We still hoped on while gleamed the blade
   Of noble Robert Lee.

Forth from its scabbard all in vain
　　Bright flashed the sword of Lee;
'Tis shrouded now in its sheath again,
It sleeps the sleep of our noble slain,
Defeated, yet without a stain,
　　Proudly and peacefully.

The Conquered Banner

By Abram J. Ryan

Furl that Banner, for 'tis weary;
Round its staff 'tis drooping dreary;
　　Furl it, fold it—it is best;
For there's not a man to wave it,
And there's not a sword to save it,
And there's not one left to lave it
In the blood which heroes gave it;
And its foes now scorn and brave it;
　　Furl it, hide it—let it rest!

Take that Banner down! 'tis tattered;
Broken is its shaft and shattered;
And the valiant hosts are scattered
　　Over whom it floated high.
Oh, 'tis hard for us to fold it,
Hard to think there's none to hold it,
Hard that those who once unrolled it
　　Now must furl it with a sigh!

Furl that Banner—furl it sadly;
Once ten thousands hailed it gladly,
And ten thousands wildly, madly,
　　Swore it should forever wave—
Swore that foeman's sword should never
Hearts like theirs entwined dissever,
And that flag should float forever
　　O'er their freedom, or their grave!

Furl it! for the hands that grasped it,
And the hearts that fondly clasped it,
   Cold and dead are lying low;
And that Banner—it is trailing,
While around it sounds the wailing
   Of its people in their woe.

For, though conquered, they adore it—
Love the cold, dead hands that bore it!
Weep for those who fell before it!
Pardon those who trailed and tore it!
But, oh, wildly they deplore it,
   Now who furl and fold it so!

Furl that Banner! True, 'tis gory,
Yet 'tis wreathed around with glory,
And 'twill live in song and story
   Though its folds are in the dust!
For its fame on brightest pages,
Penned by poets and by sages,
Shall go sounding down the ages—
   Furl its folds though now we must!

Furl that Banner, softly, slowly;
Treat it gently—it is holy,
   For it droops above the dead;
Touch it not—unfold it never,
Let it droop there, furled forever,—
   For its people's hopes are fled.

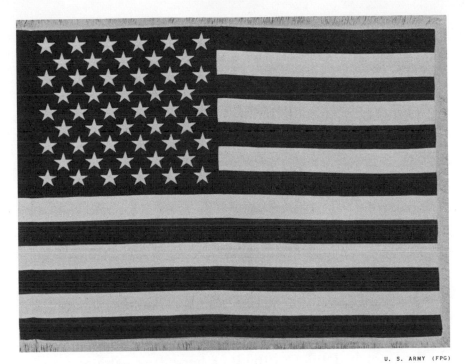

Flag Day

JUNE 14

On June 14, 1777, the American flag, consisting of thirteen stars and thirteen stripes, was approved by the Continental Congress. In the original red, white, and blue flag, each state was represented by one star and one stripe. As the country grew, so did the flag—a new star and stripe for each state. But in 1818 Congress ruled that the original thirteen stripes be restored and that on the fourth of July following the admission of a new state, a new star be added. We now have fifty stars for our fifty states.

June 14, the birthday of our flag, became a holiday in New York State in 1897. In the next few years other states joined New York. But it was not until 1916 that President Wilson established Flag Day by national proclamation.

According to the Department of State, red stands for hardiness and courage, white is the symbol of purity and innocence, and blue is the color of vigilance, perseverance, and justice.

Betsy Ross and the Flag

BY JANE MAYER

Illustrations by Grace Paull

Will you tell Mistress Ross why we have come, please?"
George Washington said to George Ross.

"We are a committee," George Ross began. And then he
went on to tell her most of the things he and the others had
discussed that day and the day before about a flag.

Betsy's first astonishment was that a committee should have
spent some of its time talking about her. She had always
kept so busy with her work or her friends or her family that
she had not had time to think of herself as gaining a repu-
tation for industry and skill.

She thanked her husband's uncle with a smile for the nice
words he was repeating about her.

"We want the flag to be well made," George Ross finished.
"We want you to make the flag."

"Have you a picture of it?" Betsy asked.

George Washington reached into his pocket again for the
sketch. He walked over to Betsy's desk, unfolded the paper
and smoothed it out. He examined the drawing carefully,
squinting his eyes to look at it.

Betsy came and stood beside him. Then the other two men
crossed the bare wood floor and leaned over the desk also to
examine the sketch once more.

After a long time Betsy said, "It is very nice. It should make
a beautiful flag."

"You see what it means, don't you?" Washington said. "A
circle of stars is union. Once the Colonies have joined, they
will never disjoin."

"One star for each state," Robert Morris said, "and every
star equal."

"Each equal part is needed to make up the whole," George Ross said.

It began to sound as if they were reciting a poem.

"Every part of the circle must be there to keep the whole circle perfect."

"A star is a symbol of light and truth."

"Blue is a strong color."

"White is a pure color."

"Red is a brave color."

Then suddenly they were all a little shy because they had said so much of what they were feeling. Robert Morris overcame his shyness by becoming practical. "Can you think of any way to improve the design?" he asked.

Betsy was almost afraid to make a suggestion, but since they all wanted the flag to be the best that it could be, and since she knew that she had a good idea, she spoke. "I think they should be five-pointed stars," she said. "They will look neater, cleaner and stronger that way."

"I agree that five-pointed stars would look better," Washington said. "But are they not harder to make?"

"Not when one is used to cutting," Betsy said, speaking with confidence now. "And once the star design is made, it will be an easy one to copy. I can make a five-pointed star."

The committee discussed this for a little, then decided that the five-pointed star would be an improvement. Soon they wanted Betsy's opinion on the proportions of the flag and materials for it. They sat down again and listened while she talked of the relation of length to width, and of fine buntings and dyes.

When she had finished George Ross said, "General, if you would care to have a new sketch made, I can bring it back here for you."

Washington made some notes on the sketch and put it back into his pocket. "Very well," he said. Then he rose to leave. "I envy you the making of the flag, Mistress Ross. It is always so much more delightful to be able to make things than to have to destroy them." He started walking from the back parlor toward the front. "That is why I feel so strongly about my plantation and growing things there and making

improvements," he said. "That is why I wish so often that I could return there and resume my old life."

At the door he stopped, tall, dignified, courteous. "We have talked so much," he said, "and we have not asked you the one important question. Can you make a flag?"

Betsy looked up at him. Her blue eyes were steady and serious. "I never have," she said, "but I'll try."

The men of the committee had told Betsy that it would be better not to talk about the flag for a while. They advised

her to wait until it was finished and then they would see how
far the Congress had gone toward declaring itself a union of
independent states. They were sure they would know soon
if the Congress wished to break away forever from England.

So Betsy told no one of the committee's visit.

Even after George Ross had returned with the new sketch,
and after she and he had examined and discussed it and
decided that it was an improvement, she still told no one.
She merely told her customers that for a time she would be
too busy to take on any new work. After that, for a few days,
there was almost no one around the shop to bother her.

From the sketch she figured out how much material of
each color she would need, and then she went out to buy it.
She knew that bunting, because it is a sturdy, loosely woven
cloth, would be the best material. Betsy could recognize good
quality when she saw it and she examined the bunting carefully. She could also tell whether the dyes used were good
or bad, for she herself had dyed much yarn at home, making
red from cochineal and blue from indigo. She was very particular about the way the yarn in this bunting was dyed.
When she was satisfied that she had found the best material
for her purpose that Philadelphia had to offer, she started
toward home.

On her way she decided that it was not enough merely
to say one would try to do something. It was also necessary
to learn *how* it could be done. For this purpose she walked

into a store where supplies for ships were sold and asked to look at some flags. If the clerk there thought it strange that a woman should be doing this, he said nothing, but brought the flags to her.

She examined the binding, then the holes where the flag could be fastened to a rope and so to a flagstaff. She examined the way designs were sewn on. She examined the seams. Everything, of course, was sewn by hand. *Humph*, she thought, *I can certainly sew finer seams than that.*

She was so particular in her examination that the clerk became curious. "Are you going to make a flag for a company of the militia?" he asked.

Betsy lowered her eyes. "No," she said demurely.

"For a regiment?"

She did not think she should answer, but she could not resist it. She could not even resist a special little smile of pride. "It may be for something larger than a regiment," she said. Then she hurried out of the shop before the clerk could ask her any more questions.

The National Flag

By Charles Sumner

There is the National Flag. He must be cold, indeed, who can look upon its folds rippling in the breeze without pride of country. If he be in a foreign land, the flag is companionship and country itself, with all its endearment . . . The very colors have a language which was officially recognized by our fathers. White is for purity; red, for valor; blue, for justice. And altogether, bunting, stripes, stars, and colors, blazing in the sky, make the flag of our country, to be cherished by all our hearts, to be upheld by all our hands.

Flag of the Free

By Walter Taylor Field

Look at the flag as it floats on high,
Streaming aloft in the clear, blue sky,
Rippling, leaping, tugging away,
Gay as the sunshine, bright as the day,
Throbbing with life, where the world may see—
Flag of our country, flag of the free!
What do we see in the flag on high,
That we bare our heads as it passes by,
That we thrill with pride, our hearts beat fast,
And we cheer and cheer as the flag goes past—
The flag that waves for you and me—
Flag of our country, flag of the free?

We see in the flag a nation's might.
The pledge of a safeguard day and night,
Of a watchful eye and a powerful arm
That guard the nation's homes from harm.
Of a strong defense on land and sea—
Flag of our country, flag of the free!
We see in the flag a union grand,
A brotherhood of heart and hand,
A pledge of love and a stirring call
To live our lives for the good of all—
Helpful and just and true to thee,
Flag of our country, flag of the free!

Flutter, dear flag, o'er the lands and seas!
Fling out your stars and your stripes to the breeze,
Righting all wrongs, dispelling all fear,
Guarding the land that we cherish so dear,
And the God of our fathers, abiding with thee,
Will bless you and trust you, O flag of the free!

Star-Spangled Banner Girl

BY CAROLYN SHERWIN BAILEY

Illustrations by Grace Paull

CAROLINE Pickersgill had learned to sew as soon as she could hold a needle. While her mother kept their little red brick house in old Baltimore spotless and shining, while she polished the brass candlesticks, scoured the floors, and spread the linen out on the garden grass to bleach, Caroline sat beside her grandmother Rebecca and stitched—first the long seams of hand-woven sheeting, so long and stiff for little fingers to hold; then a calico dress for her wooden doll. That was fun! After that, she embroidered scallops for pantalets and petticoats, and matched the countless tiny squares of colored cloth that made the pattern of patchwork quilts. Caroline could hardly have been patient enough to sit sewing, quiet and industrious, in her small red rocking chair, if old Rebecca, her grandmother, had not told her stories to shorten the work. They were thrilling stories, for Rebecca Young had made a flag for General Washington to carry when the American army took part in the siege of Boston.

The story always began with Rebecca's description of her Philadelphia flag shop. She had even advertised her craft in the *Philadelphia Ledger* in the days of the Revolution:

> Colours
> For the Army and Navy, made and sold at the most reasonable terms,
>
> REBECCA YOUNG
>
> In Walnut Street, near Third Street, and next door but one to Mr. Samuel McLane's.
>
> N.B. Any person having Bunting for sale may hear of a purchaser by applying as above.

That was how her advertisement had been printed. Then Caroline's grandmother Rebecca would go on to tell of the visit of General Washington to her shop, of his order for a flag which should have thirteen stripes of red and white, one for each of the Colonies. In the corner of this flag was a "grand union" of the old British flag, a blue field with the red and white crosses of St. Andrew and St. George.

Soon after this flag was delivered to General Washington, Rebecca had been obliged to flee with her children in an oxcart going West. Her silver spoons and the Bible had been lost in the forest. There had been her struggle in the wilderness of western Pennsylvania, and then their return to this pleasant home in Baltimore. The entire countryside remembered how Rebecca had made General Washington's battle flag. Beautiful needlework was their family pride, Rebecca told Caroline. Her own fingers were too stiff now to take the tiny stitches for which the family was celebrated, but Caroline's mother, Mary Pickersgill, who had been only a baby when they fled from Philadelphia, still made flags occasionally. Perhaps some day Caroline also would stitch well enough to sew together stripes of red and white bunting, her grandmother said.

Peace and happiness filled the house where these three, Rebecca, Mary, and Caroline, lived alone. Caroline's father was dead, but they owned their brick house near the waterfront in Baltimore, and Mary made a fair living for them stitching more and more of the banners that Caroline watched going out toward the sea, flying above merchant ships and sailing vessels. The American Revolution was nothing but history to the little girl, hard to believe when the bees hummed drowsily in their garden and the hens clucked contentedly over their nests. But Caroline often wondered at what she saw from the Baltimore wharf.

She loved to go down to the wharf, just a step from their front gate, and follow with her eyes the crimson trail her mother's flags made as the ships bearing them put out to sea from Chesapeake Bay. For almost two years many of these flags had been pulled down before they were out of sight; seamen had been taken from the American ships by British cruisers, and sometimes the ships themselves impressed into British service as the property of England if captured on the high seas.

Still this War of 1812 meant very little to Caroline Pickersgill. Other matters seemed to her vastly more important. Bonnets were much fancier in Baltimore than ever before because the girls and ladies were copying the clothes of the French Court. Caroline was making wreaths and bunches of silk flowers, a bombazine frame, and a piped green silk covering for her doll's bonnet. From scraps of her mother's bunting she had made the doll a blue cloak with a red lining, the stylish French colors. It was now fully two years since her mother's banners had first been torn from ships' rigging, and the small town of Baltimore still dozed beneath its white church steeples, its elm trees and flowering hedges. Caroline had come to think that the British and American ships were playing a game out there at sea, and by means of it helping give her mother more work. For Mary Pickersgill made a new flag for every one torn down and tattered, and Grandmother Rebecca folded each one carefully, sending it to sea with her blessing.

It was August of the year 1814. Caroline had never been so happy before. She was a tall girl now, with a flowered bonnet of her own, and with daintier dimity and muslin dresses billowing about her silk slippers than almost any other girl in Baltimore had. She was fourteen years old, and she could sew better than any of her friends. She made all her own clothes, from her embroidered chemises to the lace mitts that reached from her slender wrists to the edge of her puffed sleeves.

Sewing was not Caroline's only hand skill either. Her mother spent all her time in their flag shop, too busy to do the housework. Rebecca was seventy-five years old, and growing blind. She sat in the garden all summer long, trying to see the colors on the ships as they sailed out, and in the winter she huddled by the fireplace, telling over again the story of General Washington's visit. Caroline did the family sewing, baked bread, tended the garden, kept the pewter plates and the silver spoons shining, and raised the largest potatoes and the brightest hollyhocks in Baltimore. She also sold honey and eggs, and was always invited to quilting bees because she could quilt faster than most women. Her days were filled from morning till night with things to do and be happy about.

But all Baltimore was not as peaceful as the Pickersgill flag shop on Albermarle Street. What seemed at first to be the thunder of a summer storm was the roar of British and American ships' guns. After two years of sea warfare and the capture of American seamen by British captains, American ships had begun to imitate the methods of pirates. Many of the vessels sailing up and down the Atlantic coast were now privateers, a polite name for prize-runners. If British ships can impress our sailors, we will take their cargoes, these privateers said. A quarrel between nations that might have been peacefully settled two years before, had blazed into warfare, and at last Baltimore was threatened. British ships seeking a fleet of American privateers were on their way to attack and hold the tiny brick fort built in the shape of a star, which stood, surrounded by cow pastures and hay fields, on a low peninsula guarding the town. There seemed no hope for Baltimore. Danger such as the townspeople had not known since the Revolution stalked at their very doorsteps.

But it was adventure, not danger, that lifted the brass knocker of Caroline Pickersgill's front door on that long-ago August day. She ran to open it, and curtsied as three townsmen entered in haste and excitement. They were the three officers in charge of the few troops that Baltimore had been able to muster. According to old records of this visit, these neighbors were Commodore Barney, General Stricker, and Lieutenant-Colonel MacDonald. Their swords hung at their sides, their anxious faces were gray in the candlelight, as they spoke to Caroline's mother.

"Fort McHenry will not stand a day's siege from British guns," they said. "Our good neighbor, Dr. Beans, has been taken a prisoner of war. Our only chance is to trick the enemy into thinking us stronger than we are. We desire, Mistress Pickersgill, that you make at once a great American flag. We want this banner to measure at least thirty-six feet long and

twenty-nine feet wide. Four hundred yards of bunting will be delivered to you here in a few hours if you consent to help us. What say you? Can you deliver this flag to the fort before we are attacked from the sea? We hope that so large a flag will speak to the enemy of the high courage of our land."

"At once, good sirs," Mary Pickersgill answered. "As soon as the bunting arrives, I will begin cutting."

"Do your best, Mary," urged Rebecca, tapping the brick hearth with her cane. Then going back to her dream world, she said: "Do you not see General Washington and his aides there in our doorway, come to us for a battle flag?"

"Couldn't I help with the sewing?" begged Caroline, her eyes shining with excitement. "Surely, Mother, you can trust me to stitch stripes together." So the three, old Rebecca, young Mary, younger Caroline, daughters of the Stars and Stripes, promised to do their part in protecting their town.

The mammoth rolls of bunting were delivered at their house promptly that night, but, alas, it was soon discovered that there was not a room large enough for cutting out the flag. The parts had to be cut to fit exactly, mostly upon the floor. Much of the sewing also was done on the floor, Mary Pickersgill kneeling down and stitching each stripe, each star. What should they do? At last, in the early morning, with the help of soldiers, they carried the bunting to a deserted malt house that stood near the fort. There, on the great floor, Mary cut, basted, and stitched. Caroline ran between the malt house and their home, taking stripes to be stitched, caring for old Rebecca, and returning to kneel beside her mother to add her fine seaming to the completion of the flag.

The flag had not been started a moment too soon. Disturbances in Baltimore had begun. A group of British soldiers had broken into the garden of Dr. Beans, a well-known townsman, while he was serving tea to some friends. The intrusion had resulted in the arrest of the doctor, who was imprisoned on one of the enemy ships as a British prisoner of war. Ladies in crinoline and silks had scattered, leaving their jasmine tea, sponge cakes, and ices untouched. A gentleman guest, young Francis Scott Key, a Baltimore attorney, had gone at once with a flag of truce to attempt the doctor's rescue. He was now aboard the American cartel ship, the *Mindon*, in Chesapeake Bay two miles from the town. Should the attack upon Baltimore from the water be successful, it was rumored that the town would be set on fire.

But the flag was finished—red, white, and blue, six times as long as a man is tall, secure against storms because of the firm hand-stitching of Caroline and her mother, and bright with the courage of patriotism. They watched it being carried to Fort McHenry and raised upon a tall pole behind the guns.

In the early morning after the flag-raising, the attack upon Baltimore from the water began. For twenty-four hours British mortar ships poured bombs, rockets, and red-hot shot against the little fort, tearing gaping holes in the earth, and piercing the brick walls. A few rents were made in the flag, but it waved bravely in the sunshine. Never had such a flag taken part in battle. Aloof and peaceful, it floated above the fire of the attack. After a day of terrible shellfire and a night of the same horror, the fort still stood. The great banner stitched by Mary and Caroline Pickersgill billowed in the wind as the attacking fleet sailed away, defeated as much by the seamstress's art as by the brave militia of Baltimore.

From the water, Mr. Francis Scott Key watched the flag all that night, as it flew above the red of the rockets and the smoke of the bombs. He could not tell whether the British or the American forces were victorious. In the morning of its triumph, when he and Dr. Beans were safe on land again, he wrote a poem about the flag. We may surmise that Mr. Key wrote this poem under the protection of the red-brick

walls of Fort McHenry, with green grass for his carpet and the Stars and Stripes as a canopy:

Oh, say can you see by the dawn's early light,
What so proudly we hailed at the twilight's last gleaming?

There were many stanzas to the poem, but each ended:

The Star-Spangled Banner, oh, long may it wave,
O'er the land of the free and the home of the brave.

Soon, everybody in our country was singing Mr. Key's song about the flag that Caroline had helped to stitch. We still sing "The Star-Spangled Banner," and the old flag itself is kept as one of our most precious relics of American history in the Smithsonian Institution at Washington. The Pickersgills' house on Albermarle Street in Baltimore is well remembered; the ancient sewing baskets, the old candlesticks, the stiff straight chairs, the steel shears for cutting bunting, the sewing table, just as they were when young Caroline learned how to make a flag.

Today huge machines cut, stitch, and bind our flags. Our dresses, suits, even dolls' clothes, are fashioned by machines, and the days of patchwork quilts and hand-made banners are as far away as is Caroline in her flowered bonnet, long muslin frock, and small silk slippers. But the boy or girl who visits the Smithsonian Institution in Washington will marvel at the tiny stitches Caroline set in the Star-Spangled Banner.

The Star-Spangled Banner

By Francis Scott Key

O say, can you see, by the dawn's early light,
    What so proudly we hailed at the twilight's last gleaming?
Whose broad stripes and bright stars, through the perilous fight,
    O'er the ramparts we watched, were so gallantly streaming!
And the rockets' red glare, the bombs bursting in air,
Gave proof through the night that our flag was still there:
    O say, does that star-spangled banner yet wave
    O'er the land of the free and the home of the brave?

On the shore, dimly seen through the mists of the deep,
    Where the foe's haughty host in dread silence reposes,
What is that which the breeze, o'er the towering steep,
    As it fitfully blows, now conceals, now discloses?
Now it catches the gleam of the morning's first beam,
In full glory reflected now shines on the stream:
    'Tis the star-spangled banner! O long may it wave
    O'er the land of the free and the home of the brave!

And where is that band who so vauntingly swore
    That the havoc of war and the battle's confusion
A home and a country should leave us no more?
    Their blood has washed out their foul footsteps' pollution.
No refuge could save the hireling and slave
From the terror of flight, or the gloom of the grave:
    And the star-spangled banner in triumph doth wave
    O'er the land of the free and the home of the brave!

Oh! thus be it ever, when freemen shall stand
    Between their loved homes and the war's desolation!
Blest with victory and peace, may the heaven-rescued land
    Praise the Power that hath made and preserved us a nation.
Then conquer we must, for our cause it is just,
And this be our motto: "In God is our trust."
    And the star-spangled banner in triumph shall wave
    O'er the land of the free and the home of the brave!

The Flag Goes By

By Henry H. Bennett

Hats off!
Along the street there comes
A blare of bugles, a ruffle of drums,
A flash of color beneath the sky
Hats off!
The flag is passing by!

Blue, and crimson, and white it shines,
Over the steel-tipped, ordered lines.
Hats off!
The colors before us fly;
But more than the flag is passing by.

Sea fights and land fights, grim and great,
Fought to make and to save the state;
Weary marches and sinking ships;
Cheers of victory on dying lips;

Days of plenty, and years of peace,
March of a strong land's swift increase;
Equal justice, right and law,
Stately honor and reverent awe;

Sign of a Nation, great and strong,
To ward her people from foreign wrong;
Pride, and glory, and honor, all
Live in the colors to stand or fall.

Hats off!
Along the street there comes
A blare of bugles, a ruffle of drums;
And loyal hearts are beating high.
Hats off!
The flag is passing by!

Pledge to the Flag

By Francis Bellamy

Illustration by Steve Rubelman

I pledge allegiance to the Flag of the United States of America and to the Republic for which it stands, one nation under God, indivisible, with liberty and justice for all.

The American's Creed

By William Tyler Page

I believe in the United States of America as a Government of the people, by the people, for the people; whose just powers are derived from the consent of the governed; a democracy in a Republic; a sovereign Nation of many sovereign States; a perfect Union, one and inseparable; established upon those principles of freedom, equality, justice and humanity for which American patriots sacrificed their lives and fortunes.

I therefore believe it is my duty to my country to love it; to support its Constitution; to obey its laws; to respect its flag; and to defend it against all enemies.

Father's Day

In 1910 Mrs. John Bruce Dodd of Spokane, Washington proposed that the Spokane Ministerial Association set aside the third Sunday in June for honoring fathers. The custom became popular through the United States and Canada, and was celebrated on varying dates until it was made a national observance in 1934.

We celebrate Father's Day by giving gifts and having special treats for Father, but the other countries which have a Fathers' Day often do it differently. In Czechoslovakia, for instance, Father's Day and Mother's Day both fall shortly before Christmas. On Father's Day the children tie the father into a chair and sing, "Father's Day, Father's Day, What will you give?" Father gives gifts to the children . . . or they don't untie him.

The Night When Mother Was Away

BY CHARLOTTE ZOLOTOW

Illustrations by Reisie Lonette

ONE summer when the little girl and her mother and father were living in the country, the little girl's mother went away to shop in the city. And the little girl's daddy took care of her.

He took care of her all day and then he bathed her and put her to bed. But the little girl wasn't sleepy.

"I'm thirsty," she said.

Her father brought her a cup of water.

"I'm hungry," she said.

And her father brought her a peeled apple cut in half. She ate the apple sitting up in her bed.

"I'm hot," she said.

So her father opened the window and the soft night air came in.

She looked out into the darkness.

The stars sparkled in the sky behind the bedroom curtains.

The little girl's eyes were bright and sparkling as the stars.

And her father understood why on this soft summer night his little girl wasn't sleepy. So he took her up in his arms. He put on her slippers and carried her down the stairs.

There was only one lamp on in the living room but the moonlight shone in through the big window, making everything in the room a new shape and size.

The square gold clock on the mantelpiece seemed to say, *night-time-night-time-night-time.*

"Read me a story," the little girl said.

So her father read her a long story in his slow deep voice but when he closed the book and looked at his little girl, her eyes were still shining brightly and he knew she wasn't sleepy yet.

So her father sat down on the piano bench and the little girl leaned against him and he played some soft nighttime music, so gently and softly the sounds hung like little birds in the air, warm and feathery and sweet.

But when her father finished the song the little girl still wasn't sleepy.

"Wait," her father told her.

He went upstairs, got her summer bathrobe and put it on her. "Let's go for a walk," he suggested.

The little girl slipped her hand in his and the screen door closed behind them like a whisper in the night.

The trees hung close around the porch and in the soft night breeze the leaf of one long branch stroked the grey shingles of the house with a little scratching sound.

The moonlight slanting across the meadow looked like a

pale blanket of snow. But the little girl saw the long meadow grass and the daisies bending like dancers in the night wind and she knew it wasn't snow.

Far away a train whistle sounded. The little girl moved closer to her father as they started toward the backyard path.

It was hot and still and every now and then a lightning bug glowed almost in front of them, as though it were leading the way.

They came to the little pond they swam in, afternoons. Tonight it looked like a pool of shiny black ink.

At the water's edge two little white rabbits stopped still and stared at them before they bounded into the bushes and were gone.

They sat by the pond a long time.

On the opposite bank a family of white ducks were sleeping with their heads pillowed in their own soft feathers.

The moon, reflected in the pond, seemed so close the little girl felt she could reach into the water and hold the moon in her hands.

The night wind ruffled the little girl's hair. She sniffed.
"The scent of the lilac is blowing down from our house,"
her father said.
"It smells nice," said the little girl leaning against him.
The father took a pebble and threw it into the smooth pond.
They watched the circles rippling out and out in the black
water while the splash of the stone echoed in the stillness
of the night.

"Let's go," the father said at last, and they started home.
The lighted kitchen window shone through the darkness.

Near the house two green balls suddenly gleamed at them.
They heard the tinkling of a bell. The green glows were the
eyes of Tinkerbell, their cat, and the little bell tinkling was
the bell she wore to warn the birds away.

Whoooooooooooo

Whooooooooooooooo

WhOOOOoooooooooooooo

A long sound came from the tree behind the house as the
father opened the kitchen door.

They sat down at the kitchen table and had warm milk
and bread and butter with brown sugar. The father looked
at his little girl and saw that her eyes were dreamy and solemn
at last.

So he carried her upstairs and took off her robe and put her
in her bed. He reached over to kiss her and the little girl
kissed him back.

Outside the night owl cried again.

Whooooo whoooooooooo whooooooooooooo.

But this time the little girl was fast asleep.

And when she woke up, her mother was home.

Mr. Chairman

BY FRANK B. GILBRETH, JR., AND
ERNESTINE GILBRETH CAREY

MOTHER and Dad believed that what would work in the home would work in the factory, and what would work in the factory would work in the home.

Dad put the theory to a test shortly after we moved to Montclair. The house was too big for Tom Grieves, the handyman, and Mrs. Cunningham, the cook, to keep in order. Dad decided we were going to have to help them, and he wanted us to offer the help of our own accord. He had found that the best way to get cooperation out of employees in a factory was to set up a joint employer-employee board, which would make work assignments on a basis of personal choice and aptitude. He and Mother set up a Family Council, patterned after an employer-employee board. The council met every Sunday afternoon, immediately after dinner.

At the first session, Dad got to his feet formally, poured a glass of ice water, and began a speech.

"You will notice," he said, "that I am installed here as your chairman. I assume there are no objections. The chair, hearing no objections, will . . ."

"Mr. Chairman," Anne interrupted. Being in high school, she knew something of parliamentary procedure, and thought it might be a good idea to have the chairman represent the common people.

"Out of order," said Dad. "Very much out of order when the chair has the floor."

"But you said you heard no objections, and I want to object."

"Out of order means sit down, and you're out of order," Dad shouted. He took a swallow of ice water, and resumed his speech. "The first job of the Council is to apportion necessary work in the house and yard. Does the chair hear any suggestions?"

There were no suggestions. Dad forced a smile and attempted to radiate good humor.

"Come, come, fellow members of the Council," he said. "This is a democracy. Everybody has an equal voice. How do you want to divide the work?"

No one wanted to divide the work or otherwise be associated with it in any way, shape, or form. No one said anything.

"In a democracy everybody speaks," said Dad, "so, by jingo, start speaking." The Good Humor Man was gone now. "Jack, I recognize you. What do you think about dividing the work? I warn you, you'd better think something."

"I think," Jack said slowly, "that Mrs. Cunningham and Tom should do the work. They get paid for it."

"Sit down," Dad hollered. "You are no longer recognized."

Jack sat down amid general approval, except that of Dad and Mother.

"Hush, Jackie," Mother whispered. "They may hear you and leave. It's so hard to get servants when there are so many children in the house."

"I wish they would leave," said Jack. "They're too bossy."

Dan was next recognized by the chair.

"I think Tom and Mrs. Cunningham have enough to do," he said, as Dad and Mother beamed and nodded agreement. "I think we should hire more people to work for us."

"Out of order," Dad shouted. "Sit down and be quiet!"

Dad saw things weren't going right. Mother was the psychologist. Let her work them out.

"Your chairman recognizes the asssistant chairman," he said, nodding to Mother to let her know he had just conferred that title upon her person.

"We could hire additional help," Mother said, "and that might be the answer."

We grinned and nudged each other.

"But," she continued, "that would mean cutting the budget somewhere else. If we cut out all desserts and allowances, we could afford a maid. And if we cut out moving pictures, ice cream sodas, and new clothes for a whole year, we could afford a gardener, too."

"Do I hear a motion to that effect?" Dad beamed. "Does anybody want to stop allowances?"

No one did. After some prodding by Dad, the motion on allot-
ting work finally was introduced and passed. The boys would
cut the grass and rake the leaves. The girls would sweep, dust
and do the supper dishes. Everyone except Dad would make
his own bed and keep his room neat. When it came to appor-
tioning work on an aptitude basis, the smaller girls were assigned
to dust the legs and lower shelves of furniture; the older girls
to dust table tops and upper shelves. The older boys would push
the lawnmowers and carry leaves. The younger ones would do
the raking and weeding.

The next Sunday, when Dad convened the second meeting
of the Council, we sat self-consciously around the table, biding
our time. The chairman knew something was in the air, and it
tickled him. He had trouble keeping a straight face when he
called for new business.

Martha, who had been carefully coached in private caucus,
arose.

"It has come to the attention of the membership," she began,
"that the assistant chairman intends to buy a new rug for the
dining room. Since the entire membership will be required to
look upon, and sit in chairs resting upon, the rug, I move that
the Council be consulted before any rug is purchased."

"Second the motion," said Anne.

Dad didn't know what to make of this one. "Any discussion?"
he asked, in a move designed to kill time while he planned his
counter attack.

"Mr. Chairman," said Lillian. "We have to sweep it. We should
be able to choose it."

"We want one with flowers on it," Martha put in. "When you
have flowers, the crumbs don't show so easily, and you save motions by not having to sweep so often."

"We want to know what sort of a rug the assistant chairman
intends to buy," said Ernestine.

"We want to make sure the budget can afford it," Fred announced.

"I recognize the assistant chairman," said Dad. "This whole
Council business was your idea anyway, Lillie. What do we do
now?"

"Well," Mother said doubtfully, "I had planned to get a plain violet-colored rug, and I had planned to spend a hundred dollars. But if the children think that's too much, and if they want flowers, I'm willing to let the majority rule."

"I move," said Frank, "that not more than ninety-five dollars be spent."

Dad shrugged his shoulders. If Mother didn't care, he certainly didn't.

"So many as favor the motion to spend only ninety-five dollars, signify by saying aye."

The motion carried unanimously.

"Any more new business?"

"I move," said Bill, "that we spend the five dollars we have saved to buy a collie puppy."

"Hey, wait a minute," said Dad. The rug had been somewhat of a joke, but the dog question was serious. We had wanted a dog for years. Dad thought that any pet which didn't lay eggs was an extravagance that a man with twelve children could ill afford. He felt that if he surrendered on the dog question, there was no telling what the Council might vote next. He had a sickening mental picture of a barn full of ponies, a roadster for Anne, motorcycles, a swimming pool, and, ultimately, the poor house or a debtors' prison, if they still had such things.

"Second the motion," said Lillian, yanking Dad out of his reverie.

"A dog," said Jack, "would be a pet. Everyone in the family could pat him, and I would be his master."

"A dog," said Dan, "would be a friend. He could eat scraps of food. He would save us waste and would save motions for the garbage man."

"A dog," said Fred, "would keep burglars away. He would sleep on the foot of my bed, and I would wash him whenever he was dirty."

"A dog," Dad mimicked, "would be an accursed nuisance. He would be our master. He would eat me out of house and home. He would spread fleas from the garret to the porte-cochere. He would be positive to sleep on the foot of *my* bed. Nobody would wash his filthy, dirty, flea-bitten carcass."

He looked pleadingly at Mother.

"Lillie, Lillie, open your eyes," he implored. "Don't you see where this is leading us? Ponies, roadsters, trips to Hawaii, silk stockings, rouge, and bobbed hair."

"I think, dear," said Mother, "that we must rely on the good sense of the children. A five-dollar dog is not a trip to Hawaii."

We voted, and there was only one negative ballot—Dad's. Mother abstained. In after years, as the collie grew older, shed hair on the furniture, bit the mailman, and did in fact try to appropriate the foot of Dad's bed, the chairman was heard to remark on occasion to the assistant chairman:

"I give nightly praise to my Maker that I never cast a ballot to bring that lazy, disreputable, ill-tempered beast into what was once my home. I'm glad I had the courage to go on record as opposing that illegitimate, shameless flea-bag that now shares my bed and board. You abstainer, you!"

Like most of Dad's and Mother's ideas, the Family Council was basically sound and, although it verged sometimes on the hysterical, brought results. Family purchasing committees, duly elected, bought the food, clothes, furniture, and athletic equipment. A utilities committee levied one-cent fines on wasters of water and electricity. A projects committee saw that work was completed as scheduled. Allowances were decided by the Council, which also meted out rewards and punishment. Despite Dad's forebodings, there were no ponies or roadsters.

One purchasing committee found a large department store which gave us wholesale rates on everything from underwear to baseball gloves. Another bought canned goods directly from a manufacturer, in truckload lots.

It was the Council, too, which worked out the system of submitting bids for unusual jobs to be done.

When Lill was eight, she submitted a bid of forty-seven cents to paint a long, high fence in the back yard. Of course it was the lowest bid, and she got the job.

"She's too young to try to paint that fence all by herself," Mother told Dad. "Don't let her do it."

"Nonsense," said Dad. "She's got to learn the value of money and to keep agreements. Let her alone."

Lill, who was saving for a pair of roller skates and wanted the money, kept insisting she could do it.

"If you start it, you'll have to finish it," Dad said.

"I'll finish it, Daddy. I know I can."

"You've got yourself a contract, then."

It took Lill ten days to finish the job, working every day after school and all day week ends. Her hands blistered, and some nights she was so tired she couldn't sleep. It worried Dad so that some nights he didn't sleep very well either. But he made her live up to her contract.

"You've got to let her stop," Mother kept telling him. "She'll have a breakdown or something—or else you will."

"No," said Dad. "She's learning the value of money and she's learning that when you start something it's necessary to finish it if you want to collect. She's got to finish. It's in her contract."

"You sound like Shylock," Mother said.

But Dad stood firm.

When Lill finally completed the job, she came to Dad in tears.

"It's done," she said. "I hope you're satisfied. Now can I have my forty-seven cents?"

Dad counted out the change.

"Don't cry, honey," he said. "No matter what you think of your old Daddy, he did it for your own good. If you go look under your pillow you'll find that Daddy really loved you all the time."

The present was a pair of roller skates.

Fred headed the utilities committee and collected the fines. Once, just before he went to bed, he found that someone had left a faucet dripping and that there was a bathtub full of hot water. Jack had been asleep for more than an hour, but Fred woke him up.

"Get in there and take a bath," he said.

"But I had a bath just before I went to bed."

"I know you did, and you left the faucet dripping," Fred told him. "Do you want to waste that perfectly good water?"

"Why don't you take a bath?" Jack asked.

"I take my baths in the morning. You know that. That's the schedule."

Jack had two baths that night.

One day Dad came home with two victrolas and two stacks of records. He whistled assembly as he hit the front steps, and we helped him unload.

Mother, Father, and eleven of the twelve Gilbreth children
photographed in their family car, "Foolish Carriage."

"Kids," he said, "I have a wonderful surprise. Two victrolas
and all these lovely records."

"But we have a victrola, Daddy."

"I know that, but the victrola we have is the downstairs victrola. Now we are going to have two upstairs victrolas. Won't
that be fun?"

"Why?"

"Well from now on," said Dad, "we are going to do away
with unavoidable delay. The victrolas will go in the bathrooms—
one in the boys' bathroom and the other in the girls' bathroom.
I'll bet we'll be the only family in town with a victrola in every

bath. And when you are taking a bath, or brushing your teeth, or otherwise occupied, you will play the victrolas."

"Why?"

"Why, why, why," mimicked Dad. "Why this and why that. Does there have to be a why for everything?"

"There doesn't have to be, Daddy," Ernestine explained patiently. "But with you there usually is. When you start talking about unavoidable delay and victrolas, dance music is not the first thing that pops into our minds."

"No," Dad admitted. "It's not dance music. But you're going to find this is just as good in a way, and more educational."

"What kind of records are they?" Anne asked.

"Well," Dad said, "they are very entertaining. They are French and German language lesson records. You don't have to listen to them consciously. Just play them. And they'll finally make an impression."

"Oh, no!"

Dad soon tired of diplomacy and psychology.

"Shut up and listen to me," he roared. "I have spent one hundred and sixty dollars for this equipment. Did I get it for myself? I most emphatically by jingo well did not. I happen already to be able to speak German and French with such fluency that I frequently am mistaken for a native of both of those countries."

This was at best a terribly gross exaggeration, for while Dad had studied languages for most of his adult life, he never had become very familiar with French, although he could stumble along fairly well in German. Usually he insisted that Mother accompany him as an interpreter on his business trips to Europe. Languages came naturally to Mother.

"No," Dad continued, "I did not buy this expensive equipment for myself, although I must say I would like nothing better than to have my own private victrola and my own private language records. I bought it for you, as a present. And you are going to use it. If those two victrolas aren't going every morning from the minute you get up until you come down to breakfast, I'm going to know the reason why."

"One reason," said Bill, "might be that it is impossible to change records while you are in the bathtub."

"A person who applies motion study can be in and out of the tub in the time it takes one record to play."

That was perfectly true. Dad would sit in the tub and put the soap in his right hand. Then he'd place his right hand on his left shoulder and run it down the top of his left arm, back up the bottom of his left arm to his armpit, down his side, down the outside of his left leg, and then up the inside of his left leg. Then he'd change the soap to his left hand and do the same thing to his right side. After a couple of circular strokes on his midsection and his back, and some special attention to his feet and face, he'd duck under for a rinse and get out. He had all the boys in the bathroom several times to demonstrate just how he did it, and he sat in the middle of the living room rug one day, with all his clothes on, to teach the girls.

So there was no more unavoidable delay in the bathroom, and it wasn't long before we were all speaking at least a pidgin variety of French and German. For ten years, the victrolas ground out their lessons on the second floor of our Montclair house. As we became fairly fluent, we often would speak the languages at the dinner table. Dad was left out of the conversation when the talk was in French.

"Your German accents are not so bad," he said. "I can understand most of what you say when you talk German. But your French accents are so atrocious that no one but yourselves could possibly understand you. I believe you've developed some exotic language all your own, which has no more relation to French than it does to Pig Latin."

We giggled, and he turned furiously to Mother.

"Don't you think so, Lillie?"

"Well, dear," she said. "I don't think anyone would mistake them for natives of France, but I can usually make out what they're getting at."

"That," said Dad, with some dignity, "is because you learned your French in this country, where everybody talks with an accent, whereas my knowledge of the language came straight from the streets of Paris."

"Maybe so, dear," said Mother. "Maybe so."

That night, Dad moved the boys' bathroom victrola into his bedroom, and we heard him playing French records far into the night.

Father's Story

By Elizabeth Madox Roberts

We put more coal on the big red fire
   And while we are waiting for dinner to cook,
Our father comes and tells us about
   A story that he has read in a book.

And Charles and Will and Dick and I
   And all of us but Clarence are there.
And some of us sit on Father's legs,
   But one has to sit on the little red chair.

And when we are sitting very still,
   He sings us a song or tells a piece;
He sings, "Dan Tucker Went To Town,"
   Or he tells us about the golden fleece.

He tells us about the golden wool,
   And some of it is about a boy
Named Jason, and about a ship,
   And some is about a town called Troy.

And while he is telling or singing it through
   I stand by his arm, for that is my place,
And I push my fingers into his skin
   To make little dents in his big round face.

ILLUSTRATIONS BY DAWN STOUTSENBERGER

Walking

By Grace Ellen Glaubitz

When Daddy
Walks
With Jean and me,
We have a
Lot of fun
'Cause we can't
Walk as fast
As he,
Unless we
Skip and
Run!
I stretch,
And stretch
My legs so far,
I nearly slip
And fall—
But how
Does Daddy
Take such steps?
He doesn't stretch
At all!

It Was

By Dorothy Aldis

When he came to tuck me in
And pat me on the head
He tried to guess (he always does)
Who was in my bed.

"Is it Sally?" he guessed first
"Or her sister Joan?
It's such a wriggling little girl
It couldn't be my own.

"It can't be Mary Ann," he said
"Or Deborah because
All their eyes are much too blue
My goodness, me, I think it's you!"
And he was right, It was.

Independence Day

JULY 4

The fiery "spirit of '76" that swept the colonies into a war for independence, was sparked on January 10 by a rabble-rousing pamphlet, *Common Sense*, by Thomas Paine. Paine shouted for independence, and many of his readers shouted with him. In the following months the revolutionary spirit spread through the colonies.

At first, many colonial statesmen were hesitant about severing their bonds with Great Britain. But the crusade for independence gathered more and more support as it became increasingly apparent that only through force of arms could the colonies win the prize of liberty.

Finally, on July 4, 1776, Congress passed the Declaration of Independence, announcing to the world ". . . That these United Colonies are, and of Right ought to be, Free and Independent States; that they are Absolved from all Allegiance to the British Crown, and that all political connection between them and the State of Great Britain, is and ought to be totally dissolved. . . ."

The colonies had at last taken the step that meant either liberty or death. A union of states had never existed before. Now it was crucial that the states work and fight as one. The men who framed the Declaration had written, ". . . we mutually pledge to each other our Lives, our Fortunes, and our sacred Honor." Excited men in the streets knew that this meant, in the words of Benjamin Franklin, "We must all hang together, or assuredly we shall all hang separately."

So the thirteen colonies joined forces against Great Britain. They asserted their right to "Life, Liberty and the pursuit of Happiness," and the United States of America was born.

Fourth of July

BY LAURA INGALLS WILDER

Illustrations by Garth Williams

BOOM!

Laura was jerked out of sleep. The bedroom was dark. Carrie asked in a thin, scared whisper, "What was that?"

"Don't be scared," Laura answered. They listened. The window was hardly gray in the dark, but Laura could feel that the middle of the night was past.

BOOM! The air seemed to shake.

"Great guns!" Pa exclaimed sleepily.

"Why? Why?" Grace demanded. "Pa, Ma, why?"

Carrie asked, "Who is it? What are they shooting?"

"What time is it?" Ma wanted to know.

Through the partition Pa answered, "It's Fourth of July, Carrie." The air shook again. BOOM!

It was not great guns. It was gunpowder exploded under the blacksmith's anvil, in town. The noise was like the noise of battles that Americans fought for independence. Fourth of July was the day when the first Americans declared that all men are born free and equal. BOOM!

"Come, girls, we might as well get up!" Ma called.

Pa sang, " 'Oh, say, can you see, by the dawn's early light?' "

"Charles!" Ma protested, but she was laughing, because it really was too dark to see.

"It's nothing to be solemn about!" Pa jumped out of bed. "Hurray! we're Americans!" He sang,

> Hurray! Hurray! We'll sing the jubilee!
> Hurray! Hurray! The flag that sets men free!

Even the sun, as it rose shining into the clearest of skies, seemed to know this day was the glorious Fourth. At breakfast Ma said, "This would be a perfect day for a Fourth of July picnic."

"Maybe the town'll be far enough along to have one, come next July," said Pa.

"We couldn't hardly have a picnic this year, anyway," Ma admitted. "It wouldn't seem like a picnic without fried chicken."

After such a rousing beginning, the day did seem empty. Such a special day seemed to expect some special happening, but nothing special could happen.

"I feel like dressing up," Carrie said while they did the dishes.

"So do I, but there's nothing to dress up for," Laura replied.

When she carried out the dishwater to throw it far from the house, she saw Pa looking at the oats. They were growing thick and tall, gray-green and smoothly rippling in the wind. The corn was growing lustily, too. Its long, yellow-green, fluttering leaves almost hid the broken sod. In the garden the cucumber vines were reaching out, their crawling tips uncurling beyond patches of spreading big leaves. The rows of peas and beans were rounding up, the carrot rows were feathery green and the beets were thrusting up long, dark leaves on red stems. The ground-cherries were already small bushes. Through the wild grasses the chickens were scattered, chasing insects to eat.

All this was satisfaction enough for an ordinary day, but for Fourth of July there should be something more.

Pa felt the same way. He had nothing to do, for on Fourth of July no work could be done except the chores and housework. In a little while he came into the house and said to Ma, "There's a kind of a celebration in town today, would you like to go?"

"What kind of celebration?" Ma asked.

"Well, mostly horse racing, but they took up a collection for lemonade," Pa replied.

"Women are not likely to be at a horse race," Ma said. "And I couldn't go calling, uninvited, on Fourth of July."

Laura and Carrie stood almost bursting with eagerness while Ma considered, and shook her head. "You go along, Charles. It would be too much for Grace, anyway."

"It is much nicer at home," said Mary.

Then Laura spoke. "Oh Pa, if you go, can't Carrie and I?"

Pa's doubtful eyes brightened, and twinkled at her and Carrie. Ma smiled on them.

"Yes, Charles, it will be a nice outing for you all," she said. "Run down cellar and bring up the butter, Carrie, and while you're dressing I'll put up some bread-and-butter for you to take along."

Suddenly the day seemed really Fourth of July. Ma made sandwiches, Pa blacked his boots, Laura and Carrie hurriedly dressed up. Luckily Laura's sprigged calico was freshly washed and ironed. She and Carrie took turns at the washbasin, scrubbing their faces and necks and ears pink. Over their unbleached muslin union suits they put on crackling stiff petticoats of bleached muslin. They brushed and braided their hair. Laura wound her heavy braids around her head and pinned them. She tied the Sunday hair ribbon on the ends of Carrie's braids. Then she put on her fresh sprigged calico and buttoned it up the back. The full ruffle on the bottom of the full skirt came down to the tops of her shoes.

"Please button me up," Carrie asked. In the middle of her back there were two buttons that she couldn't reach. She had buttoned all the others outside-in.

"You can't wear your buttons turned inside, at a Fourth of July celebration," said Laura, unbuttoning them all and buttoning them again properly.

"If they're outside, they keep pulling my hair," Carrie protested. "My braids catch on them."

"I know. Mine always did," said Laura. "But you just have to stand it till you're big enough to put your hair up."

They put on their sunbonnets. Pa was waiting, holding the brown-paper packet of sandwiches. Ma looked at them carefully and said, "You look very nice."

"It's a treat to me, to be stepping out with my two good-looking girls," said Pa.

"You look nice, too, Pa," Laura told him. His boots were glossily polished, his beard was trimmed, and he was wearing his Sunday suit and broad-brimmed felt hat.

"I want to go!" Grace demanded. Even when Ma said, "No, Grace," she repeated two or three times, "I want to!" Because

she was the baby, they had almost spoiled her. Now her un-
ruliness must be nipped in the bud. Pa had to set her sternly
in a chair and tell her, "You heard your Ma speak."

They set out soberly, unhappy about Grace. But she must
be taught to mind. Perhaps next year she could go, if there
were a big celebration and they all rode in the wagon. Now
they were walking, to let the horses stay on their picket ropes
and eat grass. Horses grow tired, standing all day at hitching
posts in dust and heat. Grace was too little to walk the mile
and back, and she was too big to be carried.

Even before they reached town, they could hear a sound
like corn popping. Carrie asked what it was, and Pa said it
was firecrackers.

Horses were tied along the whole length of Main Street.
Men and boys were so thick on the sidewalk that in places
they almost touched each other. Boys were throwing lighted
firecrackers into the dusty street, where they sizzled and exploded. The noise was startling.

"I didn't know it would be like this," Carrie murmured. Laura
did not like it, either. They had never been in such a crowd
before. There was nothing to do but keep on walking up and

down in it, and to be among so many strangers made them uncomfortable.

Twice they walked the two blocks with Pa, and then Laura asked him if she and Carrie could not stay in his store building. Pa said that was a fine idea. They could watch the crowd while he circulated a little; then they would eat their lunch and see the races. He let them into the empty building and Laura shut the door.

It was pleasant to be alone in the echoing bare place. They looked at the empty kitchen behind it, where they had all lived huddled during the long hard winter. They tiptoed upstairs to the hollow, hot bedrooms under the eaves of the shingle roof, and stood looking down from the front window at the crowd, and at firecrackers squirming and popping in the dust.

"I wish we had some firecrackers," Carrie said.

"They're guns," Laura pretended. "We're in Fort Ticonderoga, and those are British and Indians. We're Americans, fighting for independence."

"It was the British in Fort Ticonderoga, and the Green Mountain boys took it," Carrie objected.

"Then I guess we're with Daniel Boone in Kentucky, and this is a log stockade," said Laura. "Only the British and Indians captured him," she had to admit.

"How much do firecrackers cost?" Carrie asked.

"Even if Pa could afford them, it's foolish to spend money just to make a little noise," Laura said. "Look at that little bay pony. Let's pick out the horses we like best; you can have first choice."

There was so much to see that they could hardly believe it was noon when Pa's boots sounded downstairs and he called, "Girls! Where are you?"

They rushed down. He was having a good time, his eyes were twinkling bright. He sang out, "I've brought us a treat! Smoked herring, to go with our bread and butter! And look what else!" He showed them a bunch of firecrackers.

"Oh, Pa!" Carrie cried. "How much did they cost?"

"Didn't cost me a cent," said Pa. "Lawyer Barnes handed them to me, said to give them to you girls."

"Why on earth did he do that?" Laura asked. She had never heard of Lawyer Barnes before.

"Oh, he's going in for politics, I guess," said Pa. "He acts that way, affable and agreeable to everybody. You want me to set these off for you now, or after we eat?"

Laura and Carrie were thinking the same thing. They knew it when they looked at each other, and Carrie said it. "Let's save them, Pa, to take home to Grace."

"All right," said Pa. He put them in his pocket and undid the smoked herring while Laura opened the packet of sandwiches. The herring was delicious. They saved some to take home to Ma. When they had eaten the last bit of bread and butter they went out to the well and drank, long and deep, from the edge of the pail that Pa drew dripping up. Then they washed their hands and their hot faces and dried them on Pa's handkerchief.

It was time to go to the races. The whole crowd was moving across the railroad tracks and out on the prairie. On a pole set up there, the American flag fluttered against the sky. The sun was shining warm and a cool breeze was blowing.

Beside the flagpole a man rose up tall above the crowd. He was standing on something. The sound of the talking died down, and he could be heard speaking.

"Well, boys," he said, "I'm not much good at public speaking, but today's the glorious Fourth. This is the day and date when our forefathers cut loose from the despots of Europe. There wasn't many Americans at that time, but they wouldn't stand for any monarch tyrannizing over them. They had to fight the British regulars and their hired Hessians and the murdering scalping red-skinned savages that those fine gold-laced aristocrats turned loose on our settlements and paid for murdering and burning and scalping women and children. A few barefoot Americans had to fight the whole of them and lick 'em, and they did fight them and they did lick them. Yes sir! We licked the British in 1776 and we licked 'em again in 1812, and we backed all the monarchies of Europe out of Mexico and off this continent less than twenty years ago, and by glory! Yessir, by Old Glory right here, waving over my head, any time the despots of Europe try to step on America's toes, we'll lick 'em again!"

"Hurray! Hurray!" everybody shouted. Laura and Carrie and Pa yelled, too, "Hurray! Hurray!"

"Well, so here we are today," the man went on. "Every man Jack of us a free and independent citizen of God's country, the only country on earth where a man is free and independent. Today's the Fourth of July, when this whole thing was started, and it ought to have a bigger, better celebration than this. We can't do much this year. Most of us are out here trying to pull ourselves up by our own boot straps. By next year, likely some of us will be better off, and able to chip in for a real big rousing celebration of Independence Day. Meantime, here we are. It's Fourth of July, and on this day somebody's got to read the Declaration of Independence. It looks like I'm elected, so hold your hats, boys; I'm going to read it."

Laura and Carrie knew the Declaration by heart, of course, but it gave them a solemn, glorious feeling to hear the words. They took hold of hands and stood listening in the solemnly listening crowd. The Stars and Stripes were fluttering bright against the thin, clear blue overhead, and their minds were saying the words before their ears heard them.

"When in the Course of human events it becomes necessary for one people to dissolve the political bands which have connected them with another, and to assume among the powers of the earth the separate and equal station to which the Laws of Nature and of Nature's God entitle them, a decent respect to the opinions of mankind requires that they should declare the causes which impel them to the separation.

"We hold these truths to be self-evident, that all men are created equal, that they are endowed by their Creator with certain unalienable rights, that among these are Life, Liberty, and the pursuit of Happiness. . . ."

Then came the long and terrible list of the crimes of the King.

"He has endeavored to prevent the population of these States . . .

"He has obstructed the administration of Justice . . .

"He has made Judges dependent on his Will alone . . .

"He has erected a multitude of New Offices, and sent hither swarms of Officers to harass our people and to eat out their substance.

. . . .

"He has plundered our seas, ravaged our coasts, burnt our towns, and destroyed the lives of our people.

"He is at this time transporting large Armies of foreign Mercenaries to complete the works of death, desolation and tyranny, already begun with circumstances of cruelty and perfidy scarcely paralleled in the most barbarous ages, and totally unworthy the head of a civilized nation.

. . . .

"WE, THEREFORE, the Representatives of the United States of America, in General Congress, Assembled, appealing to the Supreme Judge of the world for the rectitude of our intentions, do, in the name and by authority of the good People of these Colonies, solemnly publish and declare, That these United Colonies are, and of right ought to be, Free and Independent States; that they are Absolved from all Allegiance to the British Crown, and that all political connection between them and the State of Great Britain is and ought to be totally dissolved; and that as Free and Independent States, they have full Power to levy War . . . And for the support of this Declaration, with a firm reliance on the protection of Divine Providence, we mutually pledge to each other our Lives, our Fortunes, and our sacred Honor."

No one cheered. It was more like a moment to say, "Amen." But no one quite knew what to do.

Then Pa began to sing. All at once everyone was singing,

> My country, 'tis of thee,
> Sweet land of liberty,
> Of thee I sing. . . .
>
> Long may our land be bright
> With Freedom's holy light.
> Protect us by Thy might,
> Great God, our King!

The crowd was scattering away then, but Laura stood stock still. Suddenly she had a completely new thought. The Declaration and the song came together in her mind, and she thought: God is America's king.

She thought: Americans won't obey any king on earth. Americans are free. That means they have to obey their own consciences. No king bosses Pa; he has to boss himself. Why (she thought), when I am a little older, Pa and Ma will stop telling me what to do, and there isn't anyone else who has a right to give me orders. I will have to make myself be good.

Her whole mind seemed to be lighted up by that thought. This is what it means to be free. It means, you have to be good. "Our father's God, author of liberty—" The laws of Nature and of Nature's God endow you with a right to life and liberty. Then you have to keep the laws of God, for God's law is the only thing that gives you a right to be free.

Laura had no time then to think any further. Carrie was wondering why she stood so still, and Pa was saying, "This way, girls! There's the free lemonade!"

The barrels stood in the grass by the flagpole. A few men were waiting for their turns to drink from the tin dipper. As each finished drinking, he handed the dipper on, and then strolled away toward the horses and buggies by the race track.

Laura and Carrie hung back a little, but the man who had the dipper saw them and handed the dipper to Pa. He filled it from the barrel and gave it to Carrie. The barrel was almost full, and slices of lemon floated thick on the lemonade.

"I see they put in plenty of lemons, so it ought to be good," Pa said, while Carrie slowly drank. Her eyes grew round with delight; she had never tasted lemonade before.

"They've just mixed it," one of the waiting men told Pa. "The water is fresh from the hotel well, so it's cold."

Another man who was waiting said, "It depends, some, on how much sugar they put in."

Pa filled the dipper again and gave it to Laura. She had once tasted lemonade, at Nellie Oleson's party, when she was a little girl in Minnesota. This lemonade was even more delicious. She drank the last drop from the dipper and thanked Pa. It would not be polite to ask for more.

When Pa had drunk, they went across the trampled grass to the crowd by the race track. A great ring of sod had been broken, and the sod carried off. The breaking plow with its coulter had left the black earth smooth and level. In the middle of the ring and all around it the prairie grasses were waving, except where men and buggies had made trampled tracks.

"Why, hello, Boast!" Pa called, and Mr. Boast came through

the crowd. He had just got to town in time for the races. Mrs. Boast, like Ma, had preferred to stay at home.

Four ponies came out on the track. There were two bay ponies, one gray, and one black. The boys who were riding them lined them up in a straight row.

"Which'd you bet on, if you were betting?" Mr. Boast asked.

"Oh, the black one!" Laura cried. The black pony's coat shone in the sunlight and its long mane and tail blew silky on the breeze. It tossed its slender head and picked up its feet daintily.

At the word, "Go!" all the ponies leaped into a run. The crowd yelled. Stretched out low and fast, the black pony went by, the others behind it. All their pounding feet raised a cloud of dust that hid them. Then around the far side of the track they went, running with all their might. The gray pony crept up beside the black. Neck and neck they were running, then the gray pulled a little ahead and the crowd yelled again. Laura still hoped for the black. It was doing its best. Little by little it gained on the gray. Its head passed the gray's neck, its outstretched nose was almost even with the gray's nose. Suddenly all four ponies were coming head-on down the track, quickly growing larger and larger in front of the oncoming dust. The bay pony with the white nose came skimming past the black and the gray, across the line ahead of them both while the crowd cheered.

"If you'd bet on the black, Laura, you'd 've lost," said Pa.

"It's the prettiest, though," Laura answered. She had never been so excited. Carrie's eyes shone, her cheeks were pink with excitement; her braid was snared on a button and recklessly she yanked it loose.

"Are there any more, Pa? more races?" Carrie cried.

"Sure, here they come for the buggy race," Pa answered. Mr. Boast joked, "Pick the winning team, Laura!"

Through the crowd and out onto the track came first a bay team hitched to a light buggy. The bays were perfectly matched and they stepped as though the buggy weighed nothing at all. Then came other teams, other buggies, but Laura hardly saw them, for there was a team of brown horses that she knew. She knew their proud, gay heads and arching necks, the shine of light on their satiny shoulders, the black manes blowing and the forelocks tossing above their quick, bright, gentle eyes.

"Oh, look, Carrie, look! It's the brown Morgans!" she cried.

"That's Almanzo Wilder's team, Boast," said Pa. "What in creation has he got 'em hitched to?"

High up above the horses, Almanzo Wilder was sitting. His hat was pushed back on his head and he looked cheerful and confident.

He turned the team toward its place in line, and they saw that he was sitting on a high seat, on top of a long, high, heavy wagon, with a door in its side.

"It's his brother Royal's peddler's wagon," said a man standing near by.

"He don't have a chance, with that weight, against all those light buggies," said another. Everyone was looking at the Morgans and the wagon and talking about them.

"The off horse, Prince, is the one he drove last winter, that forty-mile trip that he and Cap Garland made, and brought in the wheat that kept us all from starving to death," Pa told Mr. Boast. "The other one's Lady, that ran off with the antelope herd that time. They've both got good action, and speed."

"I see that," Mr. Boast agreed. "But no team can haul that heavy cart and beat Sam Owen's bays on his light buggy. Seems like the young fellow might have rousted out a buggy somewheres in this country."

"He's an independent kind of a young cuss," someone said. "He'd rather lose with what he's got than win with a borrowed buggy."

"Too bad he don't own a buggy," Mr. Boast said.

The brown horses were by far the most beautiful on the track, and so proud. They did not seem to mind the heavy wagon at all, but tossed their heads, pricked their ears, and lifted their feet as if the ground were not quite good enough for them to step on.

"Oh, what a shame, what a *shame* they haven't a fair chance," Laura was thinking. Her hands were clenched. She wished so much that those proud, fine horses might only have a fair chance. Hitched to that heavy wagon, they could not win. She cried out, "Oh, it isn't *fair!*"

The race started. Fast came the bays, leading all the others. The shining legs trotting and the wheels whirling hardly seemed to touch the ground. Every buggy rushing by was a light, one-seated buggy. Not a team drew even the weight of a two-seated buggy, except the beautiful brown horses who came last, pulling the high, heavy peddler's cart.

"Best team in the country," Laura heard a man say, "but not a chance."

"Nope," said another. "That wagon's too heavy for them to pull. Sure as shooting, they'll break their trot."

But they were pulling it, and they were trotting. Evenly, without a break, the eight brown legs kept moving in a perfect trot. The dust-cloud rose up and hid them. Then bursting out of it, up the other side of the track the teams and buggies were speeding. One buggy—No, two buggies! were behind the peddler's cart. Three buggies were behind it. Only the bays were ahead of it.

"Oh, come on! Come on! Win Win!" Laura was begging the brown horses. She so wanted them to trot faster that it seemed her wishing was pulling them.

They were almost around the track. They were coming now around the turn and on toward the line. The bays were ahead. The Morgans could not do it, they could not win, the weight was too much for them, but still Laura kept on wishing with all of her. "Faster, faster, only a little faster. Oh, come on, come on!"

Almanzo leaned forward from the high seat and seemed to speak to them. Still smoothly trotting, they came faster. Their heads reached Mr. Owen's buggy and slowly, smoothly crept by it. All the legs were moving fast, fast, while so slowly the brown heads came up, even with the bays'. All four horses were coming now in a line, faster, faster.

"A tie. By gosh, it's a tie," a man said.

Then Mr. Owen's buggy whip flashed out. It swished down, once, twice, as he shouted. The bays leaped ahead. Almanzo had no whip. He was leaning forward, lightly holding the reins firm. Once more he seemed to speak. Fast and smooth as swallows flying, the brown Morgans passed the bays and crossed the line. They'd won!

The whole crowd shouted. It surged to surround the brown horses and Almanzo high on the cart. Laura found that she had been holding her breath. Her knees were wobbly. She wanted to yell and to laugh and to cry and to sit down and rest.

"Oh, they won! they won! they won!" Carrie kept saying, clapping her hands. Laura did not say anything.

"He earned that five dollars," said Mr. Boast.

"What five dollars?" Carrie asked.

"Some men in town put up five dollars for the best trotting team," Pa explained. "Almanzo Wilder's won it."

Laura was glad she had not known. She could not have borne it if she had known that the brown horses were running for a five-dollar prize.

"He has it coming to him," said Pa. "That young man knows how to handle horses."

There were no more races. There was nothing more to do but stand around and listen to the talking. The lemonade was low in the barrel. Mr. Boast brought Laura and Carrie a dipperful and they divided it. It was sweeter than before, but not so cold. The teams and buggies were going away. Then Pa came from the dwindling crowd and said it was time to go home.

Mr. Boast walked with them along Main Street. Pa said to him that the Wilders had a sister who was a schoolteacher back East in Minnesota. "She's taken a claim half a mile west of town here," said Pa, "and she wants Almanzo to find out if she can get this school to teach next winter. I told him to tell her to send in her application to the school board. Other things being equal, I don't know why she can't as well have it."

Laura and Carrie looked at each other. Pa was on the school board, and no doubt the others would feel as he did. Laura thought, "Maybe, if I am a very good scholar and if she likes me, maybe she might take me driving behind those beautiful horses."

Fourth of July Night

By Dorothy Aldis

Illustration by Dawn Stoutsenberger

Pin wheels whirling round
Spit sparks upon the ground,
And rockets shoot up high
And blossom in the sky—
Blue and yellow, green and red
Flowers falling on my head,
And I don't ever have to go
To bed, to bed, to bed!

America

By Samuel Francis Smith

My country, 'tis of thee,
Sweet land of liberty,
Of thee I sing;
Land where my fathers died,
Land of the pilgrims' pride,
From every mountain side
Let freedom ring.

My native country, thee,
Land of the noble free,—
Thy name I love;
I love thy rocks and rills,
Thy woods and templed hills;
My heart with rapture thrills
Like that above.

Let music swell the breeze,
And ring from all the trees;
Sweet freedom's song;
Let mortal tongues awake,
Let all that breathe partake,
Let rocks their silence break,—
The sound prolong.

Our fathers' God, to thee,
Author of liberty,
To thee I sing;
Long may our land be bright
With freedom's holy light;
Protect us by thy might,
Great God our King.

I've got a rocket
In my pocket;
I cannot stop to play.
Away it goes!
I've burnt my toes.
It's Independence Day.

Fourth of July

By Marchette Chute

Fourth of July,
   Fourth of July,
That's when the flag
   Goes waving by.

And the crackers crack,
   And the popguns pop,
And the big guns boom
   And never stop.

And we watch parades,
   And listen to speeches,
And picnic around
   On all the beaches.

And it usually rains,
   And it's always hot;
But we all like Fourth
   Of July a lot.

ILLUSTRATION BY ESTELLE HOLLINGWORTH

Paul Revere's Ride

By Henry Wadsworth Longfellow

Illustrations by Dawn Stoutsenberger

Listen, my children, and you shall hear
Of the midnight ride of Paul Revere,
On the eighteenth of April, in Seventy-five;
Hardly a man is now alive
Who remembers that famous day and year.
He said to his friend, 'If the British march
By land or sea from the town to-night,
Hang a lantern aloft in the belfry arch
Of the North Church tower as a signal light,—
One, if by land, and two, if by sea;
And I on the opposite shore will be,
Ready to ride and spread the alarm
Through every Middlesex village and farm,
For the country folk to be up and to arm.'

Then he said, 'Good-night!' and with muffled oar
Silently rowed to the Charleston shore,
Just as the moon rose over the bay,
Where swinging wide at her moorings lay
The *Somerset*, British man-of-war;
A phantom ship, with each mast and spar
Across the moon like a prison bar,
And a huge black hulk, that was magnified
By its own reflection in the tide.

Meanwhile, his friend, through alley and street,
Wanders and watches with eager ears,
Till in the silence around him he hears
The muster of men at the barrack door,
The sound of arms, and the tramp of feet,
And the measured tread of the grenadiers,
Marching down to their boats on the shore.

Then he climbed the tower of the Old North Church,
By the wooden stairs, with stealthy tread,
To the belfry-chamber overhead,
And startled the pigeons from their perch
On the somber rafters, that round him made
Masses and moving shapes of shade,—
By the trembling ladder, steep and tall,
To the highest window in the wall,
Where he paused to listen and look down
A moment on the roofs of the town,
And the moonlight flowing over all.

Beneath, in the churchyard, lay the dead,
In their night-encampment on the hill,
Wrapped in silence so deep and still
That he could hear, like a sentinel's tread,
The watchful night-wind, as it went
Creeping along from tent to tent,
And seeming to whisper, 'All is Well!'
A moment only he feels the spell
Of the place and the hour, and the secret dread
Of the lonely belfry and the dead;
For suddenly all his thoughts are bent
On a shadowy something far away,
Where the river widens to meet the bay,—
A line of black that bends and floats
On the rising tide, like a bridge of boats.

Meanwhile, impatient to mount and ride,
Booted and spurred, with a heavy stride
On the opposite shore walked Paul Revere.
Now he patted his horse's side,
Now gazed at the landscape far and near,
Then, impetuous, stamped the earth,
And turned and tightened his saddle-girth;
But mostly he watched with eager search
The belfry-tower of the Old North Church,
As it rose above the graves on the hill,
Lonely and spectral and somber and still.
And lo! as he looks, on the belfry's height
A glimmer, and then a gleam of light!
He springs to the saddle, the bridle he turns,
But lingers and gazes, till full on his sight
A second lamp in the belfry burns!

A hurry of hoofs in a village street,
A shape in the moonlight, a bulk in the dark,
And beneath, from the pebbles, in passing, a spark
Struck out by a steed flying fearless and fleet;
That was all! And yet, through the gloom and the light,
The fate of a nation was riding that night;
And the spark struck out by that steed, in his flight,
Kindled the land into flame with its heat.
He has left the village and mounted the steep,
And beneath him, tranquil and broad and deep,
Is the Mystic, meeting the ocean tides;
And under the alders that skirt its edge,
Now soft on the sand, now loud on the ledge,
Is heard the tramp of his steed as he rides.

It was twelve by the village clock,
When he crossed the bridge into Medford town.
He heard the crowing of the cock,
And the barking of the farmer's dog,
And felt the damp of the river fog,
That rises after the sun goes down.

It was one by the village clock,
When he galloped into Lexington.
He saw the gilded weathercock
Swim in the moonlight as he passed,
And the meeting-house windows, blank and bare,
Gaze at him with a spectral glare,
As if they already stood aghast
At the bloody work they would look upon.

It was two by the village clock,
When he came to the bridge in Concord town.
He heard the bleating of the flock,
And the twitter of birds among the trees,
And felt the breath of the morning breeze
Blowing over the meadows brown.
And one was safe and asleep in his bed
Who at the bridge would be first to fall,
Who that day would be lying dead,
Pierced by a British musket-ball.

You know the rest. In the books you have read,
How the British Regulars fired and fled,—
How the farmers gave them ball for ball,
From behind each fence and farm-yard wall,
Chasing the red-coats down the lane,
Then crossing the fields to emerge again
Under the trees at the turn of the road,
And only pausing to fire and load.

So through the night rode Paul Revere;
And so through the night went his cry of alarm
To every Middlesex village and farm,—
A cry of defiance and not of fear,
A voice in the darkness, a knock at the door
And a word that shall echo forevermore!
For, borne on the night-wind of the Past,
Through all our history, to the last,
In the hour of darkness and peril and need,
The people will waken and listen to hear
The hurrying hoof-beats of that steed,
And the midnight message of Paul Revere.

The Constitution of the United States

Preamble

   We, the People of the United States, in Order to form a more
perfect Union, establish Justice, insure domestic Tranquility,
provide for the common defence, promote the general Welfare,
and secure the Blessings of Liberty to ourselves and our Pos-
terity, do ordain and establish this Constitution for the United
States of America.

Labor Day

In the United States a civilization was carved out of the wilderness by the labor of the people. A powerful, modern nation emerged through the toil of its pioneers and the work of its industrial force.

Working conditions have not always been what they are today. For many years the tremendous wealth and power of a few men combined to make virtual slaves of the workers in industry. But the self-respect of these workers gave birth to the world's first large-scale organizations of labor.

At the suggestion of Peter J. McGuire, a leader in two labor organizations, "Labor's Holiday" was first celebrated in New York on September 5, 1882, to honor "the industrial spirit, the great vital force of the nation." In 1894 the United States government honored the labor unions, the workers, and the dignity of work by proclaiming Labor Day, the first Monday in September, a national holiday.

The Grand Old Man of Labor

BY JOSEPH COTTLER

H E heard the cry first in the street where he lived on the East end of London, and for the rest of his life the cry kept ringing in his ears. He was a small boy then with his nose flat against the windowpane. The tramping on the cobbles outside drew him often to the window, and he watched men, the fathers and older brothers of his playmates, moving aimlessly about. They gathered in groups; they drifted apart and together again, like scraps of rubbish blown about in the back yard. And the cry of one of them penetrated the shut window and lodged in his brain:—

"God, I've no work to do. My wife, my kids want bread, and I've no work to do."

When Sam was a grown-up of ten, his father took him out of the free school for Jewish boys, and apprenticed him to a shoemaker. His father himself was by trade a cigarmaker. Often after supper he rose from the table saying he was off to a meeting of the Cigarmakers' Society.

"I would rather be a cigarmaker," remarked Sam, the shoemaker of eight weeks standing.

"And why?" asked father Gompers.

"Because shoemakers have no society," replied Sam.

With that, the Society of Cigarmakers enrolled a new apprentice boy. Sam took his place at a long worktable. In the daily company of men his raw, open mind was molded as tightly as the rich brown velvety leaves of tobacco molded between his fingers. They talked of hard times, of wages and starvation in England. Some spoke of a land to the west, where wages were higher and they sang:—

From *Champions of Democracy*, by Joseph Cottler, copyright 1936 by Joseph Cottler. Published by Little, Brown, and Company.

> To the West, to the West, to the land of the free
> Where mighty Missouri rolls down to the sea;
> Where a man is a man if he's willing to toil,
> And the humblest may gather the fruits of the soil.

Yet even there a civil war had broken out over the freedom of workers. The English factory owners, Sam heard, were on the side of the South; but the working class was with Lincoln. In the whole world, Abraham Lincoln had no more loyal admirer than the thirteen-year-old boy Sam Gompers. When his father, one day, announced gloomily that to save themselves from starvation they would have to leave England for America, Sam thrillingly thought that he would be closer to Abraham Lincoln. His father, who once before had been driven to break the ties of family and friends by emigrating from Amsterdam to London, was in despair.

Between the East end of London and the East Side of New York there was only a step: the struggle to pay the landlord and the grocer was unchanged. The one difference for Sam lay in the many and different races of people he accosted this side of Castle Garden. His new fellow countrymen greeted him in a score of tongues. The shop where he found work was manned mostly by Germans. But at the Cooper Institute where he attended lectures and night school, his American friends were also Irish, Bohemian, Russian, Swedish.

Most of his education came to him with his wages; the shop was his university. He grew to manhood in an atmosphere choked and blended with tobacco dust. All day long he took the soft leaves stripped off their stems, one by one off the pile. He examined the leaf, and shaved off the frayed edge to a hair's breadth. Then he wrapped it around the sausage of tobacco, deftly knitting the holes in the leaf and shaping the cigar.

He enjoyed the work because, once his fingers had become expert, his mind was left free. Cigarmakers could cultivate one another's society during working hours.

"Sing us something, Otto," they coaxed. And high above the littered bench rose the dreamy spirit of the song

Kennst du das Land . . .

Sometimes it was, "Read to us, Sam." Sam had a strong, mellow voice and there was always a book or magazine in his pocket. Discussion always followed reading. Always they argued some question or other, rarely deciding anything but heaps of cigars. Now and then Sam would hastily draw out a pencil and piece of paper, and note down a striking thought or hint for homework.

"But Karl Marx says . . ." someone would remark—and Sam made the note that he must learn German, must read Karl Marx.

They talked of themselves, of their lot as workers and citizens —Sam now a voter. At such times a mood of despair prevailed, because the days of the cigarmakers seemed numbered. From every quarter they discerned threats to their existence. A tool had been invented for molding cigars, and the craftsmen saw in it a portent of the time when their skill would be thrown into the discard.

"Either we destroy the machine, or it will destroy us," believed some of Samuel Gompers' shopmates.

"But to destroy the machine is to stop the wheels of progress," objected Sam.

Then the "sweatshop" menaced them. Some merchants had bought up a block of tenements. There they installed families of immigrants whom they put to work making cigars. The immigrant family paid rent to the merchant, was forced to buy their raw tobacco and tools from him, their food even. The cigar merchant paid little for his labor, had no rent to pay for a factory, and made profit on the sale of provisions. Naturally he was able to sell his cigars at astoundingly low prices. But at whose expense? Samuel Gompers visited "sweatshops." He found that merely to keep alive, every member of the "sweatshop" family had to work early and late, seven days a week. The low price of the "sweatshop" cigar dragged down the price of the factory cigar, and that in turn beat down the wages of all craftsmen like Samuel Gompers. They found themselves unable any longer to provide their families with decent food or living quarters. The cigar smoker was content, the cigar manufacturer also, but the worker was desperate.

"Sweatshops are degrading," Sam and his friends agreed bitterly.

Then in 1873 another depression paralyzed the industry of

the country. Through the blizzards of the winter Samuel Gompers saw the lines of men outside the free-soup kitchens in every ward. What knew those bewildered, suffering men of stock market deflation or bank credits? They knew only that they begged for work and were turned away, that their families were hungry.

Again the cry rang in the ears of Samuel Gompers:—

"God, I've no work to do. My wife, my kids want bread, and I've no work to do."

Was there no answer to this cry? Some of his friends had panaceas for poverty.

"The Government should print paper money," they said. "Then money will be so plentiful that we can all have some."

"Reduce the hours of work," others said. They put their idea into the slogan: "Eight hours for work. Eight hours for rest. Eight hours for what we will."

"If the Government owned all industries," contended others, "the workers would be well off."

Samuel Gompers shook his head. He knew of no cure-all for the ills of the workingman. He knew only his distress. And he pitied him and stood ready to risk his own welfare to help him.

Sam Gompers' shopmates often told what he once risked for "Conchy."

"Conchy," as he was nicknamed, was a middle-aged sick man with very weak eyes. Sam Gompers and he worked at a bench near the windows of the dim factory. One morning when Sam came to work, he found Conchy sitting at a bench in the dimmest part of the factory.

Sam went to him. "What's the matter?" he asked.

"They put me back here and gave that new young fellow my seat near the window," Conchy said plaintively.

"What for?"

"Well, they just put him there, that's all. I don't know why."

Sam went back to his seat and sent a callboy to Mr. Smith, the new foreman. The boy came back with word that Mr. Smith was busy.

"Tell him please it's important," insisted Sam.

Mr. Smith arrived. "Well, what do you want?" he demanded.

"Why did you put Conchy away back in the dark and the young fellow down here in the light?" asked Sam.

With an oath the foreman rapped: "None of your business."

Conchy was an old employee, Sam pointed out; his sight had failed in the work. The young fellow—

"That's my business," said the foreman.

"You mean to say you're going to let the young fellow keep Conchy's seat?"

"Yes, I am. What are you going to do about it?"

Sam rose. He gathered up his tools. "Not much," he said, "except that he can have this seat, too."

There was a second of silence. Then a voice broke out— "Yes, and he can have this seat, too."

Another man rose: "And this seat."

Fifty men pushed back their chairs: "And this seat."

The men had struck.

Five minutes later the strike was settled. The factory was working as usual, with Conchy back in his old seat.

"If we always acted together," Sam Gompers told his shopmates, "we should never be either standing in free-soup lines, or working twelve hours every day."

That was his answer to the cry in the streets, the cry he could never forget since his childhood in London when he preferred the trade of cigarmaking to shoemaking because cigarmakers had a "Society."

"Let us act together," was not a new appeal in America, even among workingmen. For almost fifty years before Samuel Gompers came to work in America, workers had sometimes united to parade their grievances. In such unions the shoemakers and printers protested against low wages, the hatters and other factory hands against their fourteen hours of daily toil. The bricklayers, the plasterers, the plumbers—good men of toil— organized societies. Intelligent workers realized that if ever they were to rise out of the cellars in the slums where so many of them lived, they would have to stand united. But these unions were temporary. When indignation welled up in a trade, the workers rushed together; when their indignation was appeased or routed, they drifted apart.

"What labor needs," said Sam and his friends, speaking of the sweatshops and soup kitchens, "what labor needs is permanent strong unions."

The cigarmakers' local union, to which Sam had belonged

since the age of fourteen, was a crude club and yet as good as any of that time. It maintained little order or discipline among its members. Any day in any shop, a worker might suddenly throw down his tools and remark angrily: "I am going on strike." If enough of his friends followed him, perhaps there was a strike. But few strikes begun like that ended successfully for the workers. There was even, in New York City, a council of all crafts, called the Workingmen's Association. Perhaps its most notable act was to give Samuel Gompers the opportunity of making his first public speech. It happened in a mass meeting that the twenty-four-year-old cigarmaker rose to stammer out his feeling against sweatshops. When he sat down, one of the labor officials—a German—said kindly to him: "That was all right, Sam. You will yet a good speaker be."

Sam had made a start. As he saw it, industry was a jungle infested by beasts of prey in the shape of low wages and long hours, and withstanding them timidly, the patchwork of labor groups. To civilize the jungle, the labor patchwork would have to be knit together more solidly. Only then could the worker win a seat alongside his employer, and together lay down plans for their common welfare.

"That's a good talk, Sam," said his friends over their mugs of beer. "Now what would you do to strengthen the Cigarmakers' Union?"

To begin with, thought Sam, there were too many small unions of cigarmakers. They must give way to one big union. Its constitution would resemble the charter of an American city divided into wards over which sat a council. The shops were wards which elected delegates to the Union Council. And in all disputes with employers over the conditions of work, the Council would govern. . . .

"That's the kind of union I should like to see," said Sam.

So began Cigarmakers' Local Number 144. Its president, Samuel Gompers, remarked that it was democratic in form, and strongly knit because every member, no matter where he worked, committed himself to help every other member in debates with his employer over wages and working conditions. To their delight, the cigar workers early began to reap the benefits of their union in Local Number 144, and the name

Samuel Gompers became popular among the working class throughout New York City.

But not among certain employers. For if the workers' lot was improved, their employers' profits were cut down. Some employers resented this. In their own councils they hissed the name of Samuel Gompers. Once his boss summoned Sam to the office. Both men, face to face, respected each other; Sam for his boss's kindness, and the boss for Sam's fine work at the bench.

"Sam," said his boss in a distressed voice, "I needn't tell you what I think of you and your work. But the employers' organization to which I belong has voted to blacklist the leaders of the recent strike."

"Which means"—Sam helped him to say it— "that I'm out of a job. It's not your fault."

When he got back to the shop to pack his tools, his fellow workers indignantly rose to declare a strike. Sam climbed on a chair—he now made speeches without stammering—and the men gathered around him. . . . It was contrary to the rules of Local Number 144 to walk out in that fashion. They must be loyal not to him, but to the whole union; they must stay at work. . . . And they did.

He found a job with a manufacturer who did not belong to an employers' association. One day his new boss summoned him to his office.

"Won't you sit down, Mr. Gompers. Mr. Gompers, how would you like to be my foreman at twenty-five dollars a week?"

Sam was then earning twelve dollars. He waited to hear more.

"In fact, I look to you," said his boss, "to become my superintendent. And that is not all. If you will induce the union workers to take a reduction in pay, you can have half what I save. With your influence, it ought to be easy."

So that was it. Sam did not waste more time before packing his tools than was necessary to repay the insult. His haste swept him out before he could raise a nickel for carfare, and he walked home. He did not mind that, nor the winter slush, nor his torn shoes. If he was beside himself with anguish, the reason was his wife and kids. They would dine again on a soup of flour and water. One employer, realizing his staunchness, had sent a messenger to his wife offering her thirty dollars a week if she could induce Sam to give up the union. His loyal wife had refused. But was he fair to her and the children? He might give in, and ease the suffering of his family. But he thought of all the workers and their families, and their faith in him.

He talked the matter over with a few other leaders in the labor unions. "Let us pledge each other," he proposed, "never to rise outside the labor movement." And together they swore, like monks taking holy vows. Their purpose was to show the workers of every trade why and how they should combine in unions, so that no employer could refuse to deal with them as equals. In his vision, Sam Gompers saw the time when employer and worker—labor and capital—would sit at the same table, and talk frankly and freely of each other's needs and problems. Then, he felt, there would be no more misery among the toiling citizens of America. The vision was inspiring, but it could never become real, Sam knew, until labor stood so united that reluctant capital would not dare refuse its coöperation.

As he had been one of the principal organizers of the Cigarmakers' Local Number 144, Sam helped also to organize a union of all the trades in New York City, called the Amalgamated Trades and Labor Union. He believed that not only must one cigarmaker stand with another, one printer with another, every man with the men of his trade, but every worker must stand by every other worker. A certain Government official understood Sam Gompers, for he said: "Mr. Gompers"—the labor leader had apologized for coming to him on this occasion—"Mr. Gompers, I regard you as the spokesman for the underdog of the world."

Now, with the force of organized labor behind him, Samuel Gompers attacked the cigar sweatshops. He set about educating the public, educating representatives of the people elected to the Legislature. He showed, publicly and privately, pictures of rooms in tenement houses where children as young as six, pale and weary, squatted on a dirty floor, stripping tobacco until late in the night or until they fell over with fatigue on the tobacco heap.

The sweatshop merchants retaliated. They denied those pictures, and produced more favorable ones. They fought by advertisement, they went to law. The battle against the cigar sweatshops lasted more than ten years, but victory came finally to the forces of organized labor.

Samuel Gompers was learning how to make social change in a democracy. Though young, he knew already how to organize for the protection of workers. He was satisfied with labor unions in his own city. Now he turned his attention to the labor union of the whole country.

He talked about it with men of various trades. Many an evening, after the day's work, he sat down at a table in some public place to discuss his pet hope—the Federation of American Labor. His boon companions were printers, carpenters, tailors, stonecutters—any workers who belonged to the union of their trade. Employers were wise, Sam felt; throughout the nation they were banding together. In a few trades, the employees were doing the same thing. All the local unions of cigarmakers, for instance, had affiliated as the International Cigarmakers; likewise the printers. On special occasions a national union held a convention where a few delegates met, passed some resolutions, and went home. That was fine, agreed Sam; he would like to see those national unions stronger. But they treated of matters in their own trade. They were like State Legislatures. Now just as all the states were federated, as the United States of America, all trade-unions of the country ought likewise to federate. Such was his plan for the welfare of the American worker.

But, some people objected, the American worker already had a national union of all trades: the Knights of Labor. In December of 1869, nine tailors of Philadelphia had started the Knights of Labor, a union of workers of every kind in the country. Their purpose was to improve the lot of the American worker. The Knights of Labor were growing. Was not that the answer to Sam Gompers' hope?

No, said Sam. The purpose of the Knights of Labor was good, but they would never achieve it by their method. Take, for instance . . .

By two o'clock in the morning, Sam usually convinced or wore out his opponents.

For almost ten years Samuel Gompers preached his favorite
sermon: the Federation of American Labor. As the father of a
big family, he could ill afford to travel, yet he went out to distant conventions of labor unions to deliver his sermon. Whenever he felt discouraged, he thought of his fellow workers
living in slums, of pale and weary children in factories, of
mayhem and death coming to factory hands with no compen-
sation to their stricken families. There was his inspiration,
and he came to be known as the spokesman for the workers of
America.

At last, in December of 1886, came the moment Sam Gompers had worked for. In Columbus, Ohio, the American Federation of Labor, the union of all labor unions, was organized.
In its constitution it was modeled after the United States of
America. But just as the States in 1787 did not yield much
power to the Federal Government, so the labor unions did not
yield much power to their Federation. Weak as it was, however, it was the realization of Sam Gompers' dream. If its president were skillful and devoted, it would grow.

No one wanted the presidency of the new American Federation of Labor, for the office paid a salary of only one thousand
dollars a year. One could hardly support a family on that.
Samuel Gompers, father of the Federation, was first nominated.
He declined. But when the subsequent nominees also declined,
he stepped forward for another sacrifice in behalf of the working class of his country.

Shortly after, John Doe read "in the papers" of the American
Federation of Labor, and saw the picture of its president: a
short, stocky individual, with black hair and dark snapping
eyes. It was a picture John Doe was to see often in the years
to come.

His first office in New York, at 332 East Eighth Street, was
no more commodious than a pantry. It had a kitchen table for
a desk. The rest of the office equipment consisted of empty
grocer's boxes. Thus installed, Samuel Gompers began his new
life as professional agent of labor. Heretofore he had been
concerned largely with the problems only of his own trade,
cigarmaking. Now his concern was with the problems of every

trade. He learned to speak of his work with the glassblower and the steamfitter, as with the tailor and carpenter. They, in turn, listened more readily to his appeal to stand united in their trade, to add their trade-union to all others in the Federation. From all parts of the country workers came to him and wrote to him for advice and help.

Thus he became aware of the griefs and grievances of all workers, and he spoke for them. . . . Are the men in the steel mills of Western Pennsylvania required to work twelve hours a day? One morning the president of the steel company receives a courteous letter from Samuel Gompers, who suggests a friendly talk about the welfare of his employees. . . . The garment workers are protesting the unsafe and unsanitary condition of factories: and the factory owners have to reckon with Samuel Gompers. . . . Out on the West Coast the seamen are realizing that, in a democratic world, they alone are bound like serfs to the sea by the rule that they must not quit their ship even in a safe harbor. One day they come upon notices of a seamen's meeting called by Samuel Gompers. Mr. Gompers encourages them to stand united in their fight. Congressmen have a visit from Mr. Gompers, who explains the slavery of seamen, and suggests a new law. Congressmen get used to seeing Mr. Gompers. He comes on various errands. Now he represents a body of voters who protest the cruelty of child labor; now he appears in Congress to plead for the unemployed who have wives and kids to feed, and no work to do. We have a rich land, says Mr. Gompers warmly. Yet we allow our abundant tools to rust and our fertile soil to lie fallow while people starve. It is stupid and brutal.

Wherever he appeared and on whatever occasion, Samuel Gompers contended that the American worker had the right to a better life.

Nor was the struggle for the worker's rights always to be fought in a swivel chair. Sometimes it took a sinister form, and at such times Samuel Gompers sallied into the field like a crusader in a holy cause.

One pictures him, for instance, as the coal miners of Pennsylvania and West Virginia saw him in the '90's. Out of curiosity or hopelessness, groups of miners gathered at the roadside or in a hall to hear the stranger from New York. He told them first what they themselves knew too sorrowfully, but they marveled that any outsider should know or care: They lived lives of bondage; their homes were shacks owned by the coal company. The food they ate and the clothes they wore had to be bought from the coal company. Their sons were brought into the world by the company's doctor; at the age of eight sent into the company's mines; clothed and fed from the company's stores, buried in the company's graveyard. They were slaves. . . . And what did he advise? They must unite and demand, like self-respecting men, a decent life.

The coal companies resented Samuel Gompers; he was attacking their profits, and they tried to drive him from their towns. Their lawyers arraigned him in court. The labor leader hurt their business, they maintained; his talk was illegal.

Speech is free in America, replied Samuel Gompers.

But he was inciting the men to strike, said the protectors of profit. Strikes hurt the country; therefore he, Samuel Gompers, was his country's enemy. . . .

Samuel Gompers was not frightened by such attacks. He felt that his thinking compatriots would see through them. But too frequently strikes did break out, sometimes with violent accompaniment of mob scenes, fights, and bloodshed. At such times, the public was shocked, and demanded that workers and their employers settle their disputes peaceably.

Strikes distressed Samuel Gompers more than anyone else, and he tried all fair means to avoid them. He knew the suffering a strike brought down on the very workers he wished to help. But sometimes he was powerless to prevent a strike. At other times, however, when every other means had failed to abolish the wrongs to a group of workers, he shouldered the responsibility and fearlessly called for a strike.

In a republic, he said, strikes were necessary. They were like pain in the social body. They forced people's attention to a disease, and resulted in better industrial health. Employers and workers understood each other better after they had suffered in a strike, and the nation thereby gained. "I trust that the day will never come when the workers surrender their right to strike," he said.

He upheld the workers' right to strike because he believed in democracy. To him democracy was like a strenuous game in which groups of people joined together as in teams, for the common advantage. The zest and beauty of the game was that each player was free to choose his side. Employers lined on one side of the field, for example; workers on the opposite. Of course this sort of play was not for children. The contestants were in deadly earnest, hurt and scarred in the brunt of battle. But if the rules of the game were observed, it developed the players as did no other form of political life. . . . But the rules must be observed. To those who would prevent him from advising the workers of the country he warned: Mind the rules of democracy—free speech. Those employers who would prevent their workers from forming unions he warned: You are violating a rule of freedom. Employers unite; workers have the right to do likewise.

The employers of the country must learn, moreover, that the way to avoid strikes of their workers is not by opposing their unions, but by collaborating with them and sharing their problems. The good of the country demands a common council of labor and capital.

For forty years Samuel Gompers stood as on a platform, gavel in hand, his dark eyes snapping and his voice raised to implant his ideas for the worker's welfare in the conscience of his country. Led by him, the trade-unions flourished. He himself came to be regarded as one of the leaders of America. To many his life was like a fairy tale. "Once there was a little cigarmaker"—so the story might begin—"and he looked about him and saw Evil Things crushing the Man in Overalls. So the little cigarmaker fashioned a weapon called Trade-Unionism, and went forth to do battle with the Labor Evils in the shape of Long Hours and Low Wages. . . ." The romance told of young Samuel Gompers in his office furnished with empty grocer's boxes. That was long ago, in the days when he was little known. But in the ripeness of time, he became a mighty champion, and a power in the land to be feared and loved. Then his office contained desks and secretaries in the elegant American Federation of Labor building, within walking distance of the White House. The dwellers in the White House often called for the advice of Mr. Gompers. The little cigarmaker was not abashed, not even when he was guest of the King of Great Britain, whose ragged subject he once was. He was not abashed because he, too, represented a mighty power, Labor. He had taught Labor the value of acting through union. He had shown Capital the necessity of deliberating with Labor on their common welfare.

The real romance in the life of Samuel Gompers was his devotion to what he called "the holy cause of labor." Worldly men who appreciated his talents offered him on several occasions fortunes in money if he would give up his holy cause and enter business. But he preferred to live in his small house, comparatively poor, and continue his devotions to the holy cause. Once a capitalist proposed to him that he become the president of a corporation about to operate in Mexico. The corporation intended to run farms on a gigantic scale. With the cheap labor there, said the capitalist, millions in profits were to be made in Mexico. Now, Samuel Gompers had been thinking of Mexico. He himself was about to operate there, because of cheap labor. He intended, in fact, to make it less cheap. He declined the business offer, of course; he had other profits in mind, holier ones. His business in Mexico was to uplift the degraded worker, the peon, until he stood shoulder to shoulder with his neighbor, the worker across the Rio Grande.

In the fall of 1924, the American Federation of Labor was holding its annual convention at El Paso. Its founder, "the Grand Old Man of Labor," still sat in the presidential chair. This was fated to be the last time he would face his flock. But he did not know that. In Juarez across the Rio Grande, another mighty organization of workers, the Mexican Federation of Labor, had also convened, and to the lips of their speakers one word, a name, came often. It fell on the air with the hush of a sacred word, and then the air blazed with a "Viva!" The word was Gompers. The Grand Old Man did not know that. But one day one thousand men marched across the International Bridge and into the hall where he sat, gavel in hand. He had dreamed of this moment, when the foreign workers would sit in common council with the American. His other dream, of workers sharing in the councils of their employers and of the Government—that had already come true. Now this. His mission in life, he felt, was fulfilled; he was ready to die, and no regret.

Catching sight of the old man on the platform, the Mexicans, some of them barefooted, burst into wild applause. They cheered him, they sang to him; a few of them fell on their knees before him, blessing him for what he had done to free them from peonage.

The program of the convention called for the election of a president. Now, except for one year, Samuel Gompers had been re-elected every year for forty years. Times had changed, however. Many delegates disagreed with the old man's policies. They felt that younger labor leaders, new ideas, should prevail.

The old man looked worn out. His days were numbered. . . . A delegate rose and nominated Samuel Gompers for president, and the motion was seconded. Not a delegate present but felt that whatever his disagreement with the old man, he owed him every homage in his final hours. For the cause of labor alone, the Grand Old Man had consecrated his life. More than any other man in the country, it was he who had given Labor a voice. And that voice he had trained until it was heard with respect throughout the world, for it spoke in the interests of the workers. . . .

So Samuel Gompers was elected unanimously. The Grand Old Man was chief to the last.

I Hear America Singing

By Walt Whitman

I hear America singing, the varied carols I hear,
Those of the mechanics, each singing his as it should be blithe
    and strong,
The carpenter singing his as he measures his plank or beam,
The mason singing his as he makes ready for work or leaves
    off work,
The boatman singing what belongs to him in his boat, the deck
    hand singing on the steamboat deck,

The shoemaker singing as he sits on his bench, the hatter singing
    as he stands,
The wood-cutter's song, the ploughboy's on his way in the
    morning, or at noon intermission or at sundown,
The delicious singing of the mother, or the young wife at work,
    or the girl sewing or washing,
Each sings what belongs to him or her and to none else,
The day what belongs to the day—at night the party of young
    fellows, robust, friendly,
Singing with open mouths their strong melodious songs.

Those Who Go Forth Before Daylight

By Carl Sandburg

    The policeman buys shoes slow and careful;
    the teamster buys gloves slow and care-
    ful; they take care of their feet and
    hands; they live on their feet and
    hands.

    The milkman never argues; he works alone
    and no one speaks to him; the city is
    asleep when he is on the job; he puts a
    bottle on six hundred porches and calls
    it a day's work; he climbs two hundred
    wooden stairways; two horses are com-
    pany for him; he never argues.

    The rolling-mill men and the sheet-metal
    men are brothers of cinders; they empty
    cinders out of their shoes after the day's
    work; they ask their wives to fix burnt
    holes in the knees of their trousers;
    their necks and ears are covered with
    a smut; they scour their necks and ears;
    they are brothers of cinders.

The Man with the Hoe

By Edwin Markham

Bowed by the weight of centuries he leans
Upon his hoe and gazes on the ground,
The emptiness of ages in his face,
And on his back the burden of the world.
Who made him dead to rapture and despair,
A thing that grieves not and that never hopes,
Stolid and stunned, a brother to the ox?
Who loosened and let down this brutal jaw?
Whose was the hand that slanted back this brow?
Whose breath blew out the light within this brain?

Is this the Thing the Lord God made and gave
To have dominion over sea and land?
To trace the stars and search the heavens for power;
To feel the passion of Eternity?
Is this the dream He dreamed who shaped the suns
And markt their ways upon the ancient deep?
Down all the caverns of Hell to their last gulf
There is no shape more terrible than this—
More tongued with censure of the world's blind greed—
More filled with signs and portents for the soul—
More packt with danger to the universe.

What gulfs between him and the seraphim!
Slave of the wheel of labor, what to him
Are Plato and the swing of Pleiades?
What the long reaches of the peaks of song,
The rift of dawn, the reddening of the rose?
Through this dread shape the suffering ages look;
Time's tragedy is in that aching stoop;
Through this dread shape humanity betrayed,
Plundered, profaned and disinherited,
Cries protest to the Powers that made the world,
A protest that is also prophecy.

"The Man with the Hoe," by Jean Francois Millet.

O masters, lords and rulers in all lands,
Is this the handiwork you give to God,
This monstrous thing distorted and soul-quencht?
How will you ever straighten up this shape;
Touch it again with immortality;
Give back the upward looking and the light;
Rebuild in it the music and the dream;
Make right the immemorial infamies,
Perfidious wrongs, immedicable woes?

O masters, lords and rulers in all lands,
How will the future reckon with this Man?
How answer his brute question in that hour
When whirlwinds of rebellion shake all shores?
How will it be with kingdoms and with kings—
With those who shaped him to the thing he is—
When this dumb Terror shall rise to judge the world,
After the silence of the centuries?

The Village Blacksmith

By Henry Wadsworth Longfellow

Illustration by Estelle Hollingworth

Under a spreading chestnut-tree
The village smithy stands;
The smith, a mighty man is he,
With large and sinewy hands;
And the muscles of his brawny arm
Are strong as iron bands.

His hair is crisp, and black, and long,
His face is like the tan;
His brow is wet with honest sweat,
He earns whate'er he can,
And looks the whole world in the face,
For he owes not any man.

Week in, week out, from morn till night,
You can hear his bellows blow;
You can hear him swing his heavy sledge,
With measured beat and slow,
Like a sexton ringing the village bell,
When the evening sun is low.

And children coming home from school
Look in at the open door;
They love to see the flaming forge,
And hear the bellows roar,
And catch the burning sparks that fly,
Like chaff from a threshing-floor.

He goes on Sunday to the church,
And sits among his boys;
He hears the parson pray and preach,
He hears his daughter's voice,
Singing in the village choir,
And it makes his heart rejoice.

It sounds to him like her mother's voice,
Singing in Paradise!
He needs must think of her once more
How in the grave she lies;
And with his hard, rough hand he wipes
A tear out of his eyes.

Toiling,—rejoicing,—sorrowing,
Onward through life he goes;
Each morning sees some task begin,
Each evening sees it close;
Something attempted, something done,
Has earned a night's repose.

Thanks, thanks to thee, my worthy friend,
For the lesson thou hast taught!
Thus at the flaming forge of life
Our fortunes must be wrought;
Thus on its sounding anvil shaped
Each burning deed and thought.

Columbus Day

Christopher Columbus had one ambition—to reach the East and its fabled wealth by sailing West. There were some who thought him crazy to believe the world was round. They thought it impossible to sail "around" a flat earth. But thinking people of Columbus' day, and even earlier, knew that the world was round.

Curiosity combined with persistence finally brought Columbus the answer to his dreams. The Queen of Spain supplied him with money, and on August 3, 1492, Columbus set sail from Palos, Spain, with three ships, the *Niña*, the *Pinta*, and the *Santa María*.

On October 12, 1492, Columbus sighted by moonlight what he thought was an island of the Indies near Japan or China. The island, which Columbus called San Salvadore, was actually a tiny part of an unknown world.

Columbus made several trips back and forth across the broad reaches of the Atlantic in a continued effort to locate lands that might be Asia or Japan. Despite his great discoveries, Columbus died a disappointed man because he had failed to bring back to Spain the treasures of the East.

Columbus Looks for China and Finds America

BY ROGER DUVOISIN

Illustrations by the author

AT the time the Portuguese seamen were still looking for the southernmost end of Africa there came into Lisbon a young Italian named Christopher Columbus.

Columbus was much interested in everything which had to do with the sea and ships, and faraway islands and kings. In Lisbon, where everyone talked of all these things, Christopher Columbus helped his brother Bartholomeo to paint maps and sell books. He loved to watch the mariners unload from their sailing ships the monkeys, the bright parrots, the elephant tusks, and the other wonderful things which they had gathered in the new land of Africa. When, sometimes, he sailed on a Portuguese caravel, he liked to hear the sailors tell stories about the adventures they had met with in trying to sail to Asia, around Africa.

After a time, Columbus himself began to dream that he was sailing to Asia too, that great Land which he was trying to paint on his brother's maps. He read Marco Polo's book and other books which tried to show where China and India lay, and he pored and pored over Ptolemy's map of the world.

Now, very strangely, the two biggest mistakes Ptolemy had made on his map gave Columbus an idea. As we have already said, Ptolemy had drawn the world smaller than it really is. He had made Asia much too big toward the east, so that there was little room left on his world between the east coast of Asia and the west coast of Europe. There was only room for a small ocean.

"Ptolemy was a learned man," Columbus said. "His map must be right. Then, since the world is round, if one sails straight toward the setting sun from the west shore of Europe, one will reach Asia in a short time. And it is silly for the Portuguese seamen to try to get to India by going south round Africa and then east. It would be very much simpler to sail west from Lisbon."

"If it is true," said his brother Bartholomeo, "good caravels could, in a few days' sailing, come to Japan, for Marco Polo says that Japan lies to the east of China."

"And I will be the admiral commanding these caravels," exclaimed Columbus. "I am going to tell the King of Portugal about all this; surely he will give me the ships."

The king, John of Portugal, was amazed at Columbus' idea.

"Hum! I never thought of that," he said. "How can you be sure that Japan lies so near, across that mysterious Atlantic Ocean which we can see from any window of my palaces?"

"I have studied Ptolemy's map," answered Columbus. "I have also sailed to Iceland, the foggy isle of the north, where I heard sailors tell about a land not far to the west. I have sailed to Madeira where I was told of pieces of carved wood and strange hollow canes which the west wind had blown onto the beach. These could not have come from very far away."

"Yes, I know about the canes," the king said thoughtfully. "I have seen them."

"The sea has also brought dead pine trees of a kind we have never seen in our countries," continued Columbus. "There is land not far across the Atlantic, I know. Truly if you give me some ships I'll find the countries Polo told about—Japan, where the king's palace has roofs of gold; China, from whence comes our silk, and where there are so many rich and busy cities; India and the islands of the East from which come spices and precious stones.

"Of course, it is only fair that I have my reward for doing all this. I want to be made a knight with golden spurs; and great admiral of all the oceans; and governor of all the countries I will find. I also want the tenth part of all the riches I bring back to Lisbon."

"All that!" exclaimed the king. "Well, maybe your idea is good; maybe it is not. I am not sure. I shall call the most learned scholars of Portugal to hear what they have to say."

The old scholars came, listened, looked scornful, and finally said: "No, no! This young man, Columbus, is just a dreamer. Only God knows how large the Atlantic Ocean is, and what lies beyond. Only a fool would try to sail across it, and he would not return. Our sailors are now busy trying to sail to India and China round Africa; it is a good way. It would be unwise to try to find another one."

Columbus went home broken-hearted.

"There are other kings who will like your idea," his brother Bartholomeo told him. "Go and see the King of Spain, Ferdinand, and his Queen Isabella. They are not trying to sail round Africa and they will like to get to China before the King of Portugal does."

So Columbus took his dream into Spain and was heard by the queen and the king.

"I think there may be something in your idea," said the king.

"So do I," said the queen. "But we are very busy now chasing the Moors out of Spain, and we have no time to study all that ourselves. Let's get together some learned scholars of Spain, so they can hear what you have to say."

The Spanish scholars met but could not make up their minds at once. So they went home to think it over, and Columbus waited.

From time to time, the scholars met again but still they could not say yes and they could not say no; and again Columbus waited and waited. He talked of his dreams. He became desolate and penniless.

"Look at this man in tattered clothes," people began to whisper, "offering our king islands and continents and mountains of gold. He must be out of his mind."

Finally the scholars decided. They said no. But they added: "Wait until the Moors are out of Spain, then come back. Perhaps we will have changed our minds by then."

"No more waiting," said Columbus. "I am going to see the King of France."

And he departed for France.

But then, some of his friends went to Queen Isabella and they talked so well about Columbus that she called him back.

"Perhaps you are right, after all," she said to him. "Perhaps you can bring us the spices and silks and precious stones of the East."

"I know I can."

"Then if I give you the ships, what will you ask in return for yourself?"

Columbus repeated what he had asked the King of Portugal.

"That's too much," exclaimed the queen, her eyes big with surprise. "Much too much."

"I would not do it for less," declared Columbus.

"Then we won't give the ships."

Columbus was quite angry now. He said good-bye to his friends and again took the road to France.

However, the treasurer of the king and queen, who was a wise man, said to Isabella:

"I think you should give Columbus what he wants. What can you lose? It does not cost much to give him the golden spurs and make him a knight. If he comes back from China with his ships full of treasures, wouldn't you rather give him one tenth and keep all the rest than have the King of France have it?"

"I would," said Queen Isabella. "Go after Columbus and catch him before he gets into France."

This second time, when Columbus came back to King Ferdinand and Queen Isabella, he was granted the ships and the rewards he asked for. And it was all written down on parchment and signed by the king and queen.

It was in the port of Palos in southern Spain that Columbus made his caravels ready. There were three of them: a large one,

the *Santa Maria,* and two smaller ones, the *Pinta* and the *Niña.*
On a misty summer dawn, in August 1492, the three caravels
spread their sails with the painted cross, and sailed away.

"Now," thought Columbus, standing on the high stern of the
Santa Maria, "every minute that the wind blows, I am nearer
Japan, China, and India. Soon I will be the great admiral of
all the seas."

Columbus' sailors knew the Atlantic Ocean from Spain to
the Canary Islands, which belonged to King Ferdinand. They
were sure they would not meet horrible sea monsters until they
arrived there. But beyond, it would be another story. And so
even though their delay made Columbus unhappy, they were
glad to remain many days in the safe islands, to repair the rudder of the *Pinta* which had broken on the way.

As soon as the rudder had been repaired, it was with a sad
heart that they put out to sea again and sailed west. It was the
very first time that ships had ventured straight onto an unknown
sea with no land on either side.

"How can our captain be so sure that this ocean has an end?"
wondered a young Spaniard. "For my part, I fear that we shall
never return. Look, the wind blows steadily toward the West.
We won't be able to get back with this wind always at our bow."

"In my time," said an old sailor, "I have heard many stories
of ships swallowed by sea serpents; of ships falling off the earth
at the end of the sea. I believe they are true stories."

"They *are* true," said many sailors together. "And so are many
others, just as bad."

While they frightened one another in this way with strange
sea tales, the three caravels sailed on and on. The sailors thought
of Spain, behind them. Columbus thought of Asia ahead of
him. Sometimes birds flew in the blue summer sky, and that
made the sailors happier, for they imagined that land could
not be far away. But they were sadder than ever when more
days passed and the man in the crow's-nest never cried, "Land!"

One day they saw that the sea was green with seaweed. Another day, a black whale swam by, puffing white vapor about.
Then they were cheerful again. "Seaweed and whales," they
said, "do not go far from land."

One morning, they climbed the masts and riggings with joy

after Captain Pinzon, master of the *Pinta,* had cried "Land! Land!" But the next morning was like all the mornings before, nothing in sight but the blue waves which never tired of running after one another.

"If we go on, we are lost," growled the men. "Our place is in Spain with our wives and children, not on this awful sea with a captain who lives in a silly dream, full of Japans and Chinas."

"We shall not go on another day," they all said menacingly.

"Let's throw him overboard," an angry sailor cried. "Then we can turn round."

Columbus came out of his small cabin on the high aft castle, and looking at them without fear, said:

"There is no use complaining. I have come to seek Japan, China, and India, and with the help of God, I will find them. Do not be afraid. You will go back to your families, with your hands full of gold."

Seeing that Columbus was so resolute, the seamen went back to their posts though they still grumbled. They kept their eyes on the blue horizon, hoping for a sight of land.

As the days went by, there were many signs that land was
not far off. Once, all night long, great flights of birds flew over
the ships. One afternoon, a reed and a carved stick floated by.
At the end of that same day, as Columbus stood on the aft
castle, watching the night ahead of him and listening to the

waves as they broke on the sides of the *Santa Maria*, he suddenly saw a little light. "Look!" he cried to his sailors, "before us, at the bow. Do you see that light?"

"I see it," said one man.

"I don't!" said another.

"Perhaps it is another mistake, then," sighed Columbus.

But it was not, for soon after that, a sailor on the *Pinta* shouted:

"Land! Land! It's land, for sure."

Among cries of joy, Columbus ordered his ships to lie at anchor. Few sailors slept that night; most of them stood on the decks, their eyes peering into the dark, like people in a theatre waiting for the curtain to rise.

"What shall we see in the morning?" wondered Columbus. "The gold roofs of Japanese palaces, no doubt, for this land lies just where I thought Japan was—to the east of China. It must be Japan!"

At dawn, as darkness began to lift, a small island slowly took shape; a cool white beach: tall green palm trees, still wet with dew. All was quiet. Then a bird, hidden among the leaves whistled, and others answered it. Some naked brown men came down to the water's edge, talking and yelling among themselves in a strange language, pointing to the big sailing vessels which the night had brought. Some of them had painted their bodies red; others had blue faces; a few had dipped their noses into yellow paint.

America lay before Columbus' eyes. It was October the twelfth, fourteen hundred and ninety-two.

"I don't understand!" murmured Columbus. "There are no gold roofs. In his book Marco Polo does not say that the Japanese and the Chinese go naked and painted. He does say that they wear rich robes of silk; and he also says that the seas around Japan are full of islands. That must be one of them."

Columbus now put on his most beautiful clothes and his coat of green velvet and landed on the shore, holding in his left hand the banner of the King of Spain. Behind him came the captains of the *Niña* and the *Pinta*, carrying the flag with the green cross.

"From now on," Columbus declared, "this island will belong

to King Ferdinand, and it will be called 'San Salvador' on the map." His scribes wrote that down, and Columbus and his officers scratched their names below it.

The painted brown men stood around them and wondered what it was all about. They would have been sad had they known that the greedy white men would soon chase them out of their fairy-like islands.

They smiled, showing all their teeth, when the sailors gave them some glass beads, tinkling bells, and red bonnets. As they, too, wanted to be generous, they brought presents of cotton balls, green parrots, fruits, and arrows.

Although grateful, Columbus planned to deceive these kind, confident islanders. He ordered his men to take seven of them by force and put them on board his ships. He wanted to show them to the king, on his return to Spain.

"There is nothing much in this small island," he said. "It is time to leave it, for I am impatient to go and look for Japan and China. All aboard!"

There were many islands in these seas, all very green and beautiful. They were full of new kinds of flowers and fruits, with birds of all colors flying among the palm trees. But nowhere did the gold roofs of the palaces of the King of Japan glitter above the trees. There were but the straw huts of the naked men. Nowhere did Columbus find the rich cities, busy with hundreds of laden ships, which Marco had seen in China.

When he came to the island of Cuba, it looked so big to him

from the sea, that he was sure it was China, the country over which the great Khan ruled.

"I see only green forests and yellow huts, but that's all right," he thought. "The great Khan lives somewhere in the middle of that country. I haven't time to look for him now. I'll come back later to give him King Ferdinand's letter."

The Spanish seamen saw no gold in Cuba but they noticed that the brown men rolled large dried leaves, and made smoke with them in their mouths. It was tobacco. The sailors could not know that men would become richer by growing tobacco in America than by looking for gold.

After Cuba, Columbus came to the great island of Haiti. As it lay east of Cuba he thought it was Japan. It was like a rich garden in which grew all sorts of trees, vegetables, and flowers the Spaniards had never seen. It, too, was peopled by the kind and peaceful Indians who went about naked, with gold rings in their noses.

Since Columbus thought he had come to Japan and China, these brown men might have been called Chinese or Japanese. But they were called Indians for Columbus was also looking for India. And Indians they are still called.

"Where are those rich palaces, those people clothed in silk and precious stones?" asked Columbus. "Where are they? It is time to sail back to Spain and I have not found them. I shall have to come back and look some more."

Before they were ready to sail, while the helmsman of the *Santa Maria* went ashore one evening, instead of remaining at his post, the currents carried the ship onto the rocks where it was wrecked. As there was not enough room on the two smaller ships for all the sailors to return to Spain, forty-four of them had to remain in Haiti, where they built a fort with the beams and boards of the *Santa Maria*.

When the *Pinta* and the *Niña* made their way back across the Atlantic Ocean, they did not carry embroidered robes of silk and satin like the ones Marco Polo brought back to Venice. In their place were Indians, a few noisy green parrots, balls of cotton, fruits, arrows, and some bits of gold jewelry.

After landing in Palos, Columbus went to see King Ferdinand and Queen Isabella in the city of Barcelona. He entered it to the sound of trumpets and drums, amidst flying banners.

The king and the queen were pleased with his discoveries, for Columbus told them that he had found Japan and China, although he had not seen the richest part of these countries. Then he showed the Indians, parrots and other things which he had brought back. Everyone gazed in wonder, for no men, birds, and fruits like these had ever been seen in Europe before.

Columbus' fame spread all over Europe. He was now a knight, Don Cristóbal Columbus, great admiral of all the oceans, with golden spurs, as was written on the parchment. As proof that he was a great gentleman of Spain, the king gave him a fine escutcheon with a castle, a lion and five anchors painted on it.

So now, on the west side of the Atlantic were lands which Spain claimed as her own, and on the east side were the newly found parts of Africa, which belonged to Portugal.

"That is all very well," said the Pope in Rome. "Spain claims lands in the West; Portugal in the East. But I very much fear that these two countries are going to put their flags on the same island and fight a war over it. That would not be so good. I must do something about it."

Just like a mother who cuts an apple in two and gives one half to each of her two children, he took the map and drew a line down through the Atlantic Ocean to the South Pole and up on the Asia side. And he said: "One half of the world, that which has in it the countries found by Columbus, will belong to Spain. The other half, where Africa and India lie, will belong to Portugal." And that was that.

But Columbus was not interested in that. Amidst all his glory, he thought, and worried, and thought again about one thing:

"Where can the great Khan be? Where can the gold-roofed palaces of Japan be? Where?"

He was impatient to be again on the deck of a good caravel, sailing westward across the Atlantic. The king, who was also anxious to find the treasures of Asia, gave him seventeen ships. They were filled with soldiers, craftsmen, and farmers;

with horses, cows, and sheep; for cities were to be built, and farms started on the green islands.

Upon arriving on the other side of the Atlantic, Columbus discovered two more islands which he had not seen during his first trip—Guadeloupe, and Porto Rico.

"There are as many islands in these seas as there are flowers in a June meadow," thought Columbus. "But I don't care for them; I want the riches of Japan and China and India."

In Haiti, Columbus found that the forty-four sailors he had left there had all been killed, and their fort burned. No doubt they had done something which had angered the Indians.

It was in this island that the masons and the carpenters of Columbus built their first town: the very first white man's town built in America. Columbus named it Isabella for the Queen of Spain whom he liked very much.

Again Columbus sailed on, searching and searching for the things Marco Polo had told about, but all he discovered was the big island of Jamaica.

He went back to Spain with nothing more to tell about than more islands and still more islands, all with green palm trees, naked Indians and yellow huts on them.

A third time Columbus crossed the ocean, to the West. He found more islands, and he also found the continent of South America, and the great Orinoco River. He thought that this big continent was just another island, so he named it *Santa Isle*.

The fourth time he went, he saw the shores of Central America.

But nowhere did he see the big ships, the rich cities, and the silk-clothed Chinese, the jewel-covered kings of India, or the gold-roofed palaces of Japan!

When he returned to Spain, after this last trip, he was broken in health and very unhappy. But he was sure that somewhere among his islands lay the countries of Asia, although by that time travelers already suspected that his islands had nothing to do with Marco Polo's land of the East, but were entirely new lands.

Columbus died soon after his fourth voyage without knowing that he had added to the map one of the biggest and richest continents of the world.

Columbus

By Joaquin Miller

Illustration by William Colrus

Behind him lay the gray Azores,
   Behind, the Gates of Hercules;
Before him not the ghost of shores,
   Before him only shoreless seas.
The good mate said: "Now we must pray,
   For lo! the very stars are gone,
Brave Admiral, speak, what shall I say?"
   "Why, say 'Sail on! sail on! and on!'"

"My men grow mutinous day by day;
   My men grow ghastly wan and weak."
The stout mate thought of home; a spray
   Of salt wave washed his swarthy cheek.
"What shall I say, brave Admiral, say,
   If we sight naught but seas at dawn?"
"Why, you shall say at break of day,
   'Sail on! sail on! sail on! and on!'"

They sailed and sailed, as winds might blow,
   Until at last the blanched mate said:
"Why, now not even God would know,
   Should I and all my men fall dead.
These very winds forget their way,
   For God from these dread seas is gone,
Now, speak, brave Admiral, speak and say."
   He said, "Sail on! sail on! and on!"

They sailed. They sailed. Then spoke the mate:
   "This mad sea shows his teeth tonight.
He curls his lip, he lies in wait
   With lifted teeth, as if to bite!
Brave Admiral, say but one good word:
   What shall we do when hope is gone?"
The words leaped like a leaping sword:
   "Sail on! sail on! sail on! and on!"

Then pale and worn, he kept his deck,
   And peered through darkness. Ah, that night
Of all dark nights! And then a speck—
   A light! A light! A light! A light!
It grew, a starlit flag unfurled!
   It grew to be Time's burst of dawn.
He gained a world; he gave that world
   Its grandest lesson: "On! sail on!"

Christopher Columbus

By Stephen Vincent Benét

Illustration by Charles Child

There are lots of queer things that discoverers do
But his was the queerest, I swear.
He discovered our country in One Four Nine Two
By thinking it couldn't be there.

It wasn't his folly, it wasn't his fault,
For the very best maps of the day
Showed nothing but water, extensive and salt,
On the West, between Spain and Bombay.

There were monsters, of course, every watery mile,
Great krakens with blubbery lips
And sea-serpents smiling a crocodile-smile
As they waited for poor little ships.

There were whirlpools and maelstroms, without any doubt
And tornadoes of lava and ink.
(Which, as nobody yet had been there to find out,
Seems a little bit odd, don't you think?)

But Columbus was bold and Columbus set sail
(Thanks to Queen Isabella, her pelf),
For he said "Though there may be both monster and gale,
I'd like to find out for myself."

And he sailed and he sailed and he *sailed* and he SAILED,
Though his crew would have gladly turned round
And, morning and evening, distressfully wailed
"This is running things into the ground!"

But he paid no attention to protest or squall,
This obstinate son of the mast,
And so, in the end, he discovered us all,
Remarking, "Here's India, at last!"

He didn't intend it, he meant to heave to
At Calcutta, Rangoon or Shanghai,
There are many queer things that discoverers do.
But his was the queerest. Oh my!

UNITED NATIONS

United Nations Day

OCTOBER 24

At the close of World War II it was clear to all who had witnessed the devastation and cruelty of that great conflict that lasting peace must be established. An organization where nations could meet and settle their disputes peacefully seemed the only answer.

The League of Nations, formed after World War I, had sought the same goal of peace. But it had failed. Statesmen studied their mistakes. The United States, not a member of the League, entered negotiations. After much planning and many meetings, the United Nations was officially born on October 24, 1945, with fifty-one member nations. Nations throughout the world annually observe this day as United Nations Day. With the birth of the United Nations came new hope for a better world.

Membership is open to all "peace-loving states" willing and able to carry out the obligations stated in the United Nations Charter. New members admitted since 1945 include newly formed nations as well as older nations able to meet these standards.

A Fair World for All

BY DOROTHY CANFIELD FISHER

ARTICLE 1

All human beings are born free and equal in dignity and rights. They are endowed with reason and conscience and should act towards one another in a spirit of brotherhood.

MAYBE, in your heart, you have thought that there is some nonsense about the talk of all men being brothers. Such a feeling isn't at all what people expect of you, and so you have perhaps not wanted to say it right out. But it is quite possible that you have silently asked yourself, "How *can* I feel towards a person I don't know, that 'he is a brother'? I know that's the proper thing to say, but I don't feel so."

Yes you do, too, if you really think about it. Here are some ways to put it to yourself so that you can see that you do.

Suppose that you, with a group of neighbors, are in a market or a food shop, buying bread and fish and fruit and other things to eat. Everybody is relaxed and easy, standing around waiting for his turn to buy.

All of a sudden, a big snake (maybe brought in on a bunch of fruit) crawls along a beam of the roof and drops down amongst the shoppers. You don't need anybody to tell you how most of the crowd will scream and rush for the door, while others will try to get the creature into a basket and shut the lid down, or if they can't do that, to kill it. Just as you snatch your hand away instantly from a hot piece of iron, everybody there feels that human beings must be protected from danger.

Or, here's another picture—suppose in the same food market or grocery store, as people stand around looking at prices and waiting for a chance to buy, somebody sees through the open door a big black panther (maybe escaped from a menagerie, maybe come in from the woods) racing down the street. Not a human being in the world would stop to ask those around him, "Don't you agree with me that we had better close the door?"

Not much! He'd *know* they agree with him, he'd yell and dive to slam the door shut, and the minute the others saw what he saw, they would feel just what he feels.

But suppose that you all saw a man and woman coming towards the shop. He might be a very queer-looking man, much taller or much shorter than the men you were used to; she might have a different-colored skin from anybody you ever saw; but from as far away as you could see them, everybody would recognize them as man and woman. Nobody would yell, nobody would slam the door shut, nobody would get out a gun. You might wonder about the man's odd clothes, you might think the color of the woman's skin was queer, but if it turned out they wanted to come in to buy food, you'd all just move over to give them room.

You take this for granted, don't you? If you think about it at all, you feel it is natural. Well, it's not. It is something which has slowly been learned. Thousands of years ago people feared a human being they didn't personally know as we now fear a wild animal.

In those human beginnings of our history, a family lived in a cave, or maybe in a small hut—father, mother, children. They knew each other, probably also a grandparent or two, and maybe some neighbors who lived in a cave nearby. But that was all. At the sight of a strange man they acted like the people in the food store when they saw a panther. The children were taught to run, run, run back to the safety of the cave; the feeble old folks tried to hide; the strongest of the grownups rushed to kill the stranger, or anyhow to tie him up and to take him prisoner. They did it for the same reason—to protect themselves from danger. A stranger was as unknown to them as a panther. For all they knew he might be as dangerous.

Little by little the circle has enlarged in which men recognized other men—even strangers—as like themselves, not like unknown dangerous animals. First there were more huts close together, making a group where everybody came to know everybody else by sight. Then some of the children, as they grew up, moved to another nearby group of huts; and they were known to the first group as they came and went. At least, before people hurried to kill a strange figure, they took time for one look at him, to see if he was their kind of being.

Then, slowly, they began to notice that everybody human was the same kind of being as themselves. When fierce beasts of prey appeared, men could be pretty sure that they were going to attack to kill. Hence the safe thing to do was to attack first. But long experience taught human beings that a strange man might have in his mind some purpose entirely different from murderous attack—maybe he had something to sell, or wanted to buy something they had; maybe he came to warn them of a forest fire or a flood; maybe he was lost and wanted to ask his way.

As the centuries went on, human beings came to see more and more of each other. Boats were invented to cross streams and seas, paths and roads were constructed to cross mountains. People slowly found out that wherever they saw other men and women, no matter what color their skin, or how they were dressed, they were the very same kind of creatures. This is just a fact, as plain a fact as that tiny little sparrows and great fat hens belong to the bird family. We human beings are all as alike as members of one family, because we *are* members of one family.

So, since the children of one family are all brothers and sisters, you can see that any other human being really is a brother, even though you may never have laid eyes on him before.

It has taken a long time for men and women to grasp this idea clearly enough to think about it. Yet we have for centuries acted on it, coming and going as we do alongside other members of the human family in a street, in a crowd. We are not afraid of them; we don't want to make them afraid of us. We just go about our business, sure of what they are likely to do, as they are sure of us, as none of us would be sure of an entirely different kind of creature, like a polar bear.

But because we don't always remember—or maybe don't even realize definitely—what it is that makes us so act, this article was put first in the Declaration, to remind us of the basis of our human lives.

ARTICLE 2

Everyone is entitled to all the rights and freedoms set forth in this Declaration, without distinction of any kind, such as race, color, sex, language, religion, political or other opinion, national or social origin, property, birth or other status.

Furthermore, no distinction shall be made on the basis of the political, jurisdictional or international status of the country or territory to which a person belongs, whether it be independent, trust, non-self-governing or under any other limitation of sovereignty.

Suppose you were moving into a new place to live, and wanted to get the house which was to be your family's home perfectly clean. It wouldn't be definite enough if, as you were all talking it over together beforehand and making plans, you said only, "We must clean the house."

There are so many, many different things in a house which get dirty. You would be much surer of not forgetting any part of what you want done, if you made a list, all of you thinking about it: if you wrote down, "Clean the floor, the walls, the ceiling, the shelves, the steps on the stairs, the floor and steps leading to the front veranda and to the back door, the places where clothes are to be hung, the place in the kitchen where food is to be prepared," and so on.

That's the way Article 2 of the Declaration was written. There was perfect agreement as to what was wanted in it from every single man and woman on the Committee of eighteen who were especially working on the Declaration, and from all those in the big General Assembly of the United Nations. The first part of this Article—"Everyone is entitled to all the rights and freedoms set forth in this Declaration"—says clearly what they thought, what they all wanted to say. You might think it would have been safe to leave it at that.

But that would have been like a family's saying, "We must clean the house." If nothing more was said, they might work together at cleaning it, and move in; and then, some day, the little door under the stairs might fall open—and there would be a place full of dust and trash and dirt that they had forgotten to clean.

The United Nations wanted to mention by name every single kind of unfairness which in the past had been done to any group of people. They wanted to make sure that nobody would be overlooked in this statement of the rights agreed on by the United Nations as belonging to all.

So they put their heads together to mention all the kinds of people who had ever been shut out from such rights anywhere, so that they could be brought to mind. Men and women have sometimes been excluded from their fair rights and freedoms because of their race, so this was mentioned.

It was a little as though all the delegates to the United Nations stood up and called to the enormous crowd of human beings all around the globe, "Everybody, *no matter what race,* come on out into your fair share of freedom, as big a share as anybody."

Then, just in case the word "race" wasn't definite enough, they said, "Doesn't make any difference what color you are, step out into freedom."

Then, maybe, the women of the world, because for so long and in so many places they have been kept less free than men, might wonder if they too were to have their full human share of freedom. The voice of the Declaration speaks specially to them: "You women, you too, have the right to be as free as any other grownup."

But in many places people who believe in one kind of religion have been shut out from a full place in the freedom-world. They might be asking themselves, uncertainly, "Do you suppose *we* are in this, too?" The voice of the Declaration would ring out, "Yes, you too!"

You can make up for yourselves the reasons for the other definitely named summons to freedom: "You who have little money—you have all the rights we're setting down in this Declaration just as much as if you were ever so rich." "*You,* whose father and mother were—maybe—slaves. Don't think for a minute that that makes you a slave." "*You* who have a lot of property —you haven't any *more* of these great human rights and freedoms than the person who earns just enough each day to make both ends meet. . . . Money hasn't a thing to do with human rights."

The United Nations tried to think of every single kind of person who might have been kept out of his fair share of human rights and freedoms, and to call to them all, "Human freedom is so great an idea, that in it there's room for all!"

When you think of Article 2, listen as if to a big bell ringing out joyously: "There's room for all! There's room for all!"

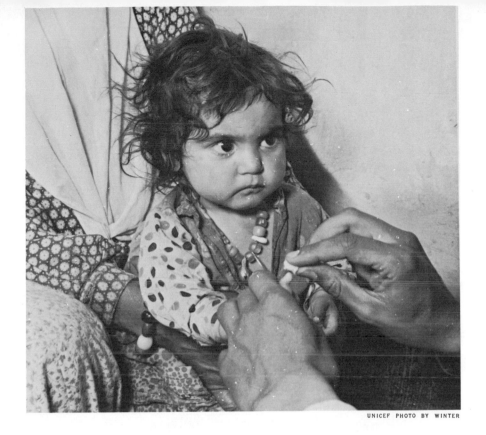

Prayer for a Better World

By Stephen Vincent Benét

Our Earth is but a small star in the great universe. Yet of it we can make, if we choose, a planet unvexed by war, untroubled by hunger or fear, undivided by senseless distinctions of race, color, or theory.

Grant us brotherhood, not only for this day but for all our years—a brotherhood not of words but of acts and deeds. We are all of us children of earth—grant us that simple knowledge. If our brothers are oppressed, then we are oppressed. If they hunger, we hunger. If their freedom is taken away, our freedom is not secure. Grant us a common faith that man shall know bread and peace—that he shall know justice and righteousness, freedom and security, an equal opportunity and an equal chance to do his best, not only in our own lands but throughout the world. And in that faith, let us march toward the clean world our hands can make.

Of Courage Undaunted

By James Daugherty

O young men of courage undaunted,
You have pledged by the Golden Gate
That the nations shall no more be haunted
By the shadows of fear and hate.

The Nations United have pledged it,
The Charter has spoken it plain,
That mercy from clouds of compassion
May fall as the healing rain,

That Peace shall flow as a river
And water the desert and plain.
The Word has gone forth to the peoples
And shall not return in vain.

O young men of courage undaunted,
Ride out toward the new frontiers,
In newness of life great-hearted,
For Love casts out all fears.

No more let the peoples be haunted
By the ghosts of fear and dread,
For brother shall share with brother
And Truth shall be their bread.

Let Us Have Peace

By Nancy Byrd Turner

The earth is weary of our foolish wars.
Her hills and shores were shaped for lovely things,
Yet all our years are spent in bickerings
    Beneath the astonished stars.

April by April laden with beauty comes,
Autumn by autumn turns our toil to gain,
But hand at sword-hilt, still we start and strain
    To catch the beat of drums.

Knowledge to knowledge adding, skill to skill,
We strive for others' good as for our own—
And then, like cavemen snarling with a bone,
    We turn and rend and kill. . . .

With life so fair, and all too short a lease
Upon our special star! Nay, love and trust,
Not blood and thunder shall redeem our dust.
    Let us have peace!

Hope for Peace

By Ilo Orleans

Search the wisdom
Of the ages
    In the books
    Upon your shelf.
Here lies alone
The hope for peace:
    "Love Thy neighbor
    As Thyself"!

Halloween

OCTOBER 31

When witches roam the skies on broomsticks and black cats lurk in alleys, when ghosts and spirits haunt the streets, you know it's Halloween.

Halloween means "holy evening" because it takes place the night before All Saints' Day. But the two have very little to do with each other.

Halloween is a holiday of magic and superstitions. The Druids, an ancient order of priests, believed that on Halloween ghosts and spirits haunted the earth, and that black cats, who were really humans being punished for evil deeds, stalked the streets.

Halloween is a time for harmless pranks, for bobbing for apples, and for "trick or treating" with huge paper bags.

The Blue-Nosed Witch

BY MARGARET EMBRY

Illustrations by Carl Rose

NOT more than four or five Halloweens ago there was a very young witch named Blanche who owned a broom, a black kitten called Brockett, and a bright blue nose. She belonged to a very special scurry of witches, Scurry No. 13, known in the best witch circles all over the country for its beautiful flight formation.

The Grand Madame, who had been leader of the club for as long as any of them could remember, flew center front. She used a vacuum cleaner instead of a broom, and when she gunned her motor it sounded as exciting as a fire siren.

On the far right was Minnie Max waving her blood-red finger nails in the dark; they really did shine like rubies. And on the far left was Blanche's best friend, Josephine, who had long yellow fluorescent teeth that gleamed like stars.

In between and a little behind flew the nine rather ordinary witches who were only expected to follow the Grand Madame's lead, and cackle with horrid glee at appropriate times.

And last came Blanche, usually far, far behind. If it hadn't been for her marvelous blue nose that she could turn on and off at will, she wouldn't have been allowed in Scurry No. 13 at all.

Blanche was always late. She had good intentions and a dependable alarm clock, but somehow she never could get started any place on time. Something always happened at the last minute to delay her. Brockett, the black kitten, would run away, or Blanche would have misplaced her broom, or she would have to finish her comic, or have just one more piece of bread and peanutbutter and honey.

"You see," said Minnie Max to Josephine, "Blanche is still just a baby, and she ought to be sent back to Scurry No. 2½.

Then she'd have to ride a whisk broom, not go any higher than the tops of the poplar trees, and never stay out after midnight with the rest of the grownups. If she's late one more time, I'm going to report her to the Grand Madame!"

"I know Blanche is young and scatterbrained," agreed Josephine, "but don't bother the Grand Madame with it. I'll take care of her. I promise she'll be on time for our next flight meeting."

"That's Halloween night," Minnie Max warned. "Sharp at midnight we're taking off from Dead Man's Bluff. Afterwards, if we make a good showing against the moon, there'll be dancing and chanting and a pot of brew. You'd better see that Blanche is at least half an hour early."

"I'll have her there on time," promised Josephine, "if I have to set her alarm an hour ahead."

As it turned out, Josephine switched the clock ahead not one hour but two, just for good measure. That probably would have been all right, but Blanche herself, as she was getting ready for bed at noon the day of Halloween, had the same good idea. She wound her clock and set it ahead an extra hour and a half—and then just a little more in case Brockett would be hard to find.

But when the alarm shrieked that evening, Brockett for once was perched demurely on the bedpost right where she belonged, her fur newly licked smooth. Blanche yawned and brushed the straw out of her hair and rolled out of bed without her usual dilly-dallying. She washed her face and hands and polished up her blue nose. Her broom was standing neatly behind the kitchen door.

Brockett hopped on eagerly without having to be coaxed. The clock said quarter of twelve, midnight. Actually, of course, it was scarcely half-past eight when they padlocked the front door and poked the key under the mat.

"It's not very dark out," said Blanche to the kitten as they soared over town. "We're probably much, much too early. Wonder if anyone is there yet?"

Blanche looked down below and saw a strange procession marching along the sidewalk. She dived lower for a better view. There was quite a tall witch in the lead.

"Why, that looks like Josephine. But whatever is she doing with that crowd? And *walking?* Maybe her broom broke down."

There were three ghosts, a pirate, a cowboy carrying a six-shooter and a lighted pumpkin, and a gypsy with spangled earrings.

Blanche settled down on the sidewalk and fell in step beside the tall witch. At once she saw it wasn't Josephine.

"Oh, excuse me," said Blanche. "I thought you were somebody I know."

The tall witch turned and stared. She had a rubbery look to her face, and her hair was stringy and obviously false. Josephine was always so careful about her hair.

"Hey!" shouted one of the ghosts, "where did you get that blue light on your nose? That's really neat!"

The little pirate, pulling at Blanche's skirts, pleaded, "Lemme see it! Lemme see it!"

"How does it work?" asked the cowboy, setting down his pumpkin.

So Blanche showed them. She made her nose glow bright and then fade palely away, then bright again and wink off and on like a turn signal.

"Gee," said the cowboy, "that's swell. I didn't see anything like that over at the dime store. Where did you buy it?"

"Lemme try it! Lemme try it?" begged the pirate, pulling again.

"I didn't buy it," Blanche said primly, "and I can't take it

off and let you try it. But I'll do it again for you if you'll quit yanking my dress."

"Leave her alone, Butch," said the tall witch, giving the pirate a shove. Turning to Blanche she explained, "He's my little brother. I told Mother he was too young to go out Halloweening with us, but he always has to tag along."

"Oh, that's all right," Blanche said generously. "I don't mind letting him see if he wants to." She leaned down so Butch could feel her nose carefully.

"Hey, if you show us how the switch works I'll give you one of my jelly doughnuts," the biggest ghost offered, holding out a brown paper bag.

Blanche grinned at them. "There really isn't a switch at all," she said. "It just works by concentration. I think about lighting up my nose and it begins to glow. When I want it to shine very bright, I think hard, like this." She wrinkled her forehead and squinted her eyes. The nose glowed a bright clear blue. "See? Simply concentration."

The ghost opened his bag. "That's really super!" he said. "Here, have a doughnut."

Blanche reached in eagerly. She hadn't had a jelly doughnut in weeks and weeks. "Where did you get these? They're wonderful!" she said, chewing happily.

"Over at Smith's. They have the best stuff. Last year it was caramel apples. Come along and we'll show you which house."

Blanche trailed along willingly, with Butch the pirate holding firmly to her hand.

"What's your name?" he asked as they walked along.

"I'm Blanche," she said.

"Blanche who?" Butch's sister, the tall witch, asked.

"Just Blanche."

"She's Blanche Witch, that's who," Butch said reasonably.

The cowboy turned around mischievously. "Which witch?"

And all the ghosts joined in with great glee, "Blanche Witch, that's which witch!"

They climbed the steps to Smith's front porch, all chanting the refrain, "Blanche Witch, that's which witch!"

The gypsy rang the doorbell.

A man with white hair opened the door. He gaped. "But—"

"Candy or cake or your windows we'll break!" they yelled at him.

"But you kids have all been here before," he protested.

"Yes, but *she* hasn't!" they laughed, pushing Blanche in front of Mr. Smith.

"Her nose turns on and off," said the pirate. "Show him!"

Blanche showed him obligingly.

"Say, that's really something!" said the man. "Come here, Mother, and see this!"

A lady sitting in a rocking chair got up and came over to the door. She gave a little gasp when she saw Blanche's nose. "Whatever will they think of next! These modern kids!"

"Sure, that's worth two doughnuts at least," said Mr. Smith. "Hold your sack."

"She hasn't got one," said the pirate, who had noticed right away.

Mrs. Smith bustled right off to her kitchen and returned with a brown paper bag.

"There, now," she said. "And here are three jelly doughnuts, and I put in some nuts and candy corn too, because you might not have time to go to many more houses."

"Thank you, ma'am," said Blanche, remembering her manners. "And please, could you tell me what time it is?"

Her husband pulled out his pocket watch. "Let's see, it's just six and a half minutes after nine o'clock."

"Just after nine o'clock?" Blanche asked bewildered. "But I thought it was nearly midnight. The time seems to be all turned around."

"It usually is on Halloween," laughed Mr. Smith. "Anything can happen tonight. Well, good night, kids, and don't soap any windows!"

"We won't," they shouted, racing down the steps. "Good night, and thanks!"

This Is Halloween

By Dorothy Brown Thompson

Goblins on the doorstep,
  Phantoms in the air,
Owls on witches' gateposts
  Giving stare for stare,
Cats on flying broomsticks,
  Bats against the moon,
Stirrings round of fate-cakes
  With a solemn spoon,

Whirling apple parings,
  Figures draped in sheets
Dodging, disappearing,
  Up and down the streets,
Jack-o'-lanterns grinning,
  Shadows on a screen,
Shrieks and starts and laughter
  This is Halloween!

Hallowe'en

By Harry Behn

Illustration by William Colrus

Tonight is the night
When dead leaves fly
Like witches on switches
Across the sky,
When elf and sprite
Flit through the night
On a moony sheen.

Tonight is the night
When leaves make a sound
Like a gnome in his home
Under the ground,
When spooks and trolls
Creep out of holes
Mossy and green.

Tonight is the night
When pumpkins stare
Through sheaves and leaves
Everywhere,
When ghoul and ghost
And goblin host
Dance round their queen.
It's Hallowe'en!

The Water Nixie

BY ANNA ELIZABETH BENNETT

Illustrations by Helen Stone

Now," said Minx, "let me decide what powder to use this time!"

The children stood staring with round eyes at the rows and rows of mysterious bottles.

"Choose the green one!" cried George.

"No, take the blue!" begged Alice.

"George asked first, so I'll take green this time," said Minx

She dumped some of the green into the magic kettle, and immediately it bubbled up into a frothy mass.

The children were silent with wonder as she stirred the green mixture.

"Don't you have to say any magic words while you do that?" asked Jack.

"Like 'abra-ca-dabra,'" said Bob.

"Oh my goodness," said Minx, loftily, "that's old-fashioned stuff. Witches don't do that sort of thing any more! In the old days they even used to have to go out and catch their own bats and toads and stuff to make their powders out of. Now it all comes out of bottles."

"Where do you buy them?" asked Frances.

"My mother sends for everything from the Witches' Market. That's located near the Never-Never Land. They send her a catalog, and she orders from that."

Now the vapor was filling the room, and something was taking shape.

The children were quiet as shadows, gazing in fascination. Alice, however, began to feel rather frightened, and started to move toward the door.

"Oh," said Minx, in a soft, breathless voice, "I believe it is— I believe it is!"

The face that appeared was thin and sharply pointed toward the chin. The skin was of the palest green, the eyes were large and filled with strange lights, and the hair was long, green, and dripping with water.

At last a slim girl body, draped in a clinging silvery green garment, took form, and leaped to the floor as lightly as a sunbeam.

"Are you a fairy?" asked Minx, tremulously.

"She has no wings," said George, skeptically.

The creature laughed with a sound like water splashing softly on pebbles.

"Of course I'm not a fairy, you funny child," she said. "Don't you know what I am?"

They all shook their heads, solemnly.

"I'm a nixie!" She danced around the room like a jet of spray.

"What's a nixie?" asked Alice.

"A nixie, poor ignorant girl child, is a sprite of the water."

"You mean—there are things—I mean people like you, living in the water?" said Frances.

"Of course! Only it's not often anyone is granted the wonderful privilege of seeing us. I hope you appreciate your good fortune!"

She began to leap and twirl again, light as spindrift.

"Oh, yes we do," said Frances, gravely.

The nixie finished her dance and said, "Now tell me what you want me for. I'm beginning to feel uncomfortably dry and warm, and I'll have to return to my lake soon."

"Well, I didn't really want you," said Minx.

The nixie looked quite hurt, and green tears began to slip down her cheeks. "You didn't really want to s-see me?"

"Oh, of course we're glad to see you," Minx reassured her, "but I've been trying and trying to make a fairy appear."

"Oh my goodness!" cried the nixie. "Fairies! They're so ordinary! I know simply hundreds of them, and they've got no more personality than a—than a clam shell!"

"But we would like to see one anyway," said Alice.

"Well—maybe I can help you! Why don't you try—"

At this moment, to the children's utter disappointment, the nixie became vapor again, and slipped through the window.

"Oh gosh!" said Jack. "Try getting her back, Minx!"

"She was just going to tell us!" said Frances.

"I'm afraid to use more of the powder," said Minx, "because my mother might notice it."

All the children looked downcast.

"But we can try again tomorrow night," said Minx, "if you can come."

"Oh, sure we can!" said Bob, promptly.

"That is—if we get home when we're supposed to, tonight," said Frances. "I think we'd better leave now."

"Maybe you'd better," said Minx, looking anxiously at the bottle of Black Spell Brew, "because sometimes my mother comes home early."

At that, the children disappeared very suddenly through the door.

Minx sighed and put back the pot on the shelf. Then she

went to the mirror, and gazed into it earnestly. "I haven't seen her today yet," she said, aloud. "Maybe I'll see her for sure tonight."

Suddenly she gave a little cry. There in the mirror—surely, oh surely it was a face! A beautiful face, pale as moonlight, with night-dark eyes, a flower-soft mouth. . . . Minx spun around quickly—but nothing was there!

She stood quite still in disappointment. Then she said, "Oh well, at least I'm sure I did see her tonight, and maybe tomorrow I'll see her outside the mirror!"

She felt very sleepy, and went over to her blanket. As she lay down, she thought, "Tomorrow I must remember to take my broomstick to school and let the children ride on it."

The next morning she awoke to find Madam Snickasnee already seated at the cluttered table, chewing greedily on a fried bat's wing.

"So you're awake at last, are you, lazybones?" the witch greeted her. "I see you finally obeyed me and made the brew!"

Minx seized a piece of bread and began to chew it hungrily. "Have some manners!" screamed the witch. "Eat like a lady!"

Although there was no clock in the house, Minx thought it must be time to get ready for school. She recalled what her teacher had told her, and going to the sink, started to splash water on her face and arms, half-heartedly.

Madam Snickasnee was so astonished that she stopped chewing for a few seconds.

"What are you doing that for?" she demanded.

"Oh, I just felt like it." Minx tried to sound casual.

"You're up to something, my lass. Don't tell me you're not. You just stay right in this house today, and don't you dare stir out of it!"

"Yes, Ma'am," said Minx, as innocent as an angel right out of heaven.

"You look too innocent, my girl! Just remember what I said!"

Madam Snickasnee tossed a well-polished bone to Scorcher, who pounced on it and started to crunch it noisily.

Minx heard the schoolbell ring, and her heart sank in despair.

"Oh, why doesn't she hurry up and go to sleep!" she thought. But she knew that if her mother discovered how anxious she felt that she would stay awake on purpose all day.

Humming a tuneless tune, Minx went to water the unhappy flowerpots.

"That reminds me," said Madam Snickasnee, darkly, fixing her little red eyes on the bottle of Black Spell Brew.

Minx's hand trembled a bit, but she continued to hum.

"Oh, please, please go to sleep," she thought, desperately.

But presently the witch's eyelids began to droop, and her head to sink down on her bony chest. At last with a thud her head dropped to the table, and the dishes began to clatter and clink with the violence of her snores.

Thankfully, Minx grabbed her broom and rushed out of the house.

"I'm late, I'm late," she thought, fearfully. "I wonder what they'll do to me!"

She was running with furious speed along the road, when suddenly she stopped short.

"My goodness!" she said. "Here I am wasting my breath on running when I could be riding!"

So she flung one slim leg over her broomstick, gave a little push with her foot, and up, up she went, into the clear October sky, riding swiftly toward the schoolhouse.

Mr. Bunch, looking out of his office window, was certainly surprised to see his newest pupil arriving in such an unusual fashion.

Veterans' Day

NOVEMBER 11

On November 11, 1918, an armistice was signed that freed the world from the horrors of its first World War. That day was kept as a reminder that such a war must never come again.

But it did—more terrible than before. It was followed by "police actions" and small wars. The United States in 1954 made November 11 a day for honoring the dead and living of all our wars. On this day, previously known as Armistice Day, we pay tribute to the men and women who, in Woodrow Wilson's phrase, have fought "to make the world safe for democracy."

The Singing Tree

BY KATE SEREDY

Illustration by the author

THIS story began one day in August 1915. We had been advancing all night . . . all through the long, silent night that followed a day of the heaviest shellfire from both lines; the Russians' and ours. Each had been trying to advance. Finally the Russians left their trenches and retreated. After sundown we were ordered to follow their retreat. We marched or rather crept and crawled and stumbled across this no-man's land of shell holes, barbed wire, burned-down forests, ruined houses, and deserted Russian gun-nests. Except for us, there was nothing alive anywhere. No rabbits scurrying underfoot, no squirrels jumping from tree to tree, no birds, not even an owl hooting, for miles around. Just odds and ends of broken things the war leaves behind.

"All night we crept and crawled and stumbled and still there was only dark night and silence to greet us. Even gunfire would have been welcome in that night, anything to break the spell of having come into a land where only we, creeping men, were alive.

"And then, when men's teeth began to chatter with fear far more benumbing than fear of injury or death, a finger of light, a tiny, weak herald of the approaching dawn, shivered on the edge of darkness, grew less weak, then stronger, changed from gray-green into the palest of yellow streaks across the horizon, turned into gold, then orange, and at last we could see again.

" 'Dawn,' a creeping man said as if he had never hoped to see a dawn again.

"Ahead of us and behind us lay a devastated forest with only skeletons of trees still standing here and there. Underfoot there was the same litter of broken things we had come to know by

touch, if not by sight . . . barbed wire, broken guns, empty
cartridges, empty tins. All around us was the same silence that
had roared in our ears all night.

"And then, as the sun broke through the clouds at last, we saw
one tree. One single apple tree that must have been near a
house; only the house was no longer there.

" 'It is alive,' a creeping man said, but with the words he rose.
'Alive,' another man said as if he never hoped to see a green
tree again.

" 'It sings,' someone whispered. 'It is alive. I can hear it.'

"Now men rose to their feet and walked and ran like *men*, toward the singing tree, which was alive with birds . . . living birds singing to the dawn in a live apple tree. Birds. Little wrens and sparrows, late robins, warblers, thrushes, orioles . . . the green tree was alive with birds all singing . . . singing to the dawn.

"Against the trunk, owls huddled sleepily; there were jackdaws, and even a crow or two had taken shelter there. Friends and foes of the bird world, side by side, all from different nests, nests that perhaps would never shelter them again, for nests must have fallen with the trees that held them. And here they were, small, feathered orphans of a man-made storm, huddled together on a green apple tree, singing to the dawn.

"Perhaps they too were merely passing time until it would be safe to travel forth and build anew, or seek the old nests. Just passing time, but while they waited, each was singing a song to dawn and each in a different way.

"The one live thing that would never go away unless a man-made gun should uproot it from the earth it grew in was the apple tree. It did not *wait* for time to pass. It did not try to sing. It just *was* what God had made it, a simple, homy tree. Small orphans . . . large ones . . . for a while found shelter on its sturdy limbs. . . . They would pass on. . . ."

The Tomb of the Unknown Soldier in Arlington (Virginia) National Cemetery is a memorial to the unidentified American soldiers killed in World War I. The Unknown Soldier, brought from an American cemetery in France, was buried in Arlington on November 11, 1921. On Memorial Day, 1958, unknown soldiers from World War II and the Korean War were buried at the head of the tomb. Each Memorial Day wreaths are placed on the tomb and services are held in a nearby amphitheatre.

HERE RESTS IN
HONORED GLORY
AN AMERICAN
SOLDIER
KNOWN BUT TO GOD

In Flanders Fields

By John McCrae

In Flanders fields the poppies blow
  Between the crosses, row on row,
That mark our place; and in the sky
  The larks, still bravely singing, fly
Scarce heard amid the guns below.

We are the dead. Short days ago
We lived, felt dawn, saw sunset glow,
  Loved, and were loved, and now we lie
  In Flanders fields.

Take up our quarrel with the foe:
To you from failing hands we throw
  The torch; be yours to hold it high.
  If ye break faith with us who die
We shall not sleep, though poppies grow
  In Flanders fields.

Soldier

By Rupert Brooke

If I should die, think only this of me:
  That there's some corner of a foreign field
That is for ever England. There shall be
  In that rich earth a richer dust concealed;
A dust whom England bore, shaped, made aware,
  Gave once her flowers to love, her ways to roam,
A body of England's breathing English air,
  Washed by the rivers, blest by suns of home.
And think, this heart, all evil shed away,
  A pulse in the eternal mind, no less
    Gives somewhere back the thoughts by England given;
Her sights and sounds; dreams happy as her day;
  And laughter, learnt of friends; and gentleness,
    In hearts at peace, under an English heaven.

Book Week

Each year one week in November is set aside for Book Week. Library tables are stacked with rare or outstanding books for young readers, schools have special assemblies, and books for young people line the counters of bookstores.

During Book Week, first celebrated in 1919, thousands of posters and millions of pieces of printed material are distributed throughout the United States in order to promote in young people a love for books and an understanding of the part they play in shaping our lives and our values.

The Library Lady

BY SYDNEY TAYLOR

Illustrations by Helen John

T HAT slowpoke Sarah!" Henny cried. "She's making us late!"

Mama's girls were going to the library, and Henny was impatient.

"If it was Charlotte, I could understand," said Ella, who was the eldest and very serious. "I'd know Charlotte was off dreaming in some corner. But what can be keeping Sarah?"

"All the best books will be gone," complained Henny. "Maybe she forgot it's Friday."

"No!" interrupted Charlotte. "Not Sarah!"

No, not Sarah, nor any of the girls could forget that Friday was library day.

Almost no East Side child owned a book when Mama's children were little girls. That was an unheard-of luxury. It was heavenly enough to be able to borrow books from the public library and that was where the children always went on Friday afternoons. Right after school, they rushed off happily to get fresh reading material for the week end. Even Gertie who was not yet old enough to "belong" took the weekly trip to look at the picture magazines.

Where *was* Sarah? Mama was beginning to be concerned too. It wasn't like the child to be late.

At last footsteps could be heard on the creaky back steps. Henny ran to open the kitchen door and poked her head out. "Here she comes," she called.

"Well, it's about time," said Ella. "Come on, let's get our books."

Henny opened the door wider. "What's the matter?" her sisters heard her asking.

From *All of a Kind Family*, by Sydney Taylor. Copyright 1951 by the Follett Publishing Company.

A woebegone little figure, face streaked with tears, walked slowly into the kitchen.

"Mama," piped up Gertie, "Sarah's crying."

"Sarah, what's the matter? What's happened?"

Sarah didn't answer. Walking over to the hard brown leather couch, she threw herself face downward, weeping bitterly. Her sisters gathered in a little group around her.

Mama came over and sat down beside Sarah. Gently she stroked her hair and let the child weep. After a while she said softly, "Sarah, tell us what happened."

Between sobs, the muffled words came slowly, "My—library book—is—lost."

Lost! The children looked at each other in dismay. Such a thing had never happened in the family before. "Ooh—how awful!" Ella said, and then was sorry that the words had escaped her for they seemed to bring on a fresh burst of tears.

"Now, now, stop crying, Sarah," Mama said. "You'll only make yourself sick. Come, we'll wash your face and then you'll tell us all about it."

Obediently Sarah followed Mama to the kitchen sink.

"Does it mean we can't go to the library ever again?" Charlotte whispered to Ella.

Ella shook her head. "I don't think so."

"Maybe we could change over to another branch," suggested Henny.

The cold water felt good on Sarah's flushed face. She was quiet now and could talk.

"It wasn't really me that lost the book. It was my friend, Tillie. You know how Tillie never takes a book out herself, but she's always wanting to read mine. When I told her about *Peter and Polly In Winter,* she begged me to lend it to her. She promised she'd give it back to me on Friday.

"When I asked her for it today, she said that she put it in my desk yesterday, but Mama, she didn't! She really didn't!"

"Are you sure?" asked Mama. "Maybe you left it in school."

"I looked a thousand times. That's why I came so late. I kept hunting and hunting all over the schoolroom."

"Maybe you brought it home with you yesterday and left it here in the house."

"Then it should be on the shelf under the whatnot," Ella said.

Hopefully, everybody rushed over to the whatnot where the library books were kept, but alas, there was no Peter and Polly book there today.

"I cleaned the house pretty thoroughly this morning," said Mama. "I don't remember seeing the book anywhere. But let's all look again anyway."

How anxiously everyone searched. The children peered into every corner of the two bedrooms and they poked under beds and dressers. No one believed it was in the front room, but still they searched it diligently. They searched and searched until they had to agree that it was useless to continue.

When they were back in the kitchen again, Sarah said tearfully, "How can I go and tell the library that the book is lost?" She was ready to cry again.

"I'm afraid they won't let you take out any more books until we pay for this one," Mama worried. "And a book costs a lot of money."

"But Tillie lost the book," argued Sarah. "She should pay."

"We can't be sure of that," Mama said. "Tillie claims she returned it. Maybe someone else took it.

"No library could make me pay for any old book." Henny was just trying to cover up how bad she felt too.

"I'm afraid the library will expect you to pay for it. And it's only right," continued Mama. "You borrowed the book and that makes you responsible. The library lets you borrow the book and you're not supposed to lend it to anybody else. I know you wanted to be kind to Tillie, but if Tillie wants to read a library book, then she should take out her own. I wish I could help you pay for this, but you know, Sarah, there's no money for such things."

"But Mama, will you come with me and talk to the library lady?"

Mama shook her head. "No, Sarah, that's something you must do yourself. If you explain just how it happened, I'm sure the library lady will understand that you didn't mean to be careless. Find out what you have to do, and we'll talk about it when you get back. Now you'll all have to hurry. There's not much time left before supper. So, the rest of you, see if you can choose your books quickly today."

Mama had said to hurry but Sarah's feet wouldn't walk. They felt like lead. In her chest was a lump of lead too. Ella put her arm around Sarah's shoulder. Even Gertie forsook her idol Charlotte and came over to Sarah. She slipped her little hand into Sarah's, her brown eyes large in sympathy.

A branch of the New York Public Library was only a few blocks from their home; soon the familiar brown building came

into view. Through the high door and up the staircase they
went. With each step, Sarah grew more despairing. They'll
take my card away, she thought. I just know they will. I'll
never be able to take out any more books.

Once inside the room, Sarah hung back, fearing to join
the line at the "in" desk. She looked back down the staircase
longingly. It would be so easy to run down the stairs and
out into the street and just never come back.

"Come on, Sarah," Ella said. "Let's get it over with." Gently
she pulled Sarah towards the desk and the five children fell
in line.

Henny nudged Sarah. "Look," she said, "isn't that a new
library lady? She's pretty!" she added.

Sarah studied the new library lady anxiously. She looked
so fresh and clean in a crisp white shirtwaist with long sleeves
ending in paper cuffs pinned tightly at the wrists. Her hair
is light, just like mine, Sarah said to herself. And she has

such little ears. I think she has a kind face. She watched as the librarian's slender fingers pulled the cards in and out of the index file. How does she keep her nails so clean, Sarah wondered, thinking of her own scrubby ones.

It was Ella's turn to have her book stamped. The library lady looked up and Sarah could see the deep blue of her eyes. The library lady smiled.

She has dimples, Sarah thought. Surely a lady with dimples could never be harsh.

The smile on the library lady's face deepened. In front of her desk stood five little girls dressed exactly alike.

"My goodness! Are you all one family?"

"Yes, all one family," Henny spoke up. "I'm Henrietta, Henny for short; I'm ten. Ella's twelve, Sarah is eight, Charlotte is six, and Gertie is four."

"A steps-and-stairs family!" The library lady laughed and the tiny freckles on her pert nose seemed to laugh with her.

"That's a good name for us," Ella said. "Some people call us an all-of-a-kind family."

"All of a very nice kind," smiled the library lady. "And you have such nice names! I'm Miss Allen, your new librarian. I'm very glad to meet you."

Her eyes travelled over the five little girls. Such sad-looking faces. Not a smile among them.

"Better tell the teacher what happened," Charlotte whispered to Sarah.

"She's not a teacher, silly. She's a library lady." Henny's scornful reply was loud enough for Miss Allen to hear. The dimples began to show again.

Sarah stepped forward. "Library lady," she began, twisting and untwisting the fingers of her hands.

Miss Allen looked at Sarah and suddenly noticed the red-rimmed eyes and the nose all swollen from weeping. Something was wrong. No wonder the faces were so unhappy.

"Let me see, now. Which one are you?" she asked.

"Sarah," the little girl replied and the tears began to swim in her eyes.

The library lady put her hand under the little girl's chin and lifted it up. "Now, now, Sarah. Nothing can be that bad."

Sarah said tearfully, "Yes, it can. I—I—" She couldn't go on.

"Here." Ella put a handkerchief to her sister's nose.

Miss Allen went on speaking as if she did not notice anything unusual. "Did you enjoy your book?"

Sarah's voice broke. "I loved it. But nobody else will ever be able to read it again . . ."

"She means she lost it!" Henny blurted out.

"She didn't lose it. It was Tillie." Charlotte rushed to Sarah's defense.

"Oh, I'm so sorry," said the library lady, looking bewilderedly from one to the other. "Who is Tillie?"

Thereupon Ella unfolded the whole story and the library lady listened sympathetically.

"Mama says I must pay for the book and I'm going to— every cent." Sarah was trembling. "But I don't have enough money now."

"How much will she have to pay?" Ella asked.

"I'll have to look it up in the catalogue," Miss Allen answered. She pulled out a big book and began to look through its pages. It really was a shame that this had happened. She knew that the people who lived on the East Side had to count their pennies carefully. Even a small sum would seem like a fortune to these children.

Her heart went out to the little group. How sincere they were and how anxious to do the right thing. She wished that she could pay for the book herself. But she could not risk hurting either the children or their parents by making the offer.

She made her voice as cheerful as she could. "Well, it's not nearly as bad as I thought. Let's see now. Do you have any spending money, Sarah?"

"A penny a day . . . and I can save my pennies. I don't care for candy anyway." She added quickly, "I have seventeen cents saved up in my penny bank."

Seventeen cents! thought the library lady. How can I tell her that the book costs a dollar? "Is that all you have?"

Sarah nodded shyly. "Yes."

"She was going to buy a doll." Gertie's voice filled the silence. "A doll with real hair."

The library lady looked at the sad little figure for a moment.

"Sarah," she said, "the book costs a dollar. If you pay the seventeen cents the next time you come, you will owe eighty-three cents. After that, I will make a special arrangement so you can pay one penny each week. I know it will take a very long time to pay the whole amount but you can save for your doll at the same time."

Sarah's eyes opened wide in unbelief. "You mean, I can save for my doll and still pay for the book?"

"That's right," said the library lady, and they both smiled.

Meanwhile the other children were whispering among themselves. Finally Ella spoke up. "Could we help pay? Each of us can bring a penny every week. We've collected three cents right now."

Henny said shamefacedly, "I already spent my penny today but I promise I'll bring it next week like the others."

"That's a wonderful idea! Sarah must be very proud to have such thoughtful sisters."

Sarah was proud. She gave them each a hug. "And when I get my doll, you can all play with her."

"Isn't it nice to have a family to share your troubles?" asked the library lady.

"Have you any sisters?" Sarah asked shyly.

"No, dear. Nor brothers. I'm the only one."

"Isn't that lonesome?" Charlotte asked. The children all felt sorry for the library lady now.

"Yes, dear, it is lonesome. But come now, aren't you going to take out any books today?"

"Can Sarah take out a book too?" questioned Henny.

"Yes, she can, so long as you'll be paying for the lost book."

Sarah clasped her hands together joyfully. "Oh, thank you! I think you're the nicest, kindest library lady in the whole world."

Miss Allen's smile was warm and friendly. "Run along now, dear, and get your book."

As she worked, Miss Allen found herself watching the five little girls. How quaint they were in their stiffly starched white aprons over dark woolen dresses. They looked for all the world like wide-open umbrellas.

Had she been able to peek under those dresses, she would have understood why they billowed out in such a manner. Underneath were *three* petticoats, a wooly, flannel one first, a simple cotton one next, with both of these topped by a fancy muslin garment which was starched to a scratchy crispness. In order to save money, Mama made those petticoats herself. Still further underneath was long woolen underwear, over which were pulled heavy knitted woolen stockings, making thin legs look like well-stuffed frankfurters. How the girls hated those stockings! They itched so! *And they never wore out!* Mama knitted them herself on long needles and she could always reknit the holes the children made.

Miss Allen could see that the stockings were bothering Sarah. She looked very comical as she kept rubbing one leg against the other. Clutching her new book tightly to her, she made her way back to the desk.

"Come on, everybody. It's late," Ella warned.

The children quickly chose their books and gave them to the library lady for stamping.

They raced home on happy feet. They couldn't wait to tell Mama that their beloved Friday afternoons at the library were not going to be spoiled after all.

There Is No Frigate Like a Book

By Emily Dickinson

There is no frigate like a book
To take us lands away,
Nor any coursers like a page
Of prancing poetry.

From

Books

BY WALTER DE LA MARE

A boy called Jack, as I've been told
Would sit for hours—good as gold—
Not with a pie, like Master Horner,
And plums, for dainties, in his corner,
But silent in some chosen nook
And spell-bound—by a story-book!
Whether the dawn brought sun or rain,
Back to its pages he'd hasten again;
He had even wheedled from his friends
A secret hoard of candle-ends,
And slumber far from his round head
Would read, till dead of night—in bed!

ILLUSTRATION BY ESTELLE HOLLINGWORTH

Rufus M

BY ELEANOR ESTES

Illustrations by Louis Slobodkin

THE library lady was sitting at the desk playing with some
cards. Rufus stepped off the matting. The cool, shiny floor felt
good to his bare feet. He went over to the shelves and luckily
did find one of the big Palmer Cox Brownie books there. It
would be fun to play the game of Find the Duke at home.
Until now he had played it only in the library. Maybe Jane
or Joe would play it with him right now. He laughed out loud
at the thought.

"Sh-sh-sh, quiet," said the lady at the desk.

Rufus clapped his chubby fist over his mouth. Goodness! He
had forgotten where he was. Do not laugh or talk out loud in the
library. He knew these rules. Well, he didn't want to stay here
any longer today anyway. He wanted to read at home with the
others. He took the book to the lady to punch.

She didn't punch it though. She took it and she put it on the
table behind her and then she started to play cards again.

"That's my book," said Rufus.

"Do you have a card?" the lady asked.

Rufus felt in his pockets. Sometimes he carried around an
old playing card or two. Today he didn't have one.

"No," he said.

"You'll have to have a card to get a book."

"I'll go and get one," said Rufus.

The lady put down her cards. "I mean a library card," she
explained kindly. "It looks to me as though you are too little
to have a library card. Do you have one?"

"No," said Rufus. "I'd like to though."

"I'm afraid you're too little," said the lady. "You have to write
your name to get one. Can you do that?"

Rufus nodded his head confidently. Writing. Lines up and down. He'd seen that done. And the letters that Mama had tied in bundles in the closet under the stairs were covered with writing. Of course he could write.

"Well, let's see your hands," said the lady.

Rufus obligingly showed this lady his hands, but she did not like the look of them. She cringed and clasped her head as though the sight hurt her.

"Oh," she gasped. "You'll just have to go home and wash them before we can even think about joining the library and borrowing books."

This was a complication upon which Rufus had not reckoned. However, all it meant was a slight delay. He'd wash his hands and then he'd get the book. He turned and went out of the library, found his scooter safe among the Christmas trees, and pushed it home. He surprised Mama by asking to have his hands washed. When this was done, he mounted his scooter again and returned all the long way to the library. It was not just a little trip to the library. It was a long one. A long one and a hot one on a day like this. But he didn't notice that. All he was bent on was getting his book and taking it home and reading with the others on the front porch. They were all still there, brushing flies away and reading.

Again Rufus hid his scooter in the pine trees, encircled the light, and went in.

"Hello," he said.

"Well," said the lady. "How are they now?"

Rufus had forgotten he had had to wash his hands. He thought she was referring to the other Moffats. "Fine," he said.

"Let me see them," she said, and she held up her hands.

Oh! His hands! Well, they were all right, thought Rufus, for Mama had just washed them. He showed them to the lady. There was a silence while she studied them. Then she shook her head. She still did not like them.

"Ts, ts, ts!" she said. "They'll have to be cleaner than that."

Rufus looked at his hands. Supposing he went all the way home and washed them again, she still might not like them. However, if that is what she wanted, he would have to do that before he could get the Brownie book . . . and he started for the door.

"Well now, let's see what we can do," said the lady. "I know what," she said. "It's against the rules but perhaps we can wash them in here." And she led Rufus into a little room that smelled of paste where lots of new books and old books were stacked up. In one corner was a little round sink and Rufus washed his hands again. Then they returned to the desk. The lady got a chair and put a newspaper on it. She made Rufus stand on this because he was not big enough to write at the desk otherwise.

Then the lady put a piece of paper covered with a lot of printing in front of Rufus, dipped a pen in the ink well and gave it to him.

"All right," she said. "Here's your application. Write your name here."

All the writing Rufus had ever done before had been on big pieces of brown wrapping paper with lots of room on them. Rufus had often covered those great sheets of paper with his own kind of writing at home. Lines up and down.

But on this paper there wasn't much space. It was already covered with writing. However, there was a tiny little empty space and that was where Rufus must write his name, the lady said. So, little space or not, Rufus confidently grasped the pen with his left hand and dug it into the paper. He was not accustomed to pens, having always worked with pencils until now, and he made a great many holes and blots and scratches.

"Gracious," said the lady. "Don't bear down so hard! And why don't you hold it in your right hand?" she asked, moving the pen back into his right hand.

Rufus started again scraping his lines up and down and all over the page, this time using his right hand. Wherever there was an empty space he wrote. He even wrote over some of the print for good measure. Then he waited for the lady, who had gone off to get a book for some man, to come back and look.

"Oh," she said as she settled herself in her swivel chair, "is that the way you write? Well . . . it's nice, but what does it say?"

"Says Rufus Moffat. My name."

Apparently these lines up and down did not spell Rufus Moffat to this lady. She shook her head.

"It's nice," she repeated. "Very nice. But nobody but you knows what it says. You have to learn to write your name better than that before you can join the library."

Rufus was silent. He had come to the library all by himself, gone back home to wash his hands, and come back because he wanted to take books home and read them the way the others did. He had worked hard. He did not like to think he might have to go home without a book.

The library lady looked at him a moment and then she said quickly before he could get himself all the way off the big chair, "Maybe you can *print* your name."

Rufus looked at her hopefully. He thought he could write better than he could print, for his writing certainly looked to him exactly like all grown people's writing. Still he'd try to print if that was what she wanted.

The lady printed some letters on the top of a piece of paper. "There," she said. "That's your name. Copy it ten times and then we'll try it on another application."

Rufus worked hard. He worked so hard the knuckles showed white on his brown fist. He worked for a long, long time, now with his right hand and now with his left. Sometimes a boy or a girl came in, looked over his shoulder and watched, but he paid no attention. From time to time the lady studied his work and she said, "That's fine. That's fine." At last she said, "Well, maybe now we can try." And she gave him another application.

All Rufus could get, with his large generous letters, in that tiny little space where he was supposed to print his name, was R-U-F. The other letters he scattered here and there on the card. The lady did not like this either. She gave him still another blank. Rufus tried to print smaller and this time he got RUFUS in the space, and also he crowded an M at the end. Since he was doing so well now the lady herself printed the *offat* part of Moffat on the next line.

"This will have to do," she said. "Now take this home and ask your mother to sign it on the other side. Bring it back on Thursday and you'll get your card."

Rufus's face was shiny and streaked with dirt where he had rubbed it. He never knew there was all this work to getting a book. The other Moffats just came in and got books. Well, maybe they had had to do this once too.

Rufus held his hard-earned application in one hand and steered his scooter with the other. When he reached home Joey, Jane and Sylvie were not around any longer. Mama signed his card for him, saying, "My! So you've learned how to write!"

"Print," corrected Rufus.

Mama kissed Rufus and he went back out. The lady had said to come back on Thursday, but he wanted a book today. When the other Moffats came home, he'd be sitting on the top step of the porch, reading. That would surprise them. He smiled to himself as he made his way to the library for the third time.

Once his application blew away. Fortunately it landed in a thistle bush and did not get very torn. The rest of the way Rufus clutched it carefully. He climbed the granite steps to the library again only to find that the big round dark brown doors were closed. Rufus tried to open them but he couldn't. He knocked at the door, even kicked it with his foot, but there was no answer. He pounded on the door but nobody came.

A big boy strode past with his newspapers. "Hey, kid," he said to Rufus. "Library's closed!" And off he went, whistling.

Rufus looked after him. The fellow said the library was closed. How could it have closed so fast? He had been here such a little while ago. The lady must still be here. He did want his Brownie book. If only he could see in, he might see the lady and get his book. The windows were high up but they had very wide sills. Rufus was a wonderful climber. He could shinny up trees and poles faster than anybody on the block. Faster than Joey. Now, helping himself up by means of one of the pine trees that grew close to the building, and by sticking his toes in the ivy and rough places in the bricks, he scrambled up the wall. He hoisted himself up on one of the sills and sat there. He peered in. It was dark inside, for the shades had been drawn almost all the way down.

"Library lady!" he called, and he knocked on the window-pane. There was no answer. He put his hands on each side of his face to shield his eyes, and he looked in for a long, long time. He could not believe that she had left. Rufus was resolved to get a book. He had lost track of the number of times he had been back and forth from home to the library, and the library home. Maybe the lady was in the cellar. He climbed down,

stubbing his big toe on the bricks as he did so. He stooped
down beside one of the low dirt-spattered cellar windows. He
couldn't see in. He lay flat on the ground, wiped one spot clean
on the window, picked up a few pieces of coal from the sill
and put them in his pocket for Mama.

"Hey, lady," he called.

He gave the cellar window a little push. It wasn't locked so
he opened it a little and looked in. All he could see was a high
pile of coal reaching up to this window. Of course he didn't
put any of that coal in his pocket for that would be stealing.

"Hey, lady," he yelled again. His voice echoed in the cellar but
the library lady did not answer. He called out, "Hey, lady,"
every few seconds, but all that answered him was an echo. He
pushed the window open a little wider. All of a sudden it swung
wide open and Rufus slid in, right on top of the coal pile, and
crash, clatter, bang! He slid to the bottom, making a great
racket.

A little light shone through the dusty windows, but on the
whole it was very dark and spooky down here and Rufus really
wished that he was back on the outside looking in. However,
since he was in the library, why not go upstairs quick, get the
Brownie book, and go home? The window had banged shut, but
he thought he could climb up the coal pile, pull the window
up, and get out. He certainly hoped he could anyway. Supposing he couldn't and he had to stay in this cellar! Well, that he
would not think about. He looked around in the dusky light

and saw a staircase across the cellar. Luckily his application was still good. It was torn and dirty but it still had his name on it, RUFUS M, and that was the important part. He'd leave this on the desk in exchange for the Brownie book.

Rufus cautiously made his way over to the steps but he stopped halfway across the cellar. Somebody had opened the door at the top of the stairs. He couldn't see who it was, but he did see the light reflected and that's how he knew that somebody had opened the door. It must be the lady. He was just going to say, "Hey, lady," when he thought, "Gee, maybe it isn't the lady. Maybe it's a spooky thing."

Then the light went away, the door was closed, and Rufus was left in the dark again. He didn't like it down here. He started to go back to the coal pile to get out of this place. Then he felt of his application. What a lot of work he had done to get a book and now that he was this near to getting one, should he give up? No. Anyway, if it was the lady up there, he knew her and she knew him and neither one of them was scared of the other. And Mama always said there's no such thing as a spooky thing.

So Rufus bravely made his way again to the stairs. He tiptoed up them. The door at the head was not closed tightly. He pushed it open and found himself right in the library. But goodness! There in the little sink room right opposite him was the library lady!

Rufus stared at her in silence. The library lady was eating. Rufus had never seen her do anything before but play cards, punch books, and carry great piles of them around. Now she was eating. Mama said not to stare at anybody while they were eating. Still Rufus didn't know the library lady ate, so it was hard for him not to look at her.

She had a little gas stove in there. She could cook there. She was reading a book at the same time that she was eating. Sylvie could do that too. This lady did not see him.

"Hey, lady," said Rufus.

The librarian jumped up out of her seat. "Was that you in the cellar? I thought I heard somebody. Goodness, young man! I thought you had gone home long ago."

Rufus didn't say anything. He just stood there. He had gone home and he had come back lots of times. He had the whole thing in his mind; the coming and going, and going and coming, and sliding down the coal pile, but he did not know where to begin, how to tell it.

"Didn't you know the library is closed now?" she demanded, coming across the floor with firm steps.

Rufus remained silent. No, he hadn't known it. The fellow had told him but he hadn't believed him. Now he could see for himself that the library was closed so the library lady could eat. If the lady would let him take his book, he'd go home and stay there. He'd play the game of Find the Duke with Jane. He hopefully held out his card with his name on it.

"Here this is," he said.

But the lady acted as though she didn't even see it. She led Rufus over to the door.

"All right now," she said. "Out with you!" But just as she opened the door the sound of water boiling over on the stove struck their ears, and back she raced to her little room.

"Gracious!" she exclaimed. "What a day!"

Before the door could close on him, Rufus followed her in and sat down on the edge of a chair. The lady thought he had gone and started to sip her tea. Rufus watched her quietly, waiting for her to finish.

After a while the lady brushed the crumbs off her lap. And then she washed her hands and the dishes in the little sink where Rufus had washed his hands. In a library a lady could eat and could wash. Maybe she slept here too. Maybe she lived here.

"Do you live here?" Rufus asked her.

"Mercy on us!" exclaimed the lady. "Where'd you come from? Didn't I send you home? No, I don't live here and neither do you. Come now, out with you, young man. I mean it." The lady called all boys "young man" and all girls "Susie." She came out of the little room and she opened the big brown door again. "There," she said. "Come back on Thursday."

Rufus's eyes filled up with tears.

"Here's this," he said again, holding up his application in a last desperate attempt. But the lady shook her head. Rufus went slowly down the steps, felt around in the bushes for his scooter, and with drooping spirits he mounted it. Then for the second time that day, the library lady changed her mind.

"Oh, well," she said, "come back here, young man. I'm not supposed to do business when the library's closed, but I see we'll have to make an exception."

So Rufus rubbed his sooty hands over his face, hid his scooter in the bushes again, climbed the granite steps and, without circling the light, he went back in and gave the lady his application.

The lady took it gingerly. "My, it's dirty," she said. "You really ought to sign another one."

"And go home with it?" asked Rufus. He really didn't believe this was possible. He wiped his hot face on his sleeve and looked up at the lady in exhaustion. What he was thinking was: All right. If he had to sign another one, all right. But would she just please stay open until he got back?

However, this was not necessary. The lady said, "Well now, I'll try to clean this old one up. But remember, young man, always have everything clean—your hands, your book, everything, when you come to the library."

Rufus nodded solemnly. "My feet too," he assured her.

Then the lady made Rufus wash his hands again. They really were very bad this time, for he had been in a coal pile, and now at last she gave Rufus the book he wanted—one of the Palmer Cox Brownie books. This one was "The Brownies in the Philippines."

And Rufus went home.

When he reached home, he showed Mama his book. She smiled at him, and gave his cheek a pat. She thought it was fine that he had gone to the library and joined all by himself and taken out a book. And she thought it was fine when Rufus sat down at the kitchen table, was busy and quiet for a long, long time, and then showed her what he had done.

He had printed RUFUS M. That was what he had done. And that's the way he learned to sign his name. And that's the way he always did sign his name for a long, long time.

Books

By Joseph Joel Keith

Books are more than words,
more than birds'
brightness, more than song.
They last long.

When the covers close
wisdom grows;
every thought is root,
leaf, and fruit.

Every good page turned
is lore learned,
higher still when found
not in bound
books, but in the vast
wood where passed,
still and deep, the sower.

Write now, grower.

ILLUSTRATION BY DAWN STOUTSENBERGER

Books

By Eleanor Farjeon

What worlds of wonder are our books!
As one opens them and looks,
New ideas and people rise
In our fancies and our eyes.

The room we sit in melts away,
And we find ourselves at play
With some one who, before the end,
May become our chosen friend.

Or we sail along the page
To some other land or age.
Here's our body in the chair,
But our mind is over *there*.

Each book is a magic box
Which with a touch a child unlocks.
In between their outside covers
Books hold all things for their lovers.

Thanksgiving

Thanksgiving, the fourth Thursday in November, is a time for family reunions and large turkey dinners, cranberry sauce, and scores of other banquet foods. Because we are so happy to be with our relatives, we sometimes forget the real purpose of this holiday, which is to thank God for the blessings received in the past year.

The first Thanksgiving in America was celebrated by the Pilgrims during their second winter in the new world. The first winter had been horrible, for nearly half the people had perished from lack of food and because of the bad weather. But the following year, thanks to help from Indians who showed them how to plant Indian corn, the Pilgrims had a successful harvest.

To show gratitude, Governor William Bradford decreed that December 13, 1621, be set aside for feasting and prayer. The Indians were invited to share in the festival. In addition to the geese, ducks, fish, corn meal bread, and pumpkins stewed in maple sap contributed by the colonists, the Indians brought wild turkey and deer meat to the three-day feast. Since then, Thanksgiving Day has been celebrated in America. However, it was only in 1941 that Congress, in a joint resolution, named the fourth Thursday in November as the official legal holiday of Thanksgiving.

UNITED PRESS INTERNATIONAL

The First Thanksgiving

BY LENA BARKSDALE

Illustrations by Lois Lenski

I AM ready to begin," said Grandma. "Where's Hannah? Come here, child, and sit on this stool at my feet. It's where your mother used to sit, my dear, when she was your age, and you must sit here today, and hear your old Grandmother tell about Thanksgiving in Pilgrim days.

"It was a long time ago, my children, that First Thanksgiving, as we like to call it, though people have always given thanks for good harvests, I am sure, and they always will. But this first feast of ours in Plymouth more than forty years ago was different, I think, from any other harvest feast ever held before, or any that can ever be held again. I want the sweet memory of it to go down in our family long after I am gone, through you to your children and grandchildren, so I am going to try to tell you something about what our first year in America was like, as well as about the harvest feast that came at the end of that year.

"Your grandfather and I were little more than children then, but we could work along with the older people. Every pair of hands counted, and if some were a little smaller none made note of it. There was much work to be done. We did what we could gladly. We'd had a long voyage, and many good people died of a strange sickness on the ship. We had thought to land in Virginia, where there were many English settlers before us. It might well be that they would be pleased to see us, and would gladly show us how to make our homes snug and comfortable against the cold, and teach us the ways of this new land. But God had other plans for us. In His wisdom He brought us here to a rocky, bleak, frozen land, as it seemed to us then, lying in stretches of desolate shore, empty of houses, where there was no one to welcome us.

"We lived on the ship for many weeks, but as soon as it seemed reasonably safe we women were set ashore to wash our linen, which sorely needed cleansing after our tedious voyage. It was good to feel solid earth under our feet again, but we dared not venture far, nor go out of sight of our protectors, for none knew where the savages were, or how they might greet us. The men would go forth in parties armed with their muskets, taking the long boat or the shallop, and landing here and there to spy out the land and find a fair place to build our town. We women on the ship could only pray for their safe return when they ventured forth. They would be gone sometimes one day, often two days or more, and we had no way to gauge the dangers that might surround them. They always returned, though such was the hazard and discomfort of the journey that their clothes were ofttimes frozen to them, in the bitter cold and wet. They found wood and water aplenty and certain places cleared where corn had been planted, and

in one place they found great store of corn buried in the
ground. Much of that they brought back with them meaning
to make full satisfaction to the owners when they could meet
and parley with them.

"Once when some of the men were returning to the ship they
brought a boatload of juniper boughs that they had cut. We
burned it in our stoves, taking comfort in the spicy smell of it.
That was our first welcoming from the land.

"At last the men came to an agreement where to build the
town, and they set to cutting down trees to build the houses,
each man working diligently, and at last the day came when
we were all set ashore, with our gear, and the ship sailed away
and left us. We were often cold, and hungry and afraid that
winter, but we got along. . . . Later, you know, Squanto came
and lived with us for a time, and he taught us to plant the
corn when the oak leaf was the size of a mouse's ear, and as
we planted the seed, he had us throw two fish in each hole to
enrich the soil, so that the yield would be more abundant. He

caught good eels for us, and taught us many other things, useful for us to know. We could not have known many of these
things otherwise, our lives having been so different in Holland, and before that, in England. Do not forget, my children,
it was an Indian who first befriended us and guided us in the
new land. Massasoit, their sagamore, also became our friend
and made a treaty of peace with us.

"In the sweet spring weather I'll never forget how comforting it was to see the trees come into leaf, and the little wild flowers blooming along the streams and in the woods. We found onions and watercress, fresh and tasty to the palate. One fair day, when my stint of work was done, I was walking beyond the village street, enjoying the sweet fresh air and the smell of blossoms. Your grandfather came down the trail, and led me to a strip of meadow that he had just noticed. It was covered with a thick mat of strawberries. We ate a few and picked many to carry home with us. Strange it is how I remember the taste of those strawberries all these years. The smell of that juniper on the ship, the tang of watercress, and the sweetness of wild strawberries—it was such simple things as these that made us begin to love the land, and feel at home at last.

"So it was that by the time our first harvest was ripe and gathered into the storing sheds that we had provided, we knew beyond any doubt that we had found a good comfortable land where we were free and could live our lives without anyone meddling. That's the great thing, children, and don't any of you forget it. God has given us freedom here to think and to worship as seems right to us. Remember to be upright in all your dealings with one another and with the Indians. Be true to God and honest and kind to your neighbor. That is what being free means, and if we forget it we shall suffer, and rightly so. Your grandpa's been true and fine all his long life, and so must you children be."

Grandma's eyes were very bright and her voice shook a little as she looked into the faces of her strong sons and daughters and all the grandchildren, sitting around her crackling fire. After a moment she went on:

"Then when the first harvest was in and we knew none would go hungry that winter, nor cold, because our houses were built of stout timbers and there was great store of wood to burn, our governor and the other men decided we would have a feast and invite Massasoit to come and bring some of his braves to eat it with us. They set a day, and sent a messenger to invite Massasoit who was pleased to accept, and who sent five deer as a gift toward the feast. For days all the women and girls were busy roasting and baking and shining the pewter. The boys cut many fresh trenchers from stout poplar wood, and spoons too, though we knew our guests would not bother overmuch with spoons, preferring to use their fingers. The men brought in wild turkey, geese and duck in abundance, as well as deer. Your grandfather brought down his first deer and that was a proud day for him. We had found cranberries growing wild that summer, and the women found ways of using them, and our harvest had yielded plenty of corn, some of which we had laboriously ground for bread, and some we had cracked for hominy. We were so happy preparing the food for that feast. You never know how wonderful it is to have plenty all 'round you until you've gone hungry as we went hungry that first winter. So we set about preparing a lavish abundance of food for our guests, but we didn't know how many guests were coming."

Grandma smiled, and the older people chuckled. They knew how many guests had come!

"It's just as well we didn't know," she went on, "we couldn't have worked any harder, and we would have worried for fear we didn't have enough. Such a good smell of roasting and baking filled the village as put us all in fine humor. Maybe Massasoit and his men smelt that good smell away off in their town. Anyway, ninety of them came, and I was the first to see them. It happened this way:

"We brought our food together at the common house that morning, all the victuals that had been cooked in the several houses where the most skilful housewives lived. We women had put on our best caps and fresh kerchiefs, and we were busily laying out the trenchers when someone remembered a basket of fresh loaves left by mistake in one of the more distant houses. I was sent to fetch it, and as I came out of the door with the basket on my arm, I looked across the fields and saw our guests coming down the trail from the woods. Of course we were used to the Indians and their outlandish ways of dressing by that time, and I thought not at all about how different they were from us, but only that they made a brave and proper sight. Tall, strong men they were, some with feathers stuck in the bands around their heads. Their long straight hair shone with bear's grease. They wore deerskins over their shoulders, and some wore long tight hose that met the leather girdles around their waists. A few had their faces painted in black or red or yellow, to suit each man's fancy. I could see the wildcat skin that one important brave had thrown over his arm. I could tell Massasoit a great way off because of the heavy chain of white bone beads that he was wont to wear around his neck. He was also wearing the copper chain with a jewel in it that our people gave him when he first visited us many months before. They came along the trail, single file as was their custom, and as I watched I saw more and more coming, until it seemed to me, in my foolish fancy, that all the Indians in America were coming to our feast. Then as I stood there idly watching, it came over me that no one else in the town had seen them, and I ran to the common house as fast as I could because I knew our elders must be warned in time to go out and greet them properly.

"All the people were dismayed to learn my news and we were much put to it to welcome our guests and serve them graciously, for we could never let them suspect that we had looked for no more than a score. We bustled around and prepared more tables out of doors. Fortunately, it was not excessively cold. Anyway, we were used to the cold and of course they were. We had built fires outside to take off the chill, and the best carpet and cushions for their principal men were ready to be spread. So by the time the Indians had got through passing that smelly pipe of theirs around among themselves and our men, the food was ready, and our guests were more than ready to eat it. But of course if you didn't know them, you would never have guessed it. It was their habit to move slowly and deliberately, as if they were pretending the food was not there until the time came to fall to. Never in all my life have I seen so many people eat so much. Those Indians must have been hollow to the knees. One big brave grabbed a whole turkey and gnawed away at it until there was nothing left but bare bones. Then he was ready to begin on a steak of venison, which he ate along with two or three tankards of beer. He finished off with a whole pie. Truly the food melted

away that day, but there was plenty left for us women when
we got a chance to eat.

"Later on they wrestled, ran races, sang, danced and played
games, probably some of the same games that you children
played this morning. The Indians could outrun and outwrestle
our boys, but when our boys began teaching the Indians some
of our English games the Indians didn't win so often. It
wouldn't have been wise to let them think they could beat us
in everything. It was a great day, and our guests liked it so
well that they wrapped up in their deerskins and spent the
night in the town, and the next day, and the next after that,

we did it all over again. Of course, there wasn't quite so much to eat after the first day, but the Indians didn't care. They were used to having a big feast, and then not bothering much about food for several days. But even at that it kept us busy cooking. We didn't mind because we had plenty, and if it meant peace and goodwill between ourselves and the Indians, we women were only too glad to do our part to help. But when it was all over and the Indians finally left, we had to do a lot of cleaning up. Soon after that the cold shut down on us and our second winter in Plymouth began. So that," said Grandma, "is the story of our First Thanksgiving."

Landing of the Pilgrim Fathers

By Felicia Dorothea Hemans

Illustration by William Colrus

The breaking waves dashed high
  On the stern and rock-bound coast,
And the woods, against a stormy sky,
  Their giant branches tossed;

And the heavy night hung dark
  The hills and waters o'er,
When a band of exiles moored their bark
  On the wild New England shore.

Not as the conquerer comes,
    They, the true-hearted, came:
Not with the roll of the stirring drums,
    And the trumpet that sings of fame;

Not as the flying come,
    In silence and in fear—
They shook the depths of the desert's gloom
    With their hymns of lofty cheer.

Amidst the storm they sang,
    And the stars heard, and the sea;
And the sounding aisles of the dim woods rang
    To the anthem of the free!

The ocean eagle soared
    From his nest by the white wave's foam,
And the rocking pines of the forest roared:
    This was their welcome home!

There were men with hoary hair
    Amidst that pilgrim band;
Why had they come to wither there,
    Away from their childhood's land?

There was woman's fearless eye,
    Lit by her deep love's truth;
There was manhood's brow, serenely high,
    And the fiery heart of youth.

What sought they thus afar?
    Bright jewels of the mine?
The wealth of seas, the spoils of war?—
    They sought a faith's pure shrine!

Aye, call it holy ground,
    The soil where first they trod!
They have left unstained what there they found—
    Freedom to worship God!

Thanksgiving Day

By Lydia Maria Child

Illustration by Estelle Hollingworth

Over the river and through the wood,
  To grandfather's house we'll go;
    The horse knows the way
    To carry the sleigh
  Through the white and drifted snow.

Over the river and through the wood,—
  Oh, how the wind does blow!
    It stings the toes
    And bites the nose
  As over the ground we go.

Over the river and through the wood,
  To have a first-rate play,
    Hear the bells ring
    "Ting-a-ling-ding!"
  Hurrah for Thanksgiving Day!

Over the river and through the wood,
  Trot fast, my dapple gray!
    Spring over the ground
    Like a hunting hound!
  For this is Thanksgiving Day!

Over the river and through the wood,
  And straight through the barnyard gate;
    We seem to go
    Extremely slow;
  It is so hard to wait!

Over the river and through the wood,
  Now grandmother's cap I spy!
    Hurrah for the fun!
    Is the pudding done?
  Hurrah for the pumpkin pie!

The Pilgrims Came

By Annette Wynne

The Pilgrims came across the sea,
And never thought of you and me;
And yet it's very strange the way
We think of them Thanksgiving Day.

We tell their story, old and true,
Of how they sailed across the blue,
And found a new land to be free
And built their homes quite near the sea.

Every child knows well the tale
Of how they bravely turned the sail,
And journeyed many a day and night,
To worship God as they thought right.

The people think that they were sad,
And grave; I'm sure that they were glad—
They made Thanksgiving Day—that's fun—
We thank the Pilgrims, every one!

Psalm 100

A Psalm of Thanksgiving

Make a joyful noise unto Jehovah, all ye lands.
Serve Jehovah with gladness:
Come before his presence with singing.
Know ye that Jehovah, he is God:
It is he that hath made us and we are his;
We are his people, and the sheep of his pasture.
Enter into his gates with thanksgiving,
And into his courts with praise:
Give thanks unto him, and bless his name.
For Jehovah is good; his loving kindness endureth for ever,
And his faithfulness unto all generations.

Hanukkah

Hanukkah, the Jewish Feast of Lights, begins on the evening of the twenty-fifth day of the Hebrew month of Kislev, which usually corresponds to the month of December. The holiday lasts for eight days, and each one is filled with songs, games, food, and the lighting of the Hanukkah candles.

Hanukkah is a joyous holiday. On the first night, Jewish families gather around the *menorah*, or eight-branched candlestick, while one candle is lit. On the second night, two candles are kindled, and so on, until the eighth night, when eight candles burn. As the candles are lit each night two blessings are recited, and then the burning *menorah* is placed in a window so that all may see it and rejoice together.

For children, the highlight of the evening comes when they receive *Hanukkah gelt*, or presents of money, and gather around in a circle to play "*dreidel.*"

The *dreidel* is a tiny spinning top with a different Hebrew letter printed on each of its four sides. Each letter has a different value in nuts or money. When the dreidel stops spinning, one letter faces up. The player with the most nuts or money at the end of the game, wins.

The Hanukkah Story

BY MORRISON DAVID BIAL

Illustrations by Stephen Kraft

MORE than two thousand years ago, the land of Judea, the land we now call Israel, was ruled by the Syrian Greeks. The Emperor Antiochus reigned. The Syrians called him Epiphanes the Illustrious, but the Jews called him Epimanes the Madman. For he ruled with cruelty and terror over a mighty empire.

Antiochus believed that he was a god, with godlike powers. He had priests who served him and placed his statue in a favored position among the many idols in their temples.

Because Antiochus admired Greek culture, all his subjects were forced to follow Greek customs, and give up their own ways of doing things. They read Greek books and acted in Greek plays. They built gymnasiums, where they held imitations of Greek games. They adopted Greek names. And they worshiped Greek gods.

Even some of the Jewish nobles in Jerusalem, the capital city, began to copy the Greeks in every way, hoping to win the Emperor's favor.

Now Jason, the Jewish High Priest, tried valiantly to keep Judaism alive as the religion of his people, and still obey the Emperor's commands. But when war broke out between Syria and Egypt, Antiochus suspected Jason of being friendly to the enemy. Jason was stripped of his holy office, and a new High Priest, Menelaus, was appointed.

The Jews hated Menelaus. They knew him to be evil, and not worthy of being a priest of God. So when word was spread that Antiochus had been slain in battle, Jason gathered an army of one thousand men. They laid siege to Jerusalem, and forced the false priest Menelaus to flee. Now the Jews could worship with their beloved leader Jason.

Antiochus, however, had not been slain after all. When the news of Jason's daring rebellion reached him, he led his great army to Jerusalem. He commanded his soldiers to execute anyone suspected of disloyalty. In his rage, Antiochus entered the Holy Temple on Mount Zion, despoiled it, and carried off its sacred treasures. Thousands of innocent Jews were slain. Jerusalem was left desolate.

Now Antiochus issued new and more dreadful commands. Every one of his subjects was to bow in worship before the Greek gods, or forfeit his life. Antiochus knew that if he was to succeed in destroying the Jews as a people, he must destroy their religion first. Their religion was the cord that bound them together; he had to break it. For the route to Egypt ran through Judea. An army marching to do battle with the Egyptians had to pass through the land of the Jews. Therefore their loyalty was necessary for the emperor to feel safe on his throne.

All the peoples of the vast realm submitted to the new decree. But the Jews refused. They were true to the faith of their fathers. Then the angry king ordered his army into the field, to root out this strange belief in the Jewish God.

Antiochus' soldiers overran Jerusalem. They halted the service

in the Temple. They placed a statue of Zeus, god of the Greeks, on the altar. They pillaged and murdered. If a woman was found lighting candles on the eve of the Sabbath, she was executed. If a man was discovered teaching his son the laws of Judaism, they paid with their lives.

A widow named Hannah lived with her seven sons, all of them true and loyal Jews. The king's men found them observing the Sabbath. One by one, beginning with the eldest, they were ordered to bow down before heathen idols. One by one, they refused. And one by one, before their mother's eyes, they were beheaded. Finally only the youngest, a lad of six, remained. But even he would not bow down, and he too died for his faith.

In the small town of Modin, in the Judean hills, dwelt an old man named Mattathias, and his five sons: John, Simeon, Eleazar, Jonathan, and Judah. When the emperor's decree reached Modin, Mattathias and his sons vowed never to desert their religion and their God. The old man mourned the desecration of the beloved Temple: "Why did I live to see the misery of my people and of Jerusalem!"

When the king's officers arrived in Modin to enforce obedience, they went to Mattathias. They asked him, as leader of the village, to be the first to offer a sacrifice to the Greek idols. They knew the villagers would follow his example. They promised him rich gifts of silver and gold, and the favor of the emperor.

Mattathias gave them his answer. "Though all nations obey

the king and fall away from the religions of their fathers, yet
must I and my sons walk in the way of the Lord. We will not
forsake the Law!"

But a man without Mattathias' courage and faith was found,
and he agreed to offer a sacrifice on the altar erected in the
village square. As the people watched in fear, Mattathias strode
forward, stabbed the traitor, struck down the king's officer,
and destroyed the altar. Then, raising his sword, he cried out:
"All who are for the Lord, follow me!"

Then Mattathias and his sons and followers fled into the
mountains, and hid in the sheltered caves among the hills.

When news of the Modin rebellion reached Jerusalem, the
army was marched forth to destroy the rebels. But each time
they attacked, the bare rocks and crevices seemed to open up,
and brave Jews swarmed forth to defeat them. Then the generals realized this strange fact: no matter how courageously
the Jews fought, they would not take up arms on the Sabbath.
So they began to attack on the Sabbath, and Mattathias watched
his followers being massacred. He called his people together, and
said: "If we follow the example of our brothers, all of us will
perish. To keep Judaism alive, we must fight for it. Even on
the Sabbath!"

Now Mattathias was very old, and the time drew near when
he must die. He gathered his sons around him. "Be true to the
Torah," he told them. "Fight for it, and, if you must, give your
lives for it. Your brother Judah has ever been strong and mighty.
He shall be your captain, and lead you in the battle of our
people."

Then he blessed his sons, and died.

Judah, called the Maccabee, or hammerer, led his people,
and they "fought with gladness the battle of the Lord."

It was not easy to deal with this band of fighters. One struck at them, and they rose again in another place. It was decided that the famed general Apollonius should lead his army against the Jews. They were a strong force, and had won many battles. Bold and powerful, Apollonius was certain of an easy victory. But the victory went to the Maccabees. Judah and his warriors defeated the Syrians, killed their general, and carried off his sword in triumph. From that time on, Judah wore the sword of Apollonius.

When Seron, commander of the Syrian army in Judea, heard of the death of his general, Apollonius, he swore revenge. He resolved to wipe out the cave-dwelling rebels forever. He mustered a huge force and marched toward the hills.

Judah and his men met Seron's mammoth army at Beth Horon.

When the Judeans saw the approaching legions, they were frightened. They said: "How can we, who are so few, fight against so strong a host?"

Judah answered them. "With the God of Heaven, it is all one to save by many or by few."

Then they fell upon Seron's army with such ferocity that they routed them and sent the survivors scurrying back to Jerusalem.

Now Antiochus gathered together all the armed force of his empire. Lysias, one of his nobles, was put in charge of the immense multitude: seven thousand horsemen and forty thousand foot soldiers and huge armored elephants. The slave dealers of neighboring nations made ready their silver and gold, to buy the vanquished children of Israel as slaves.

But Judah was a worthy leader of his people. Judah knew how to attack suddenly from the sheltering mountains. Every path, every cave, every gorge, was familiar to him. He knew how to take the enemy by surprise, strike hard, then vanish before reinforcements could overwhelm his small band. Not with the sword alone, but with strategy and skill, would Judah fight this last great battle.

Patiently he waited. Now and then he sent soldiers to slip through Lysias' lines, to worry and confuse the enemy, to make them wonder—where would the Maccabees strike next?

He waited until Lysias' generals, Gordias and Nicanor, had divided their armies into two great forces.

Then he attacked. The Judeans hurled themselves at one half of the Syrian army. The gigantic elephants, sheathed in armor, were roused to battle. Enraged and trumpeting, they carried death under their massive feet. Eleazar realized that unless the elephants were stopped, the Maccabees were doomed. Bravely and swiftly he rode his horse under the largest elephant. Dodging the arrows and spears, he plunged his lance under the elephant's armor, deep into its belly. The huge animal toppled over, crushing Eleazar beneath him.

While the bewildered Syrians watched this heroic act, the Maccabees gathered new heart from the bravery of Judah's brother. They drove the enemy from the field.

Without pause, they sped to attack the other half of the invading army. The Syrians fled, leaving behind all their equipment and booty. The Maccabees had won their fight for freedom at last.

In triumph and exaltation, Judah and his followers marched to the holy city of Jerusalem. They found their Temple desecrated, its altar profaned.

The Maccabeans began to cleanse the Temple. They scrubbed it clean, and polished it; they flung out the pagan idols; they tore down the profane altar and erected a new and beautiful one, according to the requirements of the Law.

The people rose up early on the morning of the 25th of Kislev, to offer their thanks to God. But when the priests and Levites sought to kindle the Ner Tamid, the Eternal Light, they found only one small flask of pure oil with the seal of the

High Priest. There was oil enough for only one day, and it would be eight days before more oil could be ready. They lit the lamp, and the oil miraculously burned bright for eight full days. In joy and in freedom, the people celebrated the dedication of the altar, and the rededication of their Holy Temple to the worship of God.

And so each year Hanukkah, the holiday of Dedication, is celebrated for eight days. Each day the courage of the brave Maccabees is recalled as candles commemorate the flask of oil that burned for eight days.

Festival of Lights

BY SYDNEY TAYLOR

Illustrations by Mary Stevens

LATKES for supper!" Henny's mouth watered.

There was an instant chorus of "Yum, yum!"

Mama smiled. "Well, children, it seems everybody loves *latkes*. And Hanukkah's the time to eat them. Who wants to grate the potatoes?"

"Me! Me!" the younger ones cried.

So Mama let Charlotte and Gertie take turns. When they grew tired, Ella and Henny took over. In a little while, the large mixing bowl was full to the brim with mushy potato liquid.

Then Sarah grated the onions. "Ooh, it bites my nose and eyes!" she complained. She grated very fast, her face all screwed up and the tears flowing.

"Look! Sarah's crying. She must be sorry for the onions," Henny said, grinning.

Now into the bowl went eggs, matzo flour, salt and pepper. Mama stirred and stirred the mixture. By this time the oil in the frying pan was bubbling hot. It sizzled a welcome to the spoonfuls of pancake mix Mama fed it. Soon a delicious aroma spread through the room. The children hung over the stove, eager for a taste of the very first hot potato pancake that would come off the fire.

My, it was good! All crispy, crunchy outside, all tasty, chewy on the inside! It disappeared too quickly in the mouth, rushed down to the tummy, leaving them with a craving for more. Mama knew she'd have to keep careful watch, or there'd be none left for supper.

"Here comes Papa, now."

"Just in time, I see," Papa said, as he caught a whiff of the appetizing odor.

Papa was gay, laughing and joking with the children as he washed up. Tonight the whole family was gay. It was the time for gladsomeness. It was the first night of Hanukkah—Festival of Lights—the happy holiday right in the midst of December's bleakness. Jews everywhere celebrate Hanukkah with song, games, and parties, and the giving of gifts and money.

Ella had polished the brass Menorah till it shone like a mirror. It had been placed on the top shelf of the whatnot, its eight little holders all in a row ready to receive the slim, golden yellow candles Papa had bought especially. In the middle, set up high above the others, was the *shamosh* (sexton) candle. Its flame would be used to kindle all the others.

The children grouped themselves around Papa as Mama lifted Charlie onto a chair. Papa placed a candle in the first holder of the Menorah. Then, holding the lighted *shamosh*, he turned to Charlie. "Would you like to light it?" he asked.

Charlie jumped up and down. "Yes, yes! Charlie wanna light the candle!" he cried, his little hands reaching out eagerly.

Papa's firm hand guided his son's towards the wick of candle number one. Bright and shining, it sprang to light, matching the glow on Charlie's face.

Papa's voice was deep and reverent. "Praised be Thou, O Lord our God, Ruler of the Universe, who has commanded us to kindle the Lights of Hanukkah."

Over two thousand years ago, Antiochus, King of Syria, sent forth a mighty army into Palestine, to force the Jews to give up their religion. It was forbidden to hold services in the Temple of Jerusalem, and God's house itself was turned into a Greek Temple. The Jews who refused to submit were destroyed. They were the first religious martyrs known to history.

There rose up a strong and courageous man; Judas Maccabeus was his name. He roused his people to fight for freedom. For three long years, the struggle raged, until at last victory was theirs. In triumph, the brave Jewish soldiers returned to the city of Jerusalem.

When the pagans had occupied the Temple, they had defiled it by the sacrifice of unclean animals. Anxiously, the priests searched for some unpolluted oil to rekindle the Menorah (perpetual light). All they could find was one tiny vessel of oil, its seal still unbroken. This would be enough to last only one day.

But, by a miracle, the scant supply lasted eight full days—long enough for olives to be gathered and pressed and fresh oil made!

Once again holy services could be held in the Temple, with songs and prayers offered up to God. Candles gleamed in the homes, and even the streets of the city were lit. For eight days the celebration continued. Ever since, each year, the candle lighting ceremony is repeated for eight nights, with a candle added each night.

"Tomorrow I want to hold the *shamosh* and light the two candles," Gertie said.

"Six children and Papa and Mama makes eight." Sarah had it all figured out. "It'll come out exactly right."

"Yes," Papa nodded. "Everybody will have a chance. Ella, sing for us."

So Ella sang "Rock of Ages," and in a little while, the whole family joined in.

Rock of Ages, let our song
Praise thy saving power;
Thou amidst the raging foes
Wast our sheltering tower.

Mama beamed at Papa. "Now, Papa?"

The children smiled at each other. They knew what was coming. Papa pulled out his change purse. "I'm afraid there isn't much Hanukkah money inside," he declared in mournful tones, but the girls could see that his eyes were shiny with teasing. Now he was distributing pennies, two of them to each child!

"So much money!" breathed Charlotte.

"Wait till we visit the relatives!" Henny added. "Then we'll really be rich!"

Ella was provoked. "Henny, you're not going to go around collecting! That's all right for the kids."

"Is that so?" Henny tossed her head. "Well, I'm never going to be too old to collect presents—especially money!"

Mama put a hasty end to the argument. "Come now, children," she called out, "or the *latkes* will get cold!"

On Sunday afternoon the family was about to leave for a Hanukkah party at Aunt Rivka's house. "Bundle up tight," advised Papa; "it's cold outside."

"It feels like more snow," Mama added. "We'd better take our rubbers. Ella, you get the umbrellas."

"Do we have to drag umbrellas?" Henny questioned. "It's so much fun to walk in the snow."

"Well, all right then, just rubbers for everyone," Mama decided. "And one umbrella for me. I don't want to spoil my good hat."

With Papa and Charlie in the lead, the family was soon on its way. The younger girls had a hilarious time jumping up and down the hills of snow piled up against the curb. "Take care! You'll dirty your dresses!" Mama warned.

"Mama," asked Henny, "is Uncle Hyman bringing Lena to the party?"

"I think so. Why?"

"'Cause if he does, it means we'll get an extra present," said

Henny gleefully. "Now that Uncle Hyman goes around with her, we don't see him so often. I miss him."

"Him or his pennies?" Ella asked.

Henny grinned. "Both."

"Lena isn't a relative. She doesn't have to give us anything," Sarah reminded her sister.

"Mama, do you see the way Lena eats?" Gertie asked. "She cuts her meat with the knife in her left hand and the fork in her right. Just the opposite!"

"That's the European way," Mama explained. "Very sensible, too. They don't have to keep switching their forks all the time."

"But Lena eats with her knife, too. She uses it like a shovel. Do they do that in Europe too?" Charlotte asked.

"And the way she hangs over her plate," Henny went on. "Like somebody was going to take it away from her."

"She's probably still not used to having plenty of good food," Mama said. "Things weren't so easy for Lena in the old country."

"Well, that's one thing she and Uncle Hyman have in common," Ella observed. "They sure love to eat."

"And her English is so funny, too," Charlotte added.

"That's because the language is still strange to her," Mama said, less patiently. "Do you know she can speak several languages? Russian, Polish, Jewish. Any of you speak Polish as poorly as you seem to think Lena speaks English?"

Mama's words made the girls feel a little foolish. They fell silent. But then Henny started chuckling. "When she walks, I always feel like saying, 'Here's my chest, the rest is coming!'" It set the others to giggling, and even Papa's lips twitched. But Mama's face remained unsmiling.

"Children, children!" she said earnestly. "Everyone has his own peculiar way of doing things. How do you know that we don't seem just as odd to Lena? You must learn to overlook different manners in people, because they don't matter. What is really important is whether the person has a good heart. This Lena has. More than that, she's very smart, and jolly besides. She's always ready to see the funny side, even in herself. I think she's a fine person! And last of all, if it weren't for her, we would have no little Charlie. Really, girls!"

The girls hung their heads and looked embarrassed.

"Well," Papa broke in, "I don't think the girls actually intended to be mean about Lena."

"That's right, Mama," Henny said contritely. "I'm sorry. I didn't mean to sound nasty."

"We weren't very nice," Sarah apologized.

"We really like her an awful lot, Mama," said Charlotte earnestly.

"I know." Mama smiled at them reassuringly. "But sometimes we must think a little before we speak."

Into a dimly lit hallway and up three flights of stairs the family went. Aunt Rivka's tiny boxlike flat was already overflowing with old folks and young. Joyous greetings were exchanged. "Hello, hello!" "Happy Hanukkah!"

Gradually the grownups settled themselves near the big round table while the children were distributed on the couch, laps, assorted stools, and the floor. Someone started a song. With so much fun and laughter, others were encouraged to join. Someone else told a story, and soon the company vied with one another in telling amusing tales.

Aunt Rivka brought in the refreshments. There were high mounds of steaming *latkes*, fruit, nuts, raisins and dates, and finally her great specialty, rich, brown, moist slices of honey cake. Hot tea was poured into glasses for everyone.

All at once Uncle Solomon slapped his palm on the table. "See, children!" he called out loudly. "See what I have!" He held up a leaden object which looked like a tiny alphabet block with a stem running right through its center. Each of its four sides bore a letter. "A dredel!" "A dredel!" the children cried.

Uncle Solomon smiled at them through his long white silky beard. "Whoever wants to play with the dredel must first tell what the letters are."

From various parts of the room there were shouts. "N, G, H, S!"

"That's all right," Uncle Solomon nodded his head. "But who can tell me what they stand for?"

An older boy stood up and recited in Hebrew, *"Nes Gadol Hayah Sham."*

"That's still all right," Uncle Solomon beamed. "But who knows what the words mean?"

And Ella answered proudly, her voice clear as a bell, "A great miracle happened there."

"Perfect!" Uncle Solomon handed the dredel to his son. "Here, Nathan, take the children into the kitchen and start them off. Aunt Rivka has the nuts all ready for you."

As the children trooped into the kitchen, there were wails from some of the smaller ones. "But we don't know how to play!"

"I'll teach you," Nathan said good-naturedly. "First, everyone sit down on the floor and make a circle." When everyone had done this, he continued. "Now we divide the nuts evenly amongst us. Then each puts his share in his own saucer. Now each one put a nut in the big bowl here in the center. Now watch." He gave the dredel a spin. "Let's see what letter comes up. You see, the letters also have a Jewish meaning." The dredel stopped. "Notice everybody, it's on the N. This stands for *nicht* or nothing. So I take no nuts from the big bowl." He turned to Henny. "Here, you spin next."

Henny gave the dredel a good hard turn, and it wobbled crazily till it stopped on G. "The G stands for *gantz*, meaning all. You're lucky. You get all the nuts in the bowl."

"But what do we do now, with no nuts left?" a little girl asked.

"Everybody has to put another nut into the bowl," Nathan replied. "Now the next person gets a chance to spin."

They played on. They soon learned that H stands for *halb,* half, which allows the player to take half the nuts from the bowl, and that S stands for *shtell,* or put, which means the player has to add another nut to the pile.

The children enjoyed the game immensely, and the afternoon just flew away. They didn't want to stop playing until Uncle Chaim uttered the magic words, "Hanukkah money! Come on, children!"

Thereupon the uncles and aunts made the rounds with a merry jingle of coins. "Happy Hanukkah!" they repeated over and over, as they dropped the precious pennies into open little palms.

And now parents began bundling up their little ones. It had grown late, and the party was at an end. Aunt Rivka and Uncle Chaim stood at the door bidding each one good-by. "May we always meet on happy occasions."

"It's so nice when relatives come together," Lena remarked when the family had assembled downstairs. "I'm glad Hyman brought me; I really enjoyed myself." She thrust a small parcel into Gertie's hands. "Here is my little Hanukkah present for all you girls."

"Oh!" "Oh!" Impatient fingers tore away the wrapping. The cover bounced off, and there, lined up in rows, were five shiny, satin sashes with five hair ribbons to match, in a rainbow array of colors. "Oh, Lena, they're lovely!" "Dear, dear Lena!" "You're so good to us!" Impulsively they hugged her and planted kisses on her round cheeks. All the while Uncle Hyman stood by, balancing from one leg to the other and grinning proudly.

When the hubbub had quieted down, he stepped forward. "And now we have something special for Charlie," he announced. He pulled out a big cigar and offered it to the little boy.

"Don't you think he's a little young for smoking?" Papa inquired jokingly, as Mama looked on somewhat concerned.

Charlie made a swift grab. The top of the cigar pulled out, releasing a tiny American flag in the shape of a fan. Everyone laughed as the astonished Charlie stared at the sudden change.

As Uncle Hyman and Lena waved good-by, Mama suddenly remembered something. "Oh, my! I left my umbrella!"

"I'll get it," Henny volunteered. She started back up the stairs.

"It's in the front room, by the window!" Mama shouted after her. "Ella, you wait for her," she said. "We'll go on ahead. It's way past Charlie's bedtime."

"Mama, can all of us girls wait so we can walk home together?" Sarah asked.

"All right. Ella, see they come right home."

Upstairs, as Henny picked up the umbrella, she glanced around the empty front room. It still bore traces of the recent gathering. On the partially cleared table was a large bowl of nuts. "Aunt Rivka," she called out, "can I have some nuts?"

"Why not?" Aunt Rivka shouted back from the kitchen. "Help yourself."

"How many can I take?"

She could hear Aunt Rivka laugh. "Take as much as you can carry."

Oh, boy, exclaimed Henny to herself. All I can carry! Her eyes were alight with sparks of mischief. Carefully she pushed the bowl towards the edge of the table. Pulling back several ribs of the umbrella, she tipped the bowl. In a moment, the nuts were cascading down in a rattle of sound.

As Henny sauntered past the kitchen on her way to the door, she said smoothly, "Thank you, Aunt Rivka. You certainly let me take a lot."

Unsuspecting Aunt Rivka kept right on washing the dishes. "It's all right, my child," she replied, "the more, the merrier."

Henny spluttered with laughter. "Don't you want to see how many you gave me?" she asked mischievously.

Aunt Rivka picked up a towel for her soapy hands and stepped in to the front room. When she saw the empty nut bowl, her hands flew up in amazement. "How—why, Henny, you surely can't carry them all!" Henny held up the umbrella in triumph, and Aunt Rivka burst out laughing. "What a girl! Next time I'll know better than to give you such a chance, or I'll find myself with no house left."

"What's the matter with the umbrella?" Gertie asked in amazement as Henny came tramping out of the hallway. "It looks all blown up!"

Henny chuckled. "That's because it's full of something good!"

Charlotte pulled back a rib and peered inside. Her jaw dropped. "Ooh, nuts! Millions of 'em!"

Three more heads poked themselves inside. "Look out!" Henny yelled. "You'll break Mama's umbrella and spill out all my nuts!"

Ella turned on Henny. "Does Aunt Rivka know about this?"

"Certainly!" Henny countered. "And I was very polite, too. I asked her first."

"Do you expect me to believe that she actually let you have all these?"

Henny grinned. "She said to take as much as I could carry." The grin widened from ear to ear. "So I only did what she told me."

"Mama won't like it," Sarah said immediately. "You know she always says when somebody offers you something, you're supposed to take just a little."

"It's all right. I showed Aunt Rivka how many I had, and she just laughed. I wanted to be sure there was enough for the five of us. Go on," Henny added generously, "help yourselves."

The girls fell to and soon shells were flying in all directions. The way homeward was slow, for every time one picked a butternut, she had to stop and stamp on it with her heel. After a few blocks Gertie observed, "The umbrella's getting skinnier and skinnier."

Charlotte turned back to stare at the litter of shells strewn behind them. "We're leaving a trail, just like Hansel and Gretel," she said.

By the time they reached their door, they were all full to bursting, and the little ones felt drowsy. "I'm so tired, my mouth is full of yawns," Gertie said.

Sarah stretched her arms wide. "I'm tired too. Didn't we have a good time, though? I wish every day was Hanukkah!"

A Song of Always

*By Marian Jordan and
Efraim Michael Rosenzweig*

Illustration by Stephen Kraft

The Temple is clean
    The lamp burns bright;
Judah the leader,
    Has started the light.

The sun shines by days,
    And dark is the night;
But always and always
    The lamp burns bright.

For Hanukkah

By Chaim Nachmon Bialik
Translated by Jessie Sampter

Father lighted candles for me;
    Like a torch the Shamash shone.
In whose honor, for whose glory?
    For Hanukkah alone.

Teacher bought a big top for me,
    Solid lead, the finest known.
In whose honor, for whose glory?
    For Hanukkah alone.

Mother made a pancake for me,
    Hot and sweet and sugar-strewn,
In whose honor, for whose glory?
    For Hanukkah alone.

Dreidel Song

By Efraim Rosenzweig

Twirl about, dance about,
  Spin, spin, spin!
Turn, Dreidel, turn—
  Time to begin!

Soon it is Hanukkah—
  Fast Dreidel, fast!
For you will lie still
  When Hanukkah's past.

Christmas

DECEMBER 25

Christmas means parties and gifts, Santa Claus, mistletoe, and trees. It also means prayer, for it is the season of "Peace on earth, good will to men." Christians throughout the world unite in happiness on the birthday of Jesus Christ.

The Bible tells us that the Three Wise Men and the shepherds were led by the Star of Bethlehem to the manger where Jesus was born.

Each year during the Christmas season, thousands of Christians travel to Bethlehem. There, in the Church of the Nativity, they see a huge silver star on which is written, "Here, of the Virgin Mary, Jesus Christ was born."

The word Christmas comes from the early English phrase "Cristes Masse," meaning Mass of Christ. No one is sure of the exact date of Christ's birth. Until 354 A.D., people observed His birthday on many different days. But that year Bishop Liberius of Rome ordered the people to celebrate on December 25. Like many of the other dates selected by the Romans for holidays, this is the one which most people of the world celebrate.

Miss Flora McFlimsey's Christmas Eve

BY MARIANA

Illustrations by the author

ONCE there was an old doll whose name was Flora Mc-Flimsey. She lived in a toy cupboard in the attic with a box of Tiddly-Winks and a Mother Goose book and Gulliver's Travels and a Noah's Ark and a fat sheep on wheels and an old, old, doll's trunk.

She had not always lived in the attic. No indeed! She had once belonged to the little girl with red-topped shoes, who played with her in the nursery below. But the little girl had long ago grown up and married, and Miss Flora McFlimsey had been put away in the attic and forg tten.

There she sat next to the little trunk in a corner of the toy cupboard, wearing a faded silk dress and a straw hat with a blue ribbon on it.

She led a rather lonely life, of course, as there was no one to talk to except the fat sheep who could not even say Ba-a-a any more.

Indeed she would have been quite lonely except that she had one visitor, Timothy Mouse, who often stopped in for a chat in the evenings after he'd made the rounds of the house.

Flora McFlimsey enjoyed Timothy Mouse's visits. He brought her news of the family downstairs, and what the children had for supper, and bits of gossip about the toys in the playroom.

One cold winter's night when outside the snow was falling fast, Timothy Mouse appeared as usual through the little hole in the corner of the toy cupboard.

He always said "Cheerio" when he came in, but this evening

he didn't say anything at all. He just wiggled his ears and blinked his eyes and ran three times around the floor of the cupboard after his tail.

Then he stopped and said in a low voice, "There are strange goings-on downstairs in the living room tonight, Miss McFlimsey. Stockings are hanging from the mantelpiece! And what is worse, a tree with shiny things all over it is growing right out of the floor."

"Ah," said Flora McFlimsey, sighing softly, "it must be Christmas Eve."

"What's that?" asked Timothy Mouse.

"Why that's the most wonderful night in the year," said Flora McFlimsey. "It's when Santa Claus comes down the chimney and puts presents in the children's stockings and under the Christmas tree, and people sing carols and . . ."

"Huh!" said Timothy Mouse, who did not like to think there was anything he didn't know, "it all sounds rather silly to me. I prefer birthdays with plenty of cake crumbs lying around. Well, I must be on my way," he added, and disappeared through the hole in the corner of the cupboard.

After he'd gone Miss Flora McFlimsey sat thinking about her first Christmas Eve.

She remembered how someone had taken her out of a long white box tied with satin ribbons and put her in a little red rocking-chair under the Christmas tree. She remembered the blue velvet dress she had worn with a hat to match and a muff of ermine fur and a tiny gold locket and chain.

Early Christmas morning a little girl in a fluffy white dress had come running in and cried, "Oh, isn't she beautiful!" and had hugged and kissed her.

But the velvet dress and the hat and the ermine muff and her little gold locket had disappeared long ago.

Things were different now. Maybe little girls didn't play with dolls any more. Timothy Mouse never said much about dolls in the playroom.

Miss Flora McFlimsey sighed. "I wish I could have just one little look at the Christmas tree," she said to herself.

She wished it so hard that all at once a strange thing happened. Flora McFlimsey moved one arm! It squeaked a little but the joints still worked. She kicked one leg—then the other one.

Then she stood up on both feet.

"I can walk!" she cried joyfully. "I can go downstairs and see the Christmas tree."

Four more steps and she was out of the toy cupboard. Then she walked straight to the top of the attic stairs.

Down these she climbed one by one, to the hall on the second floor. When she went past the door of the playroom where the children were sleeping, she tried to walk very softly and to keep her knees from squeaking.

Then she slid down the banisters of the front stairs and crossed the hall to the living room.

There was the tree all shining and beautiful, with an angel on the top, and in the firelight Miss Flora McFlimsey could see the stockings hanging in a row from the mantel.

Everything was still as a mouse.

She crept over into the shadows and looked up at the Christmas tree.

"It is the most beautiful tree in all the world," she whispered, "and this is the most wonderful night in all the year."

Suddenly there was a little scratching sound in the chimney.

"Goodness! What was that?"

Miss Flora McFlimsey hid in the shadow of a big chair. There was more scratching, then the sound of feet stamping on the hearth rug.

Flora McFlimsey peeked around the corner of the chair. There was Santa Claus taking a big pack off his back, and talking to himself.

"Dear, dear," he was saying, "I'm a doll short! Here's the bride doll for Suzy, and the doll with the red coat for Toto—but there's no doll for Diana! It must have dropped out when we dove through the snow cloud. Dear, dear, dear! After all those letters she wrote me, too!"

He kept on saying "dear, dear" while he was stuffing presents into the stockings and piling them up under the Christmas tree.

All at once he caught sight of Miss Flora McFlimsey peeking out from behind the chair.

"Well, well, well," he said, "and who are you, please?"

Miss Flora McFlimsey trembled but she stepped out into the firelight and said in a tiny voice:

"Good evening, sir. My name is Flora McFlimsey. I live in the attic and I came down to see the Christmas tree."

"Well, now, my dear," said Santa Claus. "It seems to me I've seen you before."

Santa Claus picked up Miss Flora McFlimsey and looked hard at her. "Why, yes, I remember you very well. It was a long time ago, to be sure."

Then his frown disappeared and his face lighted. "Why, of course! You'll be just the doll for Diana." And he sat her down under the Christmas tree with the bride doll and the doll in the red coat.

"And now, my dear," he said, "I've a great deal more to do before morning, so good night to you all and a Merry Christmas!"

And with that, he was up the chimney and away. There was a scurry of hoofs on the roof, then all was still again.

Miss Flora McFlimsey sat up straight and proud. She felt as if something wonderful were about to happen.

Then all at once Flora McFlimsey heard someone whispering. It was the tall doll in the red coat. "Did you see that scarecrow of an old doll over there?" she asked.

"Yes," answered the bride doll. "Isn't she a sight? Did you ever in all your life see such funny old-fashioned clothes? And that straw hat on Christmas Eve!" And they both laughed till they almost fell over.

"Just wait till the children see her! They'll send her right back to the attic where she belongs," said the doll in the red coat.

All the happy feeling suddenly left Flora McFlimsey.

"It's true," she said to herself. "I'm out of style and my clothes are out of style. I had better go right back to the attic before the children see me." She tried to stand up. But all her joints had grown stiff again, and she could not even move an arm.

So there was nothing to do but to sit there till the children came in the morning and saw her. Tears came into Miss Flora McFlimsey's eyes and rolled down her cheeks.

If only Timothy Mouse had not told her it was Christmas Eve! She should never, never, never have left the top cupboard in the attic.

Suddenly, from behind the fire engine, a little dark shadow darted out and ran three times around in a circle. It was Timothy Mouse. He stopped close to Miss McFlimsey and wiggled his ears and whispered, "Cheerio! help is coming soon." Then he darted off into the shadows again. Miss Flora McFlimsey straightened up.

What happened next could never be explained. Perhaps Timothy Mouse ran up the tree and whispered in the angel's ear, or perhaps the angel leaned over and saw Miss Flora McFlimsey and decided to come down and help. And down she came, right to Miss Flora McFlimsey's side and opened the trunk which had appeared miraculously under the Christmas tree. And there, on the very top, was the little gold locket and chain that Miss Flora McFlimsey had worn that first Christmas Eve. There, too, were her blue velvet dress and her hat and her little ermine muff.

The angel helped Miss Flora McFlimsey take off her faded,

dusty dress and put on the blue velvet one. She curled her hair and put the gold locket and chain around her neck. Then she found a tiny lace handkerchief in the trunk and a little bottle of Eau de Cologne. She tucked these inside Miss Flora McFlimsey's ermine muff and put a pair of white kid gloves on her little hands.

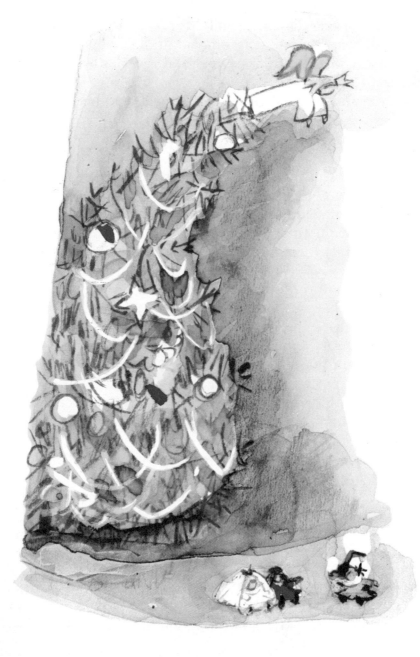

And one by one, the angel took the other things out of the trunk, and hung them all on the low branches of the Christmas tree.

Then she leaned down and kissed Flora McFlimsey on her round rosy cheek and whispered something ever so softly in her ear.

It was something about Christmas and something about love, but only Miss Flora McFlimsey heard her.

Then the angel said "good night" and climbed—no, she must have flown—back to her place on the top of the Christmas tree.

Miss Flora McFlimsey sat up very straight, holding her ermine muff in front of her. The doll in the red coat and the bride doll sat up very straight too. They were all looking toward the door where the children would come in. It would soon be morning.

"They will like me best, I think," whispered the doll in the red coat. "I am dressed in the very latest style."

"I don't know about that," said the bride doll. "There is nothing so beautiful as a bride, you know."

Miss Flora McFlimsey said nothing, but she trembled a little. At that moment she heard footsteps running down the stairs, and shouts of "Merry Christmas!"

In they came, Alex and Suzy and Billy and Diana and little round Toto. They looked so happy that Miss Flora McFlimsey forgot to be afraid.

And then the wonderful thing that she had felt was about to happen, really did happen.

It was Diana who spied her first.

"Oh, look at the old doll," she cried. "Isn't she beautiful!"

"And look at all her dresses and things," cried Suzy.

"And her trunk," said Toto.

"I love her, I love her!" cried Diana. And she took Miss Flora McFlimsey in her arms.

"Let me hold her," cried Suzy. "And please let me dress her," cried Toto.

And the doll in the red coat? And the bride doll? Well, no one paid very much attention to them.

But Miss Flora McFlimsey was happy, for once again on a Christmas morning she had been hugged and kissed by a little girl!

A Visit from St. Nicholas

By Clement O. Moore

Illustrations by William Colrus

'Twas the night before Christmas, when all through the house
Not a creature was stirring, not even a mouse;
The stockings were hung by the chimney with care,
In hopes that St. Nicholas soon would be there;
The children were nestled all snug in their beds
While visions of sugar-plums danced in their heads;
And Mamma in her 'kerchief, and I in my cap,
Had just settled our brains for a long winter's nap,
When out on the lawn there arose such a clatter,
I sprang from my bed to see what was the matter.
Away to the window I flew like a flash,
Tore open the shutters and threw up the sash.
The moon on the breast of the new-fallen snow
Gave a lustre of midday to objects below,
When, what to my wondering eyes did appear,
But a miniature sleigh and eight tiny reindeer,
With a little old driver, so lively and quick,
I knew in a moment it must be St. Nick.
More rapid than eagles his coursers they came,
And he whistled, and shouted, and called them by name:

"Now, Dasher! now, Dancer! now, Prancer and Vixen!
On, Comet! on, Cupid! on, Donder and Blitzen!
To the top of the porch! to the top of the wall!
Now dash away! dash away! dash away, all!"
As dry leaves that before the wild hurricane fly,
When they meet with an obstacle, mount to the sky,
So up to the housetop the coursers they flew,
With the sleigh full of toys, and St. Nicholas too.
And then, in a twinkling, I heard on the roof
The prancing and pawing of each little hoof.
As I drew in my head, and was turning around,
Down the chimney St. Nicholas came with a bound.
He was dressed all in fur, from his head to his foot,
And his clothes were all tarnished with ashes and soot;

A bundle of toys he had flung on his back,
And he looked like a peddler just opening his pack.
His eyes—how they twinkled! his dimples, how merry!
His cheeks were like roses, his nose like a cherry!
His droll little mouth was drawn up like a bow,
And the beard on his chin was as white as the snow;
The stump of a pipe he held tight in his teeth,
And the smoke, it encircled his head like a wreath;
He had a broad face and a little round belly
That shook, when he laughed, like a bowl full of jelly.
He was chubby and plump, a right jolly old elf,
And I laughed when I saw him, in spite of myself;
A wink of his eye and a twist of his head,
Soon gave me to know I had nothing to dread;

He spoke not a word, but went straight to his work,
And filled all the stockings; then turned with a jerk,
And laying his finger aside of his nose,
And giving a nod, up the chimney he rose.
He sprang to his sleigh, to his team gave a whistle,
And away they all flew like the down of a thistle.
But I heard him exclaim, ere he drove out of sight,

"HAPPY CHRISTMAS TO ALL,
AND TO ALL A GOOD NIGHT!"

Barney's Tale of the Wee Red Cap

BY RUTH SAWYER

Illustrations by William Colrus

DAVID watched the locked-out fairy go forth into the dusk again. He had always supposed that fairies disappeared suddenly and mysteriously, but this was not so. The little gray furry figure hopped slowly across the patch of white in front of the window, bobbed and frisked, pricked up the alert little ears, and swung his bushy tail, after the fashion of any genuine squirrel, and then dove under the low-hanging boughs of the nearest evergreens. As he disappeared, David felt an arm on his shoulder and turned to blink wonderingly into the face of big Barney bending over him and grinning.

"Well, well, who'd have thought to catch the sandman making his rounds afore supper! What sent ye to sleep, laddy?"

"Asleep!" David scoffed hotly at the accusation. "I was no more asleep than you are, Barney. Why, do you know what I've seen, what's been right here this very minute?"

Barney's grin broadened. "Well, maybe now it was the locked-out fairy!" For this was the old joke between them.

Little did Barney dream that this time he had not only touched upon the real truth, but he had actually gripped it by the scruff of the neck, as he would have put it himself. David looked wise. He was trying to make up his mind just how best to tell the wonderful news when Barney's next words held his tongue and sent the news scuttling back to his memory.

"And speaking o' fairies, I was just asking Johanna—getting supper out yonder—did she mind the tale Old Con, the tinker,

used to be telling back in the Old Country about his great-uncle
Teig and the wee red cap. Did Johanna ever tell ye, now, about
the fairies' red cap?"

David shook his head.

"It serves as an easy way o' travel for them; ye might almost
call it their private Pullman car," Barney chuckled. "Ye wait a
minute and I'll see is there time to tell the tale myself atween
now and supper."

He was away to the kitchen and back before David had much
more than time enough to rub the gathering frost from the window-pane and look out for a possible return of his fairy. Nothing
was to be seen, however, but the snow and the trees and the
trail of tiny footprints; and big Barney was beside him in the
window-nook again, with a mysterious "knowledgeable look"
on his face.

"Aye, there's time and light enough still in the west to see the
tale through." He paused for an instant.

"Ye know, laddy, over in Ireland they're not keeping Christmas
the same as ye do here—the poor, I mean. 'Tis generally the day
after, St. Stephen's Day, tho' sometimes 'tis St. Stephen's Eve
that they manage a bit of a feast and merrymaking. Them that

has little shares with them that has less; and afterward the neighbors gather about the turf fire for a story-telling. Aye, many's
the strange tale ye will hear over in Ireland on one of them
nights. And here's the tale Old Con, the tinker, used for to be
telling about his great-uncle Teig—the most close-fisted man
in all of Inneskillen."

And here again is the tale as Barney retold it and David heard
it, as he sat in the window-nook of the lodge at dusk-hour just
seven days before Christmas.

It was the Eve of St. Stephen, and Teig sat alone by his fire
with naught in his cupboard but a pinch of tea and a bare mixing of meal, and a heart inside of him as soft and warm as the
ice on the water-bucket outside the door. The turf was near
burnt on the hearth—a handful of golden cinders left, just; and
Teig took to counting them greedily on his fingers.

"There's one, two, three, an' four an' five," he laughed. "Faith,
there be more bits o' real gold hid undther the loose clay in the
corner."

It was the truth; and it was the scraping and scrooching for
the last piece that had left Teig's cupboard bare of a Christmas
dinner.

"Gold is betther nor eatin' an' dthrinkin'. An' if ye have naught
to give, there'll be naught asked of ye." And he laughed again.

He was thinking of the neighbors, and the doles of food and
piggins of milk that would pass over their thresholds that night
to the vagabonds and paupers who were sure to come begging.
And on the heels of that thought followed another: who would
be giving old Shawn his dinner? Shawn lived a stone's-throw
from Teig, alone, in a wee tumbled-in cabin; and for a score of
years past Teig had stood on the door-step every Christmas Eve,
and, making a hollow of his two hands, had called across the
road:

"Hey, there, Shawn, will ye come over for a sup?"

And Shawn had reached for his crutches, there being but one
leg to him, and had come.

"Faith," said Teig, trying another laugh, "Shawn can fast for
the once; 'twill be all the same in a month's time." And he fell
to thinking of the gold again.

A knock came to the door. Teig pulled himself down in his

chair where the shadow would cover him, and held his tongue.

"Teig, Teig!" It was the Widow O'Donnelly's voice. "If ye are there, open your door. I have not got the pay for the spriggin' this month, an' the childther are needin' food."

But Teig put the leash on his tongue, and never stirred till he heard the tramp of her feet going on to the next cabin. Then he saw to it that the door was tight barred. Another knock came, and it was a stranger's voice this time:

"The other cabins are filled; not one but has its hearth crowded. Will ye take us in, the two of us? The wind bites mortal sharp; not a morsel o' food have we tasted this day. Masther, will ye take us in?"

But Teig sat on, a-holding his tongue; and the tramp of the strangers' feet passed down the road. Others took their place—small feet, running. It was the miller's wee Cassie, and she called out as she went by:

"Old Shawn's watchin' for ye. Ye'll not be forgettin' him, will ye, Teig?"

And then the child broke into a song, sweet and clear, as she passed down the road:

"Listen all ye, 'tis the Feast o' St. Stephen,
  Mind that ye keep it, this holy even.
  Open your door and greet ye the stranger,
  For ye mind that the wee Lord had naught but a manger.
                                    Mhuire as truagh!

"Feed ye the hungry and rest ye the weary,
  This ye must do for the sake of Our Mary.
  'Tis well that ye mind—ye who sit by the fire—
  That the Lord He was born in a dark and cold byre.
                                    Mhuire as truagh!"

Teig put his fingers deep in his ears. "A million murdthering curses on them that won't let me be! Can't a man try to keep what is his without bein' pesthered by them that has only idled and wasted their days?"

And then the strange thing happened: hundreds and hundreds of wee lights began dancing outside the window, making the room bright; the hands of the clock began chasing each other round the dial, and the bolt of the door drew itself out. Slowly, without a creak or a cringe, the door opened, and in there trooped a crowd of the Good People. Their wee green cloaks were folded close about them, and each carried a rush-candle.

Teig was filled with a great wonderment, entirely, when he saw the fairies, but when they saw him they laughed.

"We are takin' the loan o' your cabin this night, Teig," said they. "Ye are the only man hereabouts with an empty hearth, an' we're needin' one."

Without saying more, they bustled about the room making ready. They lengthened out the table and spread and set it; more of the Good People trooped in, bringing stools and food and drink. The pipers came last, and they sat themselves around the chimneypiece a-blowing their chanters and trying the drones. The feasting began and the pipers played, and never had Teig seen such a sight in his life. Suddenly a wee man sang out:

"Clip, clap, clip, clap, I wish I had my wee red cap!"

And out of the air there tumbled the neatest cap Teig had ever laid eyes on. The wee man clapped it on his head crying:

"I wish I was in Spain!" And—whist!—up the chimney he went, and away out of sight!

It happened just as I am telling it. Another wee man called for his cap, and away he went after the first. And then another and another until the room was empty and Teig sat alone again.

"By my soul," said Teig, "I'd like to thravel like that myself! It's a grand savin' of tickets an' baggage; an' ye get to a place before ye've had time to change your mind. Faith, there is no harm done if I thry it."

So he sang the fairies' rhyme and out of the air dropped a wee cap for him. For a moment the wonder had him, but the next he was clapping the cap on his head, crying: "Spain!"

Then—whist!—up the chimney he went after the fairies, and before he had time to let out his breath he was standing in the middle of Spain, and strangeness all about him.

He was in a great city. The doorways of the houses were hung with flowers and the air was warm and sweet with the smell of them. Torches burned along the streets, sweetmeat-sellers went about crying their wares, and on the steps of a cathedral crouched a crowd of beggars.

"What's the meanin' o' that?" asked Teig of one of the fairies.

"They are waiting for those that are hearing Mass. When they come out they give half of what they have to those who have nothing, so that on this night of all the year there shall be no hunger and no cold."

And then far down the street came the sound of a child's voice, singing:

> "Listen all ye, 'tis the Feast o' St. Stephen,
> Mind that ye keep it, this holy even."

"Curse it!" said Teig. "Can a song fly after ye?" And then he heard the fairies cry, "Holland!" and he cried, "Holland!" too.

In one leap he was over France, and another over Belgium, and with the third he was standing by the long ditches of water frozen fast, and over them glided hundreds upon hundreds of lads and maids. Outside each door stood a wee wooden shoe, empty. Teig saw scores of them as he looked down the ditch of a street.

"What is the meanin' o' those shoes?" he asked the fairies.

"Ye poor lad!" answered the wee man next to him. "Are ye

not knowing anything? This is the Gift Night of the year, when every man gives to his neighbor."

A child came to the window of one of the houses, and in her hand was a lighted candle. She was singing as she put the light down close to the glass, and Teig caught her words:

"Open your door and greet ye the stranger,
    For ye mind that the wee Lord had naught but a manger.
                            Mhuire as truagh!"

" 'Tis the de'il's work!" cried Teig, and he set the red cap more firmly on his head. "I'm for another country."

I cannot be telling you half of the adventures Teig had that night, nor half the sights that he saw. But he passed by fields that held sheaves of grain for the birds, and door-steps that held bowls of porridge for the wee creatures. He saw lighted trees, sparkling and heavy with gifts; and he stood outside the churches and watched the crowds pass in, bearing gifts to the Holy Mother and Child.

At last the fairies straightened their caps and cried, "Now for the great hall in the King of England's palace!"

Whist!—and away they went, and Teig after them; and the first thing he knew he was in London, not an arm's-length from the King's throne. It was a grander sight than he had seen in any other country. The hall was filled entirely with lords and ladies; and the great doors were open for the poor and the homeless to come in and warm themselves by the King's fire and feast from the King's table. And many a hungry soul did the King serve with his own hands.

Those that had anything to give gave it in return. It might be a bit of music played on a harp or a pipe, or it might be a dance or a song; but more often it was a wish, just, for good luck and safe-keeping.

Teig was so taken up with the watching that he never heard the fairies when they wished themselves off; moreover, he never saw the wee girl that was fed and went laughing away. But he heard a bit of her song as she passed through the door:

"Feed ye the hungry and rest ye the weary,
    This ye must do for the sake of Our Mary."

Then the anger had Teig. "I'll stop your pestherin' tongue once an' for all time!" And, catching the cap from his head, he threw it after her.

No sooner was the cap gone than every soul in the hall saw him. The next moment they were about him, catching his coat and crying:

"Where is he from? What does he here? Bring him before the King!"

And Teig was dragged along by a hundred hands to the throne where the King sat.

"He was stealing food," cried one.

"He was stealing the King's jewels," cried another.

"He looks evil," cried a third. "Kill him!"

And in a moment all the voices took it up and the hall rang with, "Aye, kill him, kill him!"

Teig's legs took to trembling, and fear put the leash on his tongue; but after a long silence he managed to whisper:

"I have done evil to no one, no one!"

"Maybe," said the King. "But have ye done good? Come, tell us, have ye given aught to any one this night? If ye have, we will pardon ye."

Not a word could Teig say; fear tightened the leash, for he was knowing full well there was no good to him that night.

"Then ye must die," said the King. "Will ye try hanging or beheading?"

"Hanging, please, your Majesty," said Teig.

The guards came rushing up and carried him off. But as he was crossing the threshold of the hall a thought sprang at him and held him.

"Your Majesty," he called after him, "will ye grant me a last request?"

"I will," said the King.

"Thank ye. There's a wee red cap that I'm mortal fond of, and I lost it awhile ago; if I could be hung with it on I would hang a deal more comfortable."

The cap was found and brought to Teig.

"Clip, clap, clip, clap, for my wee red cap. I wish I was home!" he sang.

Up and over the heads of the dumfounded guard he flew,

and—whist!—and away out of sight. When he opened his eyes
again he was sitting close by his own hearth, with the fire
burnt low. The hands of the clock were still, the bolt was
fixed firm in the door. The fairies' lights were gone, and the
only bright thing was the candle burning in old Shawn's cabin
across the road.

A running of feet sounded outside, and then the snatch of
a song:

> " 'Tis well that ye mind, ye who sit by the fire,
>   That the Lord He was born in a dark and cold byre.
>   Mhuire as truagh!"

"Wait ye, whoever ye are!" And Teig was away to the corner,
digging fast at the loose clay, as the terrier digs at a bone. He
filled his hands full of the shining gold, then hurried to the
door, unbarring it.

The miller's wee Cassie stood there, peering at him out of
the darkness.

"Take those to the Widow O'Donnelly, do ye hear? And
take the rest to the store. Ye tell Jamie to bring up all that
he has that is eatable an' dhrinkable; an' to the neighbors ye
say, 'Teig's keepin' the feast this night.' Hurry now!"

Teig stopped a moment on the threshold until the tramp of
her feet had died away; then he made a hollow of his two
hands and called across the road:

"Hey, there, Shawn, will ye come over for a sup?"

"And hey, there, the two o' ye, will ye come out for a sup?"

It was Johanna's cheery voice bringing David back from a
strange country and stranger happenings. She stood in the open
doorway, a lighted candle in her hand.

"Ye'd hurry faster if ye knew what I had outside for supper.
What would a wee lad say, now, to a bit o' real Irish currant-
bread, baked in the griddle, and a bowl of chicken broth with
dumplings!"

A Star for Hansi

BY MARGUERITE VANCE

Illustrations by Grace Paull

SOPHIE is a friendly name. You cannot think that a little girl to whom it belonged would sulk, or refuse to answer to "How do you do?" or take the largest currant muffin.

Sophie Ebbert, who lived in the large, lemon-colored house behind the very high green hedge, was just the little girl to be called by a friendly name. Her eyes were gray, and a dimple near the corner of the left one gave to her face when she smiled what Grossmutter called her "twinkly look." When Sophie smiled —and she did very often—you thought of hidden fairy lights shining from those merry twinkly eyes. Sophie's cheeks were red and round as snow apples, and her brown hair, in two neat, short pigtails, bobbed across her shoulders.

Sometimes they were tied with blue ribbons, and sometimes with red, but on important days, or when there were guests, plaid ribbons, red and blue and gold all together, finished the ends of the fat brown braids.

One of the things that always made Sophie happy was that her birthday—and this time it had been her eighth—came just a week before Christmas when one was growing a little impatient for the great day itself to come. A birthday, though not so important, did a great deal to make a pleasant break in the time of waiting.

Today, however, was one of the very rare times when the "twinkly look" was gone and even the brave plaid bows on her braids drooped.

It was Sunday afternoon. Snow drifted softly down on the garden. The bushes looked like huge white frosted cakes, the pine trees like the sugar trees in the candy shops, which would stand on Christmas dinner tables next week. Inside, the lamps had not been lighted, but from the hearth a pink warm light stole out to touch the edges of things. Sophie watched the white snowflakes lose themselves in the gray twilight, and sighed. Grossmutter closed her book anr lighted the lamp—the one with the pink china shade. Then she came and stood beside Sophie.

"What is it, Liebchen?" she asked. "You are quiet today and just now you sighed much too deeply for a little girl just half-way between her birthday party and Christmas. What is it?"

"Nothing —" began Sophie, and then, before she could stop them, big tears were sliding down her cheeks and Grossmutter was wiping them with her handkerchief which smelled of lavender and spice.

"Come, come, tell me what is troubling you, little child. Maybe I can help. Here on my lap—come."

She drew Sophie onto her lap and listened while the little story was told.

"I had saved my allowance to buy Mother and Father and you and Peter Christmas gifts," she began. "I got Peter's boat, and Father's pencil, and—and your gift. The man in the perfume shop has a little bottle shaped like a green lantern. It is filled with the cologne Mother likes. He is saving it for me. I had enough money to buy it, and Father was going to take me to town tomorrow afternoon to get it—and now—" Sophie's voice trailed off and stopped.

"And now what?"

"Well—you see when Karen came for my party last week we went to the village and—I—I spent all I had left for gingerbread men, and now—" Again the big tears began to slip down Sophie's cheeks.

Grossmutter looked grave, even with the pink lamp and the firelight making everything so warm and friendly.

"So you spent your money all on gingerbread men," she said. "Ach, that is bad, little Sophie, very bad. Now, now, don't cry so!" for now the tears were coming faster and faster. "See, I shall tell you the story of the applewood box. Would you like that?"

Sophie nodded.

"What did it look like?" she asked.

"It was round—round as a chestnut, and just that color. Now listen well.

"Once long ago there stood on the edge of the great Black Forest a beautiful castle. Around it spread its parks where deer and antelope walked softly through the speckled shadows. Beyond the park was the hamlet where lived the people who served the baron of the castle. In their little cottages they lived —woodcutters, shepherds, farmers, the blacksmith, shopkeepers, the school-teacher, the pastor, the bürgermeister.

"In the little house of the bürgermeister besides himself, there lived his wife and their three children, Tomas, little Hans, and a little girl about your age. And what do you suppose her name was?"

Sophie shook her head, and almost the dimple peeped out. "I don't know. What was it?"

"Sophie."

"Sophie—like me?"

"Yes, Liebchen, very much like you. I think that other Sophie looked just a little like you, too. Tomas was two years older than his sister and four years older than little Hans.

"In all the Black Forest region there was no child just like little Hans. His hair was like pale sunshine caught and rolled into soft curls all over his head. His dark eyes seemed to see far-away places; and when little Hans laughed Tomas put down his whittling and Sophie stopped her knitting the better to listen to so sweet a sound. Little Hans did not play their games, nor did he go with them to tend geese in the swamp. He sat and played quietly in a sunny spot where his chair was placed. Sometimes his father carried him into the woods and he called to the birds in his high sweet voice, by little names he made up for them.

"Sophie and Tomas and their parents all loved one another dearly, but their love for little Hans was quite different. It was as though there must be enough love for Hansi to remember forever and ever.

"Now, though the bürgermeister had his snug cottage, and though his family was clothed and fed, still he was not a rich man, and his children earned whatever they could to buy the little extra things that girls and boys like. Tomas helped the woodcutter gather the lighter branches as they fell under his ax and saw, and tied them in neat, tight bundles. On baking days, when his mother's loaves were ready to be carried to the village oven for baking, he stopped at the cottage of the black-smith, the tailor, and the doctor, and carried the loaves their wives had set, too, and later returned each golden loaf, crusty and hot from the oven to its owner.

"Sophie crocheted fine lace for the linen pillowcases in the castle, and knitted pretty worsted caps and mufflers for the children of the baron. Each morning when she drove her moth-

er's geese to the swamp, she drove the geese of the miller and the storekeeper, too.

"For these little tasks the children received a few coppers. That is how Tomas came to own his jackknife for whittling, and how Sophie had the white knitting needles with tiny roses and violets painted on them.

"One day in early autumn the school-teacher called Sophie to him and said:

"'I have something here for you, Sophie, which I hope you will always treasure. Look, it was given me by my teacher when I was your age.'

"He put into Sophie's hands a small round box."

"Was it the applewood box, Grossmutter?"

"Yes, exactly, and this is what he said: 'This little box is only for a careful child, and I believe you are that. There is a coin in it now. See that there is at least one coin, however small, in it at all times. There is only one exception to this rule. When your heart quite plainly says, "Now, now is the time to spend the last coin," then spend it gladly. Otherwise, remember, always keep at least one coin in the box. It will call in others. When you have grown to be an old lady search well for another careful child and pass the box on to him or her with this same advice.'

"So he gave the applewood box to the happy little girl, and—"

"And did it have a coin in it?"

"Yes, a pfennig; and Sophie promised that she would never let the little box be empty unless her heart quite plainly said, 'Now, now is the time to spend the last coin.'

"She was so proud of her new prize that she ran home through the woods and burst in on her mother, who was spinning beside the fire."

"What did Tomas and little Hans say?"

"Tomas was away in the woods with the woodcutter, but little Hans held the box against his cheek and laughed softly and said, 'It is smooth and cool like the moon.'

"The days flew and Sophie worked very diligently at all the tasks at home, at school, and at those other tasks which brought coins to the little box.

"One day a peddler came to the village with strange and beautiful toys from across the Russian border—little carved squirrels that climbed a string, small tops of many colors, music-boxes that played wild, sweet tunes that seemed to come from far-away lovely places behind the snowy sunset. Tomas selected a set of tops, spent his last coin, and grieved when evening came and his tops were broken. Sophie knew that little Hans would have loved a music-box, but as he had not seen ANY of the toys, she carried the prettiest brown squirrel home to him instead and shared his fun as he watched it run up and down the string. In the applewood box there was still the last coin to begin fresh saving for other useful or amusing things.

"Again, when the family all went to the fair in the early winter, Sophie was tempted. There was the man selling cardamom cakes, another selling chocolate and herb tea delicately spiced. In one tent a big black bear danced and boxed with his trainer; in another a troupe of dwarfs tumbled and did amusing tricks. Still farther on a strong man lifted mighty weights. Tomas spent his last coin, poor lad, yet saw only half that he wanted to. Sophie chose a cardamom cake and saw the dancing bear, and went home happy, with a cake for little Hans, and a coin still rattling in the applewood box. More lace to be crocheted, more cold mornings helping with the geese and chickens, and soon there would be more coins to make a gay tinkling in the box.

"Soon it was time for the lovely Christmas festival. Mother baked pfeffernüsse and springerlein until the little cottage was sweet with spicy fragrance. Father brought in fresh wood and laid pine cones between the kindling to make a more snapping Christmas fire while he told the children stories of other Christmases in the Black Forest.

"One evening he told the story of the first Christmas and how a great, beautiful, silver star had led the way to the Baby Jesus. Little Hans was in his arms, listening to the story. His sunny hair made a great splash of gold against his father's coat.

" 'Did they find Him, Father?' he asked.

" 'Of course,' Father answered; 'they just followed where the star led, and there at last they found the Child, and He held out His little arms to them.'

"The other children did not say anything, but little Hans smiled.

" 'That was nice,' he said, 'nice.'

"The next day was Christmas Eve, so Sophie and Tomas took their coins and went to the village, and what fun they had! A bit of beeswax for Mother's ironing-board, a new goose quill for Father's writing-pad, a jumping-jack and a stick of candy for little Hans. For each other they chose a collection of small things which, of course, they would not show until the tree was lighted after sunset. Hugging their packages, they ran home through the twilight, hoping Mother had not finished trimming the tree and placing the little manger beneath it."

"But, was it a really, truly manger, Grossmutter?"

"Yes, a tiny stable, and just inside, a manger filled with real hay for the Child Jesus to lie upon. And then grouped all around were the little figures of Mary and Joseph and the Wise Men and shepherds—all made of wax.

"Tomas ran to hide his packages and Sophie threw off her hood and cape and went to little Hans. He was not in his chair by the window this evening, but in his little bed, for he was tired. So Sophie put the lumpy jumping-jack in its brown wrapping on the bed beside him.

" 'Guess what Sophie brought for you, Hansi,' she said, and waited while his fingers moved over the stiff paper. Never, never would he guess!

" 'Is it—Sophie, is it—a star?' he whispered at last, and his own dark eyes were like stars.

"Sophie's heart sank. A jumping-jack! and he had wanted a star! For a few pfennigs a beautiful star, all shimmering and silvery white, could be had in a shop at the other end of the village! But she had spent all her money—all but—! Suddenly Sophie straightened up. There was that last coin which must never be touched unless quite plainly her heart said, 'Now, now is the time to spend the last coin,' and now her heart spoke.

"She smiled down at little Hans, and he smiled happily back.

" 'Is it—is it truly a star?' he asked again, very softly.

"Sophie kissed his fingers resting on the package.

" 'Just you wait, Hansi, until Sophie comes back,' she whispered, and taking the jumping-jack, she ran to the woodshed where Tomas was helping Father with the little tree for which Mother was clearing a space on the table.

" 'Hide this with your other things, Tomas,' she said. 'I'm going to run back to the village. I'll not be gone long—I'll hurry.'

"She threw on her cape, and holding the applewood box tightly, ran through the woods to the village, thinking she never had heard anything more comforting than the sound of the coin rattling away merrily in the little box as she ran. The shopkeeper smiled at her serious face.

" 'A star for little Hansi, eh?' he exclaimed. Together they looked over the rows of beautiful white-and-silver stars hanging like a sparkling girdle around the shop walls, and at last the shopkeeper took down the shiniest one he had and held it out to her.

" 'There,' he said, 'there is the brightest star in the shop, and little Hans is just the child it was meant to shine for. Be sure to wish him a good Christmas for me, eh?'

"Sophie gave him her last coin happily, and holding the star carefully under her cape, sped back over the snow to the cottage at the edge of the wood.

"Now the sun had set and from the windows of the bürgermeister's little house a warm welcoming light streamed out, making a gay pattern on the snow.

" 'The whole house seems to glow,' thought Sophie, hurrying toward it, 'as though it were full of lovely stars!'

"Softly she opened the door, and softly—not knowing why— hurried through the passage. At the door of the family room

she stopped. There was a hush in the room—as when a bird
stops singing or a bubbling fountain ceases to play.

"The little tree standing on the table shone quietly in the soft
white light of its candles. Before it, all together, was the family
—Mother, Father, Tomas, and in Father's arms little Hans.
Mother knelt beside Father's chair, with her cheek against
Hansi's curls, and Sophie could see that she had forgotten Father
and Tomas and even Christmas—everything but little Hans.
Father was telling the Christmas story again, very slowly, very
carefully, so that even if one were tired and drowsy, still one
could hear and understand.

" 'They followed where the star led,' Father said, 'and there
at last—'

"Little Hans opened his eyes. He saw Sophie. He smiled all over his little face.

" 'Look, Hansi,' she whispered, and slid to her knees before Father's chair and held up the great quivering silver star.

" 'For me! For me!' the little boy said, softly, and held out his hands and laughed; and looking at his Christmas star, he fell asleep there before the Baby Christ in the manger who held out His little arms to him. And Sophie knew she had done well to take the last coin from the applewood box. And that is the end of the story, Liebchen."

Sophie stirred.

"Tell some more," she begged. "Did little Hans wake up after a while and see his star again? and did Sophie grow up? and what did she do with the box?"

Grossmutter smiled gently.

"Little Hans woke—yes, and never was tired any more. Sophie grew up, and what do you suppose she did with the applewood box? Jump down, dear; I am going to show you something."

Grossmutter went to her room, and in a moment she was back, carrying a small object in her hands.

"This is from one Sophie to another," she said, smiling—"to you."

Sophie could not believe her eyes, for there in her hands was a small, round, dark box of polished wood!

"Is it—oh, Grossmutter, IS IT THE APPLEWOOD BOX?" Sophie's dimple was back and so was the "twinkly look."

Grossmutter nodded.

"Then are you—were you—that Sophie?"

Again Grossmutter nodded, or tried to, because Sophie's arms were around her neck in a bear hug, and her flushed round cheek pressed so tightly to Grossmutter's that she scarcely could move.

"Oh, it was the lovliest, LOVELIEST story, Grossmutter!" she said, "and I'll be so proud of my box!"

"Then see, child; here, let us open it."

Carefully Sophie took off the polished lid. The box was quite filled with coins.

"Now then," Grossmutter asked, "how much shall we need to buy the lantern filled with cologne?"

Sophie's dimple disappeared.

"Fifty cents," she answered, and just saying it made it sound twice as much.

Grossmutter emptied the coins on the table and together they counted them.

"Just exactly fifty pennies!" Grossmutter beamed. Sophie shrieked with glee.

"Goody! Goody!" she cried. "Now in the morning the first thing Father and I can go to town and buy the lantern! Fifty cents is exactly what I needed and now I have it! I'm so happy! So happy!" She danced around the room. Then suddenly she noticed that Grossmutter was looking at her a little strangely, a little sadly.

"I am afraid," she said, "that my little Sophie does not remember the most important part of all in the story of the box. What about the last coin?"

Sophie stopped short in her dance.

"Oh—I forgot," she said—"I forgot."

"When does Father give you your next allowance?"

"Tomorrow. Peter and I get it every Monday morning."

"Well, then—?"

"Oh, I see!" The dimple came twinkling out again. "I see! Look, Grossmutter, I'll leave five pennies instead of only one in the box. That will leave forty-five pennies I can keep out. Then tomorrow I'll add five pennies from my allowance, and that will give me enough to buy the lantern and still leave coins in the box to 'call in others,' as the school-teacher said when he gave the box to So—I mean to you."

Grossmutter patted her cheek.

"That is my little Sophie," she said. "That is being a 'careful child,' a worthy owner of the applewood box."

So on Christmas Eve, tucked in her snug bed, Sophie thought happily of Mother's cologne lantern hanging bravely on the tree downstairs. Above, the Christmas stars shone softly down, and one, larger, brighter than the others, she thought must look very like the one the other Sophie had brought to little Hans on that long-ago Christmas Eve in the Black Forest. As she drifted into happy Christmas dreams she made a solemn promise always to guard her last coin carefully, but to spend it gladly, thankfully when her heart quite plainly said, "Now, now is the time."

"So Hallowed and So Gracious Is the Time—"

BY ANNE THAXTER EATON

Illustrations by Valenti Angelo

THROUGH the centuries since the starry night when the Christ Child was born in a manger at Bethlehem, people in all countries have joyously told and retold legends of that first Christmas Eve. In so many of these Christmas legends there are animals and birds and other creatures that it seems as though man must always have felt that, in this best-loved festival, all living things should have a share. Among the Albanians the first Christmas meat-cake is given to the house dog as a sign of the sympathy which people believe animals have with the Nativity, and in parts of Scotland it used to be the custom to see that every animal about the place had additional food on Christmas morning.

Many are the stories of countrymen quietly entering the stable at midnight on Christmas Eve to find the cattle on their knees and sometimes praising God in human words. The deer are said to kneel in northern forests in the moonlight at this same hour and look upward. Cocks are said to crow at all hours the night before Christmas.

In some parts of England it is believed that if you listen outside the bee-hives at midnight on Christmas Eve, you will hear the bees within, humming, or "singing" in honour of the Holy Child. There is also a story about the little beetle who made his home on the roof of the stable in Bethlehem and so heard the angels when they brought the good tidings of the Christ Child's birth to the shepherds. Flying to one of the angels he begged that he might be allowed to tell the other animals the good news. The angel was pleased with him and he placed a tiny glowing spark from his own shining hair between the beetle's wings. Animals, birds, and insects saw the little light and knew what it meant. When the little beetle returned to the stable, he continued to fly about all night, giving out a faint light by which Mary and Joseph could watch the Child. Ever since then the beetle has been known as the glow-worm.

Spiders, too, have played their part, for once, it is said, they found the Christmas Tree all trimmed and waiting, and in their eagerness to see the pretty things that hung from the branches, they crawled over it from top to bottom, leaving their little grey webs behind them. When the Christ Child came to bless the Tree and found it hung with spiderwebs, in order that the mother might not be disappointed when she saw the state of the Tree she had so carefully trimmed, He touched the grey webs and turned them to gleaming threads of gold.

The robin's breast is red, one legend tells us, because he fluttered his little wings to quicken the dying fire which had been built to warm the Christ Child as He lay in the manger. As the fire grew brighter, the feathers on the robin's breast caught the glow from the flames and has remained red ever since. In Belgium the young wrens are said to return at midnight on Christmas Eve to the nest where they were born.

In that country on Christmas Eve, the farmers put out in front of the barns oats and water which are blessed at midnight. These oats are given to the horses in summer and keep them well. Some of the oats are thrown to the hens, and when they have eaten it, it will keep them safe from wolves and foxes. The holy water is sprinkled round the house, the stables, and the barns to keep away mice and witches. Always during Christmas Eve, in every flock of sheep, a lamb is born.

In Norway and Sweden a wheat sheaf is placed outside for the birds on Christmas Eve and little clay birds are made and sold as children's playthings at Christmas time. This is in memory of the legend that when Jesus was a child He and other children amused themselves by making birds out of clay. The birds of the other children remained clay, but when Jesus clapped His hands His birds came to life and flew away.

There is an ancient tradition that during the fourteen days before Christmas there was a great calm on the ocean because the halcyon, or kingfisher, built his nest on the waves and hatched out its young. These were known as the "halcyon days." John Milton describes them in his "Ode on the Morning of Christ's Nativity."

The winds with wonder whist,
Smoothly the waters kissed,
Whispering new joys to the mild Ocean,
Who now hath quite forgot to rave,
While birds of calm sit brooding on the charmèd wave.

A quaint sheet of carols was published and sold in London in 1701, headed "Christus Natus Est:—Christ Is Born," with a woodcut showing the stable at Bethlehem, Christ in the manger, Mary and Joseph, shepherds and angels, a man playing on the bagpipes, and a woman with a basket of fruit on her head. There, too, are the animals; a sheep, an ox, a raven, and a crow on the hayrack; a cock is crowing above them and there are angels in the sky. In the mouths of the animals are labels, with Latin inscriptions. The cock crows, "Christus Natus Est—Christ is born"; the raven asks, "Quando?—When?"; the crow answers, "Hac Nacte—This night"; the Ox cries, "Ubi,

Ubi?—Where?"; the sheep bleats, "Bethlehem, Bethlehem,"
while from the sky above the angels sing "Gloria in Excelsis
—Glory in the Highest."

When Joseph of Arimathea came to live in Glastonbury
in England, it is said that he thrust his staff into the ground
where it took root, put forth leaves, and on the next day,
which was Christmas, burst into snow-white blossoms. Every
Christmas Eve thereafter it bloomed again.

Is There a Santa Claus?

BY FRANCIS PHARCELLUS CHURCH

Illustration by Estelle Hollingworth

In September, 1897, the Editor of The Sun opened a letter from a little girl named Virginia. "Is there a Santa Claus?" she wanted to know. The answer, from Francis Pharcellus Church, has become the most famous editorial-article that has ever been written.

W E take pleasure in answering at once and thus prominently the communication below, expressing at the same time our great gratification that its faithful author is numbered among the friends of The Sun:

"Dear Editor:
I am 8 years old.
Some of my little friends say there is no Santa Claus.
Papa says 'If you see it in The Sun it's so.'
Please tell me the truth, is there a Santa Claus?
Virginia O'Hanlon,
115 West 95th Street"

Virginia, your little friends are wrong. They have been affected by the skepticism of a skeptical age. They do not believe except they see. They think that nothing can be which is not comprehensible by their little minds. All minds, Virginia, whether they be men's or children's, are little. In this great universe of ours man is a mere insect, an ant, in his intellect, as compared with the boundless world about him, as measured by the intelligence capable of grasping the whole of truth and knowledge.

Yes, Virginia, there is a Santa Claus. He exists as certainly as love and generosity and devotion exist, and you know that they abound and give to your life its highest beauty and joy. Alas! how dreary would be the world if there were no Santa Claus! It would be as dreary as if there were no Virginias. There would be no childlike faith then, no poetry, no romance to make tolerable this existence. We should have no enjoyment, except in sense and sight. The eternal light with which childhood fills the world would be extinguished.

Not believe in Santa Claus! You might as well not believe in fairies! You might get your papa to hire men to watch in all the Chimneys on Christmas eve to catch Santa Claus, but even if they did not see Santa Claus coming down, what would that prove? Nobody sees Santa Claus, but that is no sign that there is no Santa Claus. The most real things in the world are those that neither children nor men can see. Did you ever see fairies dancing on the lawn? Of course not, but that's no proof that they are not there. Nobody can conceive or imagine all the wonders there are unseen and unseeable in the world.

You tear apart the baby's rattle and see what makes the noise inside, but there is a veil covering the unseen world which not the strongest man, nor even the united strength of all the strongest men that ever lived, could tear apart. Only faith, fancy, poetry, love, romance, can push aside that curtain and view and picture the supernal beauty and glory beyond. Is it all real? Ah, Virginia, in all this world there is nothing else real and abiding.

No Santa Claus! Thank God he lives, and he lives forever. A thousand years from now, Virginia, nay, ten times ten thousand years from now, he will continue to make glad the heart of childhood.

Prayer

By John Farrar

Last night I crept across the snow,
Where only tracking rabbits go,
And then I waited quite alone
Until the Christmas radiance shone!

At midnight twenty angels came,
Each white and shining like a flame.
At midnight twenty angels sang,
The stars swung out like bells and rang.

They lifted me across the hill,
They bore me in their arms until
A greater glory greeted them.
It was the town of Bethlehem.

And gently, then, they set me down,
All worshipping that holy town,
And gently, then, they bade me raise
My head to worship and to praise.

And gently, then, the Christ smiled down.
Ah, there was glory in that town!
It was as if the world were free
And glistening with purity.

And in that vault of crystal blue,
It was as if the world were new,
And myriad angels, file on file,
Gloried in the Christ-Child's smile.

It was so beautiful to see
Such glory, for a child like me,
So beautiful, it does not seem
It could have been a Christmas dream.

Christmas Carol

By Kenneth Grahame

Villagers all, this frosty tide,
Let your doors swing open wide,
Though wind may follow and snow betide
Yet draw us in by your fire to bide:
Joy shall be yours in the morning.

Here we stand in the cold and the sleet,
Blowing fingers and stamping feet,
Come from far away, you to greet—
You by the fire and we in the street—
Bidding you joy in the morning.

For ere one half of the night was gone,
Sudden a star has led us on,
Raining bliss and benison—
Bliss tomorrow and more anon,
Joy for every morning.

Good man Joseph toiled through the snow—
Saw the star o'er the stable low;
Mary she might not further go—
Welcome thatch and litter below!
Joy was hers in the morning.

And then they heard the angels tell,
"Who were the first to cry Nowell?
Animals all as it befel,
In the stable where they did dwell!
Joy shall be theirs in the morning."

In the Week When Christmas Comes

By Eleanor Farjeon

This is the week when Christmas comes.

Let every pudding burst with plums,
And every tree bear dolls and drums,
　In the week when Christmas comes.

Let every hall have boughs of green,
With berries glowing in between,
　In the week when Christmas comes.

Let every doorstep have a song
Sounding the dark street along,
　In the week when Christmas comes.

Let every steeple ring a bell
With a joyful tale to tell,
　In the week when Christmas comes.

Let every night put forth a star
To show us where the heavens are,
　In the week when Christmas comes.

Let every stable have a lamb
Sleeping warm beside its dam,
　In the week when Christmas comes.

This is the week when Christmas comes.

Christmas Morning

By Elizabeth Madox Roberts

If Bethlehem were here today,
   Or this were very long ago,
There wouldn't be a winter time
   Nor any cold or snow.

I'd run out through the garden gate,
   And down along the pasture walk;
And off beside the cattle barns
   I'd hear a kind of gentle talk.

I'd move the heavy iron chain
   And pull away the wooden pin;
I'd push the door a little bit
   And tiptoe very softly in.

The pigeons and the yellow hens
   And all the cows would stand away;
Their eyes would open wide to see
   A lady in the manger hay,
If this were very long ago
   And Bethlehem were here today.

And Mother held my hand and smiled—
   I mean the lady would—and she
Would take the woolly blankets off
   Her little boy so I could see.

Illustrations by Dawn Stoutsenberger

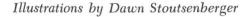

His shut-up eyes would be asleep,
   And he would look just like our John,
And he would be all crumpled too,
   And have a pinkish color on.

I'd watch his breath go in and out.
   His little clothes would all be white.
I'd slip my finger in his hand
   To feel how he could hold it tight.

And she would smile and say, "Take care,"
   The mother, Mary, would, "Take care";
And I would kiss his little hand
   And touch his hair.

While Mary put the blankets back,
   The gentle talk would soon begin.
And when I'd tiptoe softly out
   I'd meet the Wise Men going in.

For Christmas

By Rachel Field

Now not a window small or big
But wears a wreath of holly sprig;
Nor any shop too poor to show
Its spray of pine or mistletoe.
Now city airs are spicy-sweet
With Christmas trees along the street,
Green spruce and fir whose boughs will hold
Their tinselled balls and fruits of gold.
Now postmen pass in threes and fours
Like bent, blue-coated Santa Claus.
Now people hurry to and fro
With little girls and boys in tow,
And not a child but keeps some trace
Of Christmas secrets in his face.

Hark! The Herald Angels Sing

By Charles Wesley

Hark! the herald angels sing,
"Glory to the newborn King,
Peace on earth and mercy mild;
God and sinners reconciled,"
Joyful, all ye nations, rise,
Join the triumph of the skies;
With angelic hosts proclaim,
"Christ is born in Bethlehem!"
Hark! the herald angels sing,
"Glory to the newborn King."

Christ by highest heaven adored;
Christ, the everlasting Lord;
Late in time behold Him come
Offspring of the Virgin's womb.
Veiled in flesh the Godhead see;
Hail the incarnate Deity,
Pleased as man with man to dwell;
Jesus, our Emmanuel!
Hark! the herald angels sing,
"Glory to the newborn King."

Hail the heav'n-born Prince of Peace!
Hail the Sun of Righteousness!
Light and life to all He brings,
Ris'n with healing in His wings.
Mild He lays His glory by,
Born that men no more may die,
Born to raise the sons of earth,
Born to give them second birth.
Hark! the herald angels sing,
"Glory to the newborn King."

It Came Upon the Midnight Clear

By E. H. Sears

It came upon the midnight clear,
That glorious song of old,
From angels bending near the earth
To touch their harps of gold:
"Peace on the earth, good will to men,
From heaven's all-gracious King."
The world in solemn stillness lay
To hear the angels sing.

Still through the cloven skies they come
With peaceful wings unfurled,
And still their heavenly music floats
O'er all the weary world;
Above its sad and lowly plains
They bend on hovering wing,
And ever o'er its Babel-sounds
The blessed angels sing.

Yet with the woes of sin and strife
The world has suffered long;
Beneath the heavenly strain have rolled
Two thousand years of wrong;
And man, at war with man, hears not
The tidings which they bring;
O hush the noise, ye men of strife,
And hear the angels sing!

O ye, beneath life's crushing load
Whose forms are bending low,
Who toil along the climbing way
With painful steps and slow,
Look now, for glad and golden hours
Come swiftly on the wing.
O rest beside the weary road
And hear the angels sing!

For lo! the days are hastening on,
By prophets seen of old,
When with the ever-circling years
Shall come the time foretold,
When peace shall over all the earth
Its ancient splendors fling,
And the whole world give back the song
Which now the angels sing.

Silent Night

By Joseph Mohr

Silent night, Holy night!
All is calm, all is bright
Round yon Virgin Mother and Child,
Holy Infant, so tender and mild,
Sleep in heavenly peace,
Sleep in heavenly peace.

Silent night, Holy night!
Shepherds quake at the sight,
Glories stream from heaven afar,
Heav'nly hosts sing Alleluia;
Christ the Saviour is born!
Christ the Saviour is born.

Silent night, Holy night!
Son of God, love's pure light
Radiant beams from Thy holy face,
With the dawn of redeeming grace,
Jesus, Lord, at Thy birth!
Jesus, Lord, at Thy birth!

O Little Town of Bethlehem

By Phillips Brooks

O little town of Bethlehem,
How still we see thee lie!
Above thy deep and dreamless sleep
The silent stars go by;
Yet in thy dark streets shineth
The everlasting Light;
The hopes and fears of all the years
Are met in thee to-night.

For Christ is born of Mary,
And, gathered all above,
While mortals sleep, the angels keep
Their watch of wondering love.
O morning stars, together
Proclaim the holy birth!
And praises sing to God the King,
And peace to men on earth.

How silently, how silently,
The wondrous gift is given!
So God imparts to human hearts
The blessings of His heaven.
No ear may hear His coming,
But in this world of sin,
Where meek souls will receive him still,
The dear Christ enters in.

O holy Child of Bethlehem,
Descend to us, we pray;
Cast out our sin, and enter in,
Be born in us to-day.
We hear the Christmas angels
The great glad tidings tell;
Oh, come to us, abide with us,
Our Lord Emmanuel!

INDEX of Authors and Titles

Titles of stories are set in *italic* type; titles of poems in roman type.

ACKNOWLEDGMENTS

The publishers wish to express their appreciation to the following publishers, agents, authors, and artists who have granted permission to use material appearing in this book. Any errors or omissions are unintentional and will be corrected in future printings if notice is sent to The Crowell-Collier Publishing Company.

ABINGDON PRESS *Mr. Plum and the Little Green Tree*, by Helen Earle Gilbert, illustrated by Margaret Bradfield, copyright 1946 by Stone and Pierce; used by permission of Abingdon Press, publishers.

BEHRMAN HOUSE, INC. Excerpt from *The Hanukkah Story*, by Morrison David Bial, illustrated by Stephen Kraft, copyright 1952 by Behrman House, Inc.; two illustrations from *The Hanukkah Story* used to illustrate the poems "Dreidel Song" and "For Hanukkah"; reprinted by permission of the publisher, Behrman House, Inc., 1261 Broadway, New York 1, N.Y.

BRANDT & BRANDT "Christopher Columbus," "George Washington," by Stephen Vincent Benet, and "Nancy Hanks" by Rosemary Carr Benet, from *A Book of Americans*, copyright 1933 by Rosemary and Stephen Vincent Benet; "Prayer for a Better World," from *We Stand United and Other Radio Scripts*, by Stephen Vincent Benet, copyright 1942 by Stephen Vincent Benet; Holt, Rinehart & Wilson, Inc.

BEATRICE CHUTE "Archie and the April Fools," by Beatrice Chute, from *Child Life*, copyright 1942 by *Child Life*; reprinted by permission of Beatrice Chute.

ELIZABETH COATSWORTH "April Fool" and "Easter" by Elizabeth Coatsworth, from *Girls Today*. Reprinted by permission of the author.

JOSEPH COTTLER "The Grand Old Man of Labor," from *Champions of Democracy*, by Joseph Cottler, copyright 1936 by Joseph Cottler; reprinted by permission of Joseph Cottler.

THOMAS Y. CROWELL COMPANY "Mr. Chairman" from *Cheaper by the Dozen* by Frank B. Gilbreth, Jr., and Ernestine Gilbreth Carey, copyright 1948 by Frank B. Gilbreth, Jr., and Ernestine Gilbreth Carey; "Light Bread and Apple Butter" from *Rifles for Watie* by Harold Keith, copyright 1957 by Harold Keith; Thomas Y. Crowell Company, New York.

THE CURTIS PUBLISHING COMPANY "The Valentine Box" by Maud Hart Lovelace, reprinted from *Jack and Jill*, copyright 1945 by The Curtis Publishing Company and Maud Hart Lovelace; by special permission of The Curtis Publishing Company and Maud Hart Lovelace.

MRS. GRAHAM DOAR "A Valentine," by Eleanor Hammond; reprinted by permission of Mrs. Graham Doar.

DODD, MEAD & COMPANY, INC. "The Soldier," by Rupert Brooke, reprinted by permission of Dodd, Mead & Company from *The Collected Poems of Rupert Brooke*, copyright 1915 by Dodd, Mead & Company, Inc.; 1943 by Edward Marsh.

DOUBLEDAY & COMPANY, INC. "Abraham Lincoln," from *Abraham Lincoln*, written and illustrated by Ingri and Edgar d'Aulaire, copyright 1939, 1957 by Doubleday & Company, Inc.; "New Year's Day," from *A Little Book of Days*, by Rachel Field, copyright 1927 by Doubleday & Company, Inc.; reprinted by permission of the publisher.

E. P. DUTTON & CO., INC. "Easter Parade," from the book *Around And About*, by Marchette Chute, copyright 1946 by Marchette Chute; "Fourth of July" by Marchette Chute; *A Star For Hansi*, by Marguerite Vance, illustrated by Grace Paull, copyright 1936 by Marguerite Vance; reprinted by permission of E. P. Dutton & Co., Inc.

FOLLETT PUBLISHING COMPANY "The Library Lady," from *All-of-a-Kind Family*, by Sydney Taylor, illustrated by Helen John, copyright 1951 by Follett Publishing Company; "Festival of Lights," from *More All-of-a-Kind Family*, by Sydney Taylor, illustrated by Mary Stevens, copyright 1954 by Sydney Taylor; reprinted by permission of Follett Publishing Co., Chicago.

GINN AND COMPANY "Flag of the Free," by Walter Taylor Field, reprinted with the permission of Ginn and Company, owners of the copyright.

HARCOURT, BRACE & WORLD, INC. Excerpt from *Rufus M.*, by Eleanor Estes, illustrated by Louis Slobodkin, copyright 1943 by Eleanor Estes; "Trees" and "Hallowe'en," from *The Little Hill*, by Harry Behn, copyright 1949 by Harry Behn; used by permission of Harcourt, Brace & World, Inc.

ACKNOWLEDGMENTS 429

ILO ORLEANS   "April Pranks" and "Hope For Peace," by Ilo Orleans; reprinted by permission of the author.

G. P. PUTNAM'S SONS   "Night and Morning," from *Everything and Anything,* copyright 1925, 1926, 1927 by Dorothy Aldis; "Fourth of July Night," from *Hop, Skip and Jump,* copyright 1934 by Dorothy Aldis; "It Was" from *Here, There and Everywhere,* copyright 1927, 1929 by Dorothy Aldis; all by Dorothy Aldis; used by permission of G. P. Putnam's Sons.

RANDOM HOUSE, INC.   "Childhood on the Potomac," from *George Washington: Frontier Colonel,* by Sterling North, illustrated by Lee Ames, copyright 1957 by Sterling North; "Betsy Ross and the Flag," from *Betsy Ross and the Flag* by Jane Mayer, illustrated by Grace Paull, copyright 1952 by Jane Mayer; reprinted by permission of Random House, Inc.

SATURDAY REVIEW   "Books," by Joseph Joel Keith, reprinted from *Saturday Review,* March 21, 1953, by permission of *Saturday Review.*

SCOTT, FORESMAN AND COMPANY   "A Reply to Nancy Hanks," by Julius Silberger, from *Children and Books,* by May Hill Arbuthnot, copyright 1947 by Scott, Foresman and Company, Chicago.

CHARLES SCRIBNER'S SONS   "Christmas Carol," reprinted from *The Wind in the Willows,* by Kenneth Grahame, copyright 1908, 1933, 1953 by Charles Scribner's Sons; "The War for Independence," reprinted from *George Washington, An Initial Biography,* by Genevieve Foster, copyright 1949 by Genevieve Foster; used by permission of Charles Scribner's Sons.

THE SOCIETY OF AUTHORS   Excerpt from "Books," by Walter de la Mare, reprinted by permission of The Literary Trustees of Walter de la Mare and The Society of Authors as their representative.

DOROTHY BROWN THOMPSON   "This Is Halloween," from *Child Life,* Rand McNally and Company, publishers, and "Arbor Day," both by Dorothy Brown Thompson; reprinted by permission of the author.

NANCY BYRD TURNER   "Let Us Have Peace" and "Washington," by Nancy Byrd Turner; reprinted by permission of the author.

UNION OF AMERICAN HEBREW CONGREGATIONS   "Dreidel Song" and "A Song of Always," from *Now We Begin,* by Marian J. and Efraim M. Rosenzweig; "For Hanukkah," from *Far Over the Sea,* by Chaim Nachman Bialik, translated by Jessie Sampter; reprinted by permission of the Union of American Hebrew Congregations, publishers and copyright holders.

THE VIKING PRESS, INC.   "Christmas Morning" and "Father's Story," from *Under the Tree,* by Elizabeth Madox Roberts, copyright 1922 by B. W. Huebsch, Inc.; 1950 by Ivor S. Roberts; "Dobry," from *Dobry,* by Monica Shannon, illustrated by Atanas Katchmakoff, copyright 1934 by Monica Shannon; "Nino's Easter," from *Nino,* written and illustrated by Valenti Angelo, copyright 1938 by Valenti Angelo; "Of Courage Undaunted," from *West of Boston,* by James Daugherty; excerpt from *The Singing Tree* written and illustrated by Kate Seredy, copyright 1939 by Kate Seredy; "So Hallowed and So Gracious Is The Time. . .," from *The Animals' Christmas,* by Anne Thaxter Eaton, illustrated by Valenti Angelo, copyright 1944 by Anne Thaxter Eaton and Valenti Angelo; "The Star-Spangled Banner Girl," from *Children of the Handcrafts,* by Carolyn Sherwin Bailey, illustrated by Grace Paull, copyright 1935 by Carolyn Sherwin Bailey; reprinted by permission of The Viking Press, Inc.

JERRY VOGEL MUSIC CO., INC.   The poem "Trees," by Joyce Kilmer; used by special permission of copyright owner, Jerry Vogel Music Co., Inc., 112 West 44 Street, New York 36, N.Y.

HENRY Z. WALCK, INC.   "St. Patrick," from *Ten Saints,* by Eleanor Farjeon, illustrated by Helen Sewell, copyright 1936 by Henry Z. Walck, Inc.; reprinted by permission.

YALE UNIVERSITY PRESS   "Prayer," from *Songs for Parents,* by John Farrar; reprinted by permission of Yale University Press.